Edexcel

George Face

A2 Chemistry

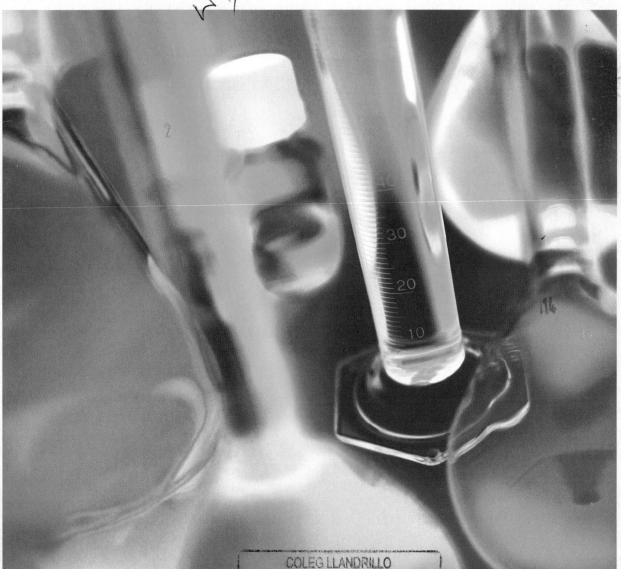

This book is dedicated to Judy, my wife of 40 years, who has supported me throughout the research and writing of this textbook.

Philip Allan Updates
Market Place
Deddington
Oxfordshire
OX15 0SE

Tel: 01869 336420
Fax: 01869 337590
e-mail: sales@philipallan.co.uk
www.philipallan.co.uk

© Philip Allan Updates 2006

ISBN-13: 978-1-84489-213-6
ISBN-10: 1-84489-213-1

This textbook has been written specifically to support students studying Edexcel A2 Chemistry. The content has been neither approved nor endorsed by Edexcel and remains the sole responsibility of the author.

All efforts have been made to trace copyright on items used.
Front cover photograph reproduced by permission of TEK Image/Science Photo Library

Design by Juha Sorsa
Printed in Great Britain by CPI Bath

P588

Contents

Introduction

This textbook covers the Edexcel specification for A2 chemistry. Generally, the order follows that of the specification. However, in order to bring all the Unit 5 organic chemistry together in consecutive chapters, the chapter on kinetics precedes those on aromatic chemistry and organic mechanisms. To give the student a better understanding of, and feel for, some topics, the content of the book occasionally goes beyond the confines of the A2 specification.

The first eight chapters describe and explain the material of **Unit 4: Periodicity, quantitative equilibria and functional group chemistry**. The following eight chapters cover the material of **Unit 5: Transition metals, quantitative kinetics and applied organic chemistry.** The final section comprises one chapter on the synoptic assessment. Each section concludes with a practice unit test.

Margin comments are provided throughout the book. These comprise valuable reminders and snippets of information and include examiner's tips (indicated by an ⓔ symbol), which clarify what you need to know and common sources of confusion.

This book is not a guide to the practical chemistry that all A2 candidates will study. However, many of the reactions that will be met in the laboratory are detailed throughout the book. Chapter 15 will also be a help to those students who take the practical examination.

At the back of the book (p. 334), there is a periodic table. This should be referred to for atomic numbers, atomic masses and symbols of the elements. The table is similar to the one printed on the back of the examination papers.

Required previous knowledge and skills

It is assumed that all A2 chemistry students have successfully completed the AS course. All students should be:
- familiar with the use of a calculator
- able to change the subject of an algebraic equation
- able to draw straight-line and curved graphs from supplied data and to extrapolate graphs
- able to draw tangents to curves and to calculate the slope of the tangent and of straight-line graphs
- confident in the use of scientific (standard) notation, for example that the number 1234 can be written as 1.234×10^3 and that 1.234×10^{-3} is the same as 0.001234

Scheme of assessment

Assessment objectives

AO1: knowledge with understanding

Candidates should be able to remember specific chemical facts, such as reactions, equations and conditions. They should be able to use correct chemical terminology. This skill is primarily one of factual recall, which many students find difficult. It is a skill that needs much practice.

AO2: application of knowledge and understanding, analysis and evaluation

Candidates have to be able to:

- explain and interpret chemical phenomena
- select and use data presented in the form of continuous prose, tables or graphs
- carry out calculations
- apply chemical principles to compounds similar to those covered by the specification
- assess the validity and accuracy of chemical experiments and suggest improvements

AO3: experiment and observation

This is examined either by internal assessment of practical work or in the practical examination.

AO4: synthesis of knowledge, understanding and skills

Candidates should be able to bring together knowledge, principles and concepts from different areas of chemistry and apply them to particular contexts.

The unit tests

Candidates take three theory papers. These are offered in June each year (Unit Test 4 is also offered in January). They can be taken more than once, with the best scores of the AS and A2 papers counting towards the A-level grade.

The A2 course includes of synoptic assessment. This involves drawing together knowledge and understanding from all parts of the AS and A2 courses. The emphasis will be on the application of principles rather than factual recall. Currently, Unit Test 5 includes a synoptic element because it examines all the organic chemistry covered by the AS and A2 specifications. Unit Test 6B is completely synoptic, examining all areas of the A-level course.

The marks for Unit Test 6B are added to the marks obtained from either the internal assessment of practical work or the practical exam. These, together with the marks from Unit Tests 4 and 5, are converted to 'uniform marks'. The total of these and the uniform marks awarded at AS determine the A-level grade.

Examination technique

Mark allocation

In all three A2 papers the marks for each part of the question are given in brackets. This is a much better guide as to how much to write than the number of dotted lines provided for the answer. If there are 2 marks, two statements must be made. For example, if the question asks for the conditions for a particular reaction and there are 2 marks available, there must be two different conditions given, such as solvent, temperature or catalyst.

Alternative answers

Do *not* give alternative answers. If one of them is wrong, the examiner will not award any marks for this part of the question. If both answers are correct, you *would* score the mark. However, there is no point in risking one answer being wrong. Beware also of contradictions, such as giving the reagent as concentrated sulphuric acid and then writing $H_2SO_4(aq)$ in an equation.

Writing your answers

In Edexcel A2 chemistry exams, the answers are written in the spaces on the question paper. If part of your answer is written elsewhere on the page, alert the examiner by writing, for example, 'see below' or 'continued on page 5'. Exam papers will be marked online, so question papers and answers will be electronically scanned. For this reason, it is essential *not to write outside the borders* marked on the page.

Correction fluid and red pens

Do not use either of these. Mistakes should be crossed out neatly before writing the new answer. Red ink is for the examiner's use only. Also, it will not show up when the paper is scanned ready for online marking.

Command words

It is important that you respond correctly to key words or phrases in the question.

- **Define** — definitions of important terms such as relative atomic mass or standard enthalpy of formation are frequently asked for. You *must* know these definitions. They are printed in red in this book.
- **Name** — give the full name of the substance, *not* its formula.
- **Identify** — give either the name or the formula.
- **Write the formula** — a molecular formula, such as C_2H_5Cl, will suffice, as long as it is unambiguous. It is no use writing C_2H_4O for the formula of ethanal, or C_3H_7Br for the formula for 2-bromopropane. This also applies to equations. For example, the equation $C_2H_4 + Br_2 \rightarrow C_2H_4Br_2$ would not score a mark, because the formula $C_2H_4Br_2$ is ambiguous.
- **Draw or write the structural formula** — this must clearly show any double bonds and the position of the functional group. For example, CH_3COOH is not acceptable as the structural formula of ethanoic acid. It must be written as:

An acceptable structural formula of but-1-ene is $H_2C=CHCH_2CH_3$.

- **Draw the full structural formula** — all the atoms and all the bonds in the molecule *must* be shown. For example, the full structural formula of ethanoic acid is:

- **State** — give the answer without any explanation. For example, if asked to state in which direction the position of equilibrium moves, the answer is simply 'to the left' or 'to the right'.
- **State, giving your reasons** — this is a difficult type of question. First, look at the mark allocation. Then state the answer (1 mark) and follow this with an explanation containing enough chemical points to score the remaining marks.
- **Explain** — look at the mark allocation and then give the same number of pieces of chemical explanation, or even one extra. For example, in answer to the question 'explain why but-2-ene has two geometric isomers (2)', the first point is that there is restricted rotation about the double bond and the second point is that there are two different groups on each double-bonded carbon atom.
- **Deduce** — the data supplied in the question, or an answer from a previous part of the question, are used to work out the answer. The data could be numerical or they could be the results of qualitative tests on an unknown substance. Alternatively, knowledge from another part of the specification may be needed to answer a question about a related topic or similar substance.
- **Suggest** — candidates are not expected to know the answer. Knowledge and understanding of similar compounds have to be used to work out (deduce) the answer. For example, the shape of SF_6 is covered in the specification, so students should be able to deduce the shape of the PCl_6^- ion. Alternatively, the question might ask candidates to suggest the identity of an organic compound because there are not sufficient data to decide between two possible isomers.
- **Compare** *or* **explain the difference between** — valid points must be made about *both* substances. For example, if the question asks for an explanation for the difference in the boiling points of hydrogen fluoride and hydrogen chloride, the different types and strengths of intermolecular forces in *both* substances must be described, together with an explanation of what causes these differences.
- **Calculate** — it is essential to show all working. Calculations at A2 are not structured in the same way as they are at AS. This means that you must make clear what you are doing at each stage. If you make a mistake early in the calculation, you could be awarded marks for the subsequent steps. However, this depends on the examiner being able to follow your working. An answer without working will score a maximum 1 mark. Always give your final answer to the number of significant figures justified by the number of significant figures in the data.
- **Identify the reagent** — give the *full* name or formula. Answers such as 'acidified dichromate' or 'OH⁻ ions' do not score full marks.

- **State the conditions** — do not automatically write down 'heat under reflux'. The answer might be 'at room temperature' or you might be expected to know the necessary solvent (e.g. ethanol for the elimination of HBr from bromoalkanes) or a specific catalyst (e.g. platinum or nickel in the addition of hydrogen to alkenes). If a concentrated acid is needed in a reaction, this must be stated. In the absence of any knowledge of the reaction, then try 'heat under reflux' — it might be correct!

Equations

- Equations must always be balanced. Word equations never score any marks.
- Ionic equations and half-equations must also balance for charge.
- State symbols must be included:
  - if the question asks for them
  - in all thermochemical equations
  - if a precipitate or a gas is produced
- The use of the symbols [O] and [H] in organic oxidation and reduction reactions, respectively, is acceptable. Equations using these symbols must still be properly balanced.
- Organic formulae used in equations must be written in such a way that their structures are unambiguous.

Stability

'A secondary carbocation is stable' has no meaning. 'Stability' must be used only when comparing two states or two sets of compounds. You have to know and understand the difference between thermodynamic stability (ΔH, ΔS and E_{cell}) and kinetic stability (activation energy and rate of reaction).

Graphs

Normally, there is a mark for labelling the axes. When sketching a graph, make sure that any numbers are on a linear scale. The graph should start at the right place, have the correct shape and end at the right place. An example is the Maxwell–Boltzmann distribution, which starts at the origin, rises in a curve to a maximum and tails off as an asymptote to the x-axis.

Diagrams of apparatus

Make sure that a flask and condenser are not drawn as one continuous piece of glassware. The apparatus must work. Be particularly careful when drawing a condenser. There must be an outlet to the air somewhere in the apparatus. In distillation, the top should be closed and the outlet should be at the end of the condenser. For heating under reflux, the top of the condenser must be open. Never draw a Bunsen burner as the heater. It is always safer to draw an electrical heater, in case one of the reagents is flammable.

Safety

A statement that laboratory coats or safety glasses must be worn will not score a mark. Safety issues must be linked to particular dangers associated with the chemicals referred to in the question.

Read the question

Questions are often very similar to, but slightly different from, those previously asked. Make sure that you answer this year's question, not last year's! Look for the words 'using your answer to...' or 'hence...'. For example, if you have been asked to calculate oxidation numbers and are then asked to 'hence explain why this is a redox reaction', your answer must be in terms of changes in oxidation number and not in terms of loss or gain of electrons.

George Facer

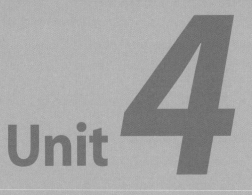

Unit 4

Periodicity, quantitative equilibria and functional group chemistry

Energetics

Chapter 1

Introduction

The coverage of energetics in this chapter builds on the content of the AS specification. Therefore, it is essential that you know the following:

■ In an **exothermic reaction** the temperature increases because chemical energy is converted into heat energy. ΔH for an exothermic reaction is negative.

The **standard enthalpy of formation** of a compound, ΔH_f°, is the enthalpy change when *1 mol* of the compound is formed from its constituent *elements* in their *standard states* at 1 atm pressure and a stated temperature, usually 298 K (25°C).

> *e* The enthalpy of formation of an element is, by definition, zero. It is the base line from which all enthalpy changes are measured, in the same way as sea level is the base line from which all heights are measured.

■ The **standard enthalpy of combustion**, ΔH_c°, is the enthalpy change when *1 mol* of the substance is completely burnt in *excess* oxygen under standard conditions.
■ The **standard enthalpy of a reaction**, ΔH_r° is the enthalpy change when the number of moles in the equation *as written* react under standard conditions.
■ The average **bond enthalpy** is the enthalpy change when *1 mol* of those bonds is broken homolytically in the gaseous phase.
■ **Hess's law** states that the value of an enthalpy change for any reaction is independent of the path from reactants to products.
■ The **first ionisation energy** of an element is the energy required to remove *one* electron from each gaseous atom in *1 mol* of atoms. It is always a positive number (indicating an endothermic process). It is represented by the equation:

$$M(g) \rightarrow M^+(g) + e^-$$

■ The **second ionisation energy** of an element is the energy required to remove one electron from each ion of 1 mol of gaseous singly charged positive ions. It is always a positive number (an endothermic process). It is represented by the equation:

$$M^+(g) \rightarrow M^{2+}(g) + e^-$$

■ The **first electron affinity**, EA, of an element is the energy change when one electron is added to *each* atom in *1 mol* of gaseous atoms. It is usually negative (exothermic).

$$M(g) + e^- \rightarrow M^-(g)$$

e If the temperature rises, the reaction is exothermic and ΔH is negative.

e Organic compounds burn to form carbon dioxide and water.

e Bond breaking is endothermic; bond making is exothermic.

A singly charged positive ion is always formed in this process, even from a non-metal.

e The second electron affinity is always endothermic, because the electron is repelled as it comes towards the negatively charged ion.

Energetics of ionic bonding

Ion-pair formation

It is often taught at GCSE that a sodium atom 'gives' one electron to a chlorine atom 'so that they both gain the stability of a noble gas'. This is a gross oversimplification. The enthalpy change for the formation of separate sodium and chloride ions from their atoms is the sum of the energies for the endothermic removal of an electron from the sodium atom and for the exothermic addition of an electron to the chlorine atom, thus:

$$Na(g) \rightarrow Na^+(g) + e^- \qquad \Delta H = +494 \text{ kJ mol}^{-1}$$
$$Cl(g) + e^- \rightarrow Cl^-(g) \qquad \Delta H = -364 \text{ kJ mol}^{-1}$$

$$Na(g) + Cl(g) \rightarrow Na^+(g) + Cl^-(g) \quad \Delta H = +130 \text{ kJ mol}^{-1}$$

This is very endothermic and, therefore, cannot be the driving force for the reaction. In addition, sodium metal has to be vaporised and chlorine molecules have to be split into atoms, making the whole process even more endothermic.

CHARLES D. WINTERS/SPL

Sugar burning in ammonium nitrate — an exothermic reaction. Ammonium nitrate is used in the manufacture of fertilisers and explosives.

When sodium and chlorine react, solid sodium chloride is formed and not separate sodium and chloride ions. The energy released when the ions come together and form the solid more than compensates for the endothermic formation of the separate ions. This energy is called the **lattice energy**.

> The lattice energy, ΔH_{latt} or LE, of an ionic compound is the energy change when *1 mol* of the *solid* is formed from its constituent *gaseous ions* that start infinitely far apart.

Born–Haber cycles

The enthalpy of formation of NaCl(s) is the enthalpy change for the reaction of solid sodium with gaseous chlorine molecules. The enthalpy change for this direct one-step reaction will, by Hess's law, be equal to the sum of the enthalpy changes involved if the reaction were to take place in several steps. Born and Haber were the first to think of the formation of an ionic compound in this way. In this case, the steps are:

■ turning solid sodium atoms into gaseous atoms
■ splitting chlorine molecules into atoms
■ removing an electron from each gaseous sodium atom
■ adding an electron to each gaseous chlorine atom
■ bringing the ions together into an ionic lattice

These processes are shown below:

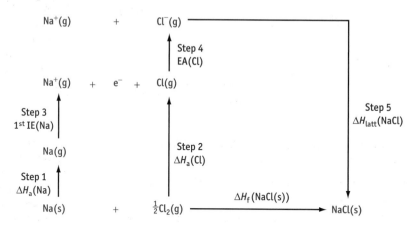

Step 1: the enthalpy of atomisation of sodium, $\Delta H_a(Na)$ (+109 kJ mol^{-1})
Step 2: the enthalpy of atomisation of chlorine, $\Delta H_a(Cl)$ (+121 kJ mol^{-1})
Step 3: the first ionisation energy of sodium, 1st IE(Na) (+494 kJ mol^{-1})
Step 4: the first electron affinity of chlorine, EA(Cl) (−364 kJ mol^{-1})
Step 5: the lattice energy of sodium chloride, $\Delta H_{latt}(NaCl)$ (−771 kJ mol^{-1})

$\Delta H_f(NaCl(s))$ = sum of the ΔH values for steps 1–5
= $\Delta H_a(Na) + \Delta H_a(Cl) + 1^{st}$ IE(Na) + EA(Cl) + $\Delta H_{latt}(NaCl)$
= +109 + 121 + 494 + (−364) + (−771) = −411 kJ mol^{-1}

The enthalpy of atomisation, ΔH_a, of an element is the enthalpy change when *1 mol* of *gaseous* atoms is made from an element in its standard state.

For example, the enthalpy of atomisation of:

- chlorine is for the change $\frac{1}{2}Cl_2(g) \rightarrow Cl(g)$
- bromine is for the change $\frac{1}{2}Br_2(l) \rightarrow Br(g)$
- sulphur is for the change $\frac{1}{8}S_8(s) \rightarrow S(g)$

If the ionic radii and the arrangement of the ions in the lattice are known, theoretical lattice energies can be calculated. The only way that they can be found experimentally is by using a Born–Haber cycle.

$$\Delta H_f(NaCl(s)) = \Delta H_a(Na) + \Delta H_a(Cl) + 1^{st}\ IE(Na) + EA(Cl) + \Delta H_{latt}(NaCl)$$
$$\Delta H_{latt}(NaCl) = \Delta H_f(NaCl(s)) - \{\Delta H_a(Na) + \Delta H_a(Cl) + 1^{st}\ IE(Na) + EA(Cl)\}$$
$$= -411 - \{+109 + (+121) + (+494) + (-364)\} = -771\ kJ\ mol^{-1}$$

Born–Haber cycles can also be drawn as energy-level diagrams. For example, for calcium chloride, $CaCl_2$, the energy-level diagram is:

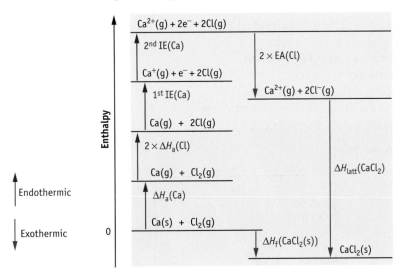

◀ Note that as 2 Cl atoms are formed from Cl_2, the enthalpy change is $2 \times \Delta H_a$. Also, because 2 Cl^- ions are formed, the enthalpy change is $2 \times EA$.

$$\Delta H_f(CaCl_2(s)) = \Delta H_a(Ca) + 2 \times \Delta H_a(Cl) + 1^{st}\ IE(Ca) + 2^{nd}\ IE(Ca)$$
$$+ 2 \times EA(Cl) + \Delta H_{latt}(CaCl_2)$$
$$\Delta H_{latt}(CaCl_2) = \Delta H_f(CaCl_2(s)) - \{\Delta H_a(Ca) + 2 \times \Delta H_a(Cl) + 1^{st}\ IE(Ca)$$
$$+ 2^{nd}\ IE(Ca) + 2 \times EA(Cl)\}$$
$$= -795 - \{+193 + 2(+121) + (+590) + (+1150) + 2(-364)\}$$
$$= -2242\ kJ\ mol^{-1}$$

Factors that affect lattice energy

The magnitude of the lattice energy depends on the strength of the forces acting on the ions. In a lattice, each ion is surrounded by a number of ions of opposite charge, resulting in strong forces of attraction and some forces of repulsion. This is illustrated in Figure 1.1.

The strength of these forces depends on:

- the magnitude of the charges on the ions
- the sum of the radii of the cation and the anion

ℯ The second ionisation energy is the energy change when an electron is removed from a gaseous 1+ ion. It is the energy required to remove the second electron, not the energy for the removal of both electrons.

- the arrangement of the ions in the lattice
- the relative sizes of the ions
- the extent of covalency

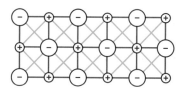

In Figure 1.1, the red lines represent forces of attraction; the blue lines represent forces of repulsion.

Figure 1.1 *The forces acting between the ions in a planar slice through a crystal of sodium chloride*

Charge and size of ions

The force between two ions of opposite charge depends upon the value of the ionic charges and how close the centres of the ions are. The stronger the force of attraction between the ions in the solid, the more exothermic is the lattice energy.

The lattice energy is proportional to the product of the charges on the two ions divided by the sum of their radii:

$$\Delta H_{latt} \propto \frac{q(+) \times q(-)}{\{r(+) + r(-)\}}$$

where $q(+)$ = the charge on the cation
$q(-)$ = the charge on the anion
$r(+)$ = the ionic radius of the cation
$r(-)$ = the ionic radius of the anion

e There are small forces of repulsion between neighbouring ions of the same charge. This is only significant when the anion is much larger than the cation, which causes the anions to be crowded together.

CROWN COPYRIGHT/HEALTH & SAFETY LABORATORY/SPL

Energy is released in the thermit process because the lattice energy of the aluminium oxide produced is much greater than the lattice energy of the iron(III) oxide reactant.

The exothermic thermit process — an aluminium wrench striking a rusty iron block

Worked example 1

Explain why the lattice energy of sodium fluoride is more exothermic than the lattice energy of potassium chloride.

Answer

It is because Na^+ has a smaller ionic radius than K^+, and F^- is smaller than Cl^-. Therefore, the forces between sodium ions and fluoride ions are stronger than those between potassium ions and chloride ions.

Worked example 2

Explain why the lattice energy of calcium oxide is approximately four times larger than that of potassium fluoride.

Answer

This is because in calcium oxide the product of the ionic charges is 4, whereas in potassium fluoride it is 1. The sums of the ionic radii of the two compounds are not very different. However, the value is smaller in CaO than in KF, so the lattice energy ratio is further increased.

The answer to worked example 2 can be explained more fully by looking at the values involved (Table 1.1).

Substance	ΔH_{latt}/kJ mol^{-1}	Product of ionic charges	Sum of ionic radii/nm
CaO	−3513	4	0.239
KF	−801	1	0.269

Table 1.1 Lattice energy and ionic charge

The lattice energy depends on the product of the charges on the ions divided by the sum of the ionic radii.

$$\text{ratio} = \frac{\text{product of ionic charges divided by sum of ionic radii for CaO}}{\text{product of ionic charges divided by sum of ionic radii for KF}}$$

$$= \frac{4/0.239}{1/0.269} = 4.5$$

$$\text{ratio} = \frac{\Delta H_{latt}(\text{CaO})}{\Delta H_{latt}(\text{KF})}$$

$$= \frac{-3513}{-801} = 4.4$$

The fact that these two values are so similar supports the theory.

Arrangement and relative size

Ions take up an arrangement in the lattice that maximises the lattice energy released. This is the position of minimum potential energy of the ions. If a small cation is surrounded by too many larger anions, a considerable amount of repulsion occurs between the larger anions. This is shown by the structures of ionic compounds of formula AB that are given in Table 1.2.

ⓔ The coordination number of an ion in an ionic lattice is the number of ions of opposite charge that are most closely arranged around it.

In sodium chloride, fitting eight chloride ions around the smaller sodium ion would result in considerable repulsion between the closely packed chloride ions. Each Na^+ ion is surrounded by six Cl^- ions; each Cl^- ion is surrounded by six Na^+ ions. This is called 6:6 coordination. This arrangement minimises repulsion.

Substance	Cationic radius/ nm	Anionic radius/ nm	Ratio of anionic radius: cationic radius	Coordination number
CsCl	0.169	0.181	1.1	8
NaCl	0.095	0.181	1.9	6
ZnS	0.074	0.184	2.5	4

Table 1.2 Ionic radii and coordination numbers

The type of lattice depends upon the ratio of the ionic radii. Compounds with a ratio of approximately 1:1 have a lattice structure similar to that of caesium chloride. Those with a ratio nearer to 2:1 have a structure similar to that of sodium chloride.

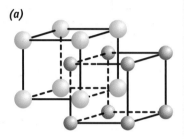

(a)

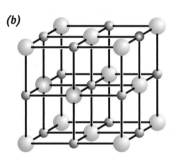

(b)

Structures of (a) caesium chloride and (b) sodium chloride

Extent of covalency: polarisation of the anion

Cations with a large charge and a small radius are highly polarising. Anions with a large charge and a large radius are highly polarisable. If either type of ion is present, the anion will be significantly polarised, resulting in the bond being partially covalent. This causes the experimental (or Born–Haber) lattice energy to be greater than the theoretical value, which is calculated assuming that the solid is 100% ionic.

Cation	Radius/nm	Anion	Radius/nm
Na^+	0.095	Cl^-	0.181
K^+	0.133	I^-	0.216
Mg^{2+}	0.065	S^{2-}	0.184

Table 1.3 Ionic radii

The polarising power of a cation depends on its charge density, which is proportional to the charge divided by the square of the radius. Therefore, the magnesium ion is the most polarising cation in Table 1.3. The iodide ion is the biggest anion, so magnesium iodide should be the most covalent compound and have the biggest difference between the experimental and the theoretical lattice energies (Table 1.4).

Substance	Experimental lattice energy/kJ mol^{-1}	Theoretical lattice energy/kJ mol^{-1}	Extent of covalency
NaCl	−780	−770	Almost none
K_2S	−2052	−1933	Significant
MgI_2	−2327	−1944	Considerable

Table 1.4 Lattice energies

The effect that covalency has on the experimental value of lattice energy is very much less than the effects of the charges and the radii of the ions.

> **Worked example**
> Explain why calcium chloride is more covalent than potassium chloride.
>
> **Answer**
> The calcium ion is 2+ and has a smaller radius than the 1+ potassium ion. Therefore, its charge density is greater. This means that it polarises the Cl^- ion to a greater extent, causing the bond in calcium chloride to be more covalent than the bond in potassium chloride.

Table 1.5 shows that:
- the magnitude of the lattice energy steadily decreases down a group of the periodic table as the size of the cation increases
- the magnitude of the lattice energy steadily decreases down the group as the size of the anion increases
- lattice energy increases as the charge on either or both the cation and the anion increases

			Lattice energy/kJ mol^{-1}		
Halides	LiF −1022	NaF −902	KF −801	RbF −767	CsF −716
	LiCl −846	NaCl −771	KCl −701	RbCl −675	CsCl −645
	LiBr −800	NaBr −733	KBr −670	RbBr −647	CsBr −619
	LiI −744	NaI −684	KI −629	RbI −609	CsI −585
	$BeCl_2$ −3006	$MgCl_2$ −2500	$CaCl_2$ −2237	$SrCl_2$ −2112	$BaCl_2$ −2018
Oxides	Li_2O −2814	Na_2O −2478	K_2O −2232	Rb_2O −2161	Cs_2O −2063
	BeO −4444	MgO −3890	CaO −3513	SrO −3310	BaO −3152
Sulphides	Li_2S −2500	Na_2S −2200	K_2S −2052	Rb_2S −1944	Cs_2S −1850
	BeS −3832	MgS −3300	CaS −3013	SrS −2850	BaS −2725
Hydroxides		$Mg(OH)_2$ −2842	$Ca(OH)_2$ −2553	$Sr(OH)_2$ −2354	$Ba(OH)_2$ −2228

Table 1.5 Lattice energies of some ionic compounds

Formulae of ionic compounds

The reason why sodium and chlorine form NaCl rather than $NaCl_2$ is not because of the mythical stability of a noble gas electronic configuration. The answer lies in comparing the enthalpy change of the two reactions:

$$Na(s) + \tfrac{1}{2}Cl_2(g) \rightarrow NaCl(s)$$
$$Na(s) + Cl_2(g) \rightarrow NaCl_2(s)$$

ΔH_f for the formation of NaCl(s) can be measured. The value is −411 kJ mol^{-1}.

ΔH_f for the formation of $NaCl_2(s)$ can be calculated from a Born–Haber cycle, assuming that the lattice energy of $NaCl_2$ would be similar to that of $MgCl_2$ (-2500 kJ mol^{-1}).

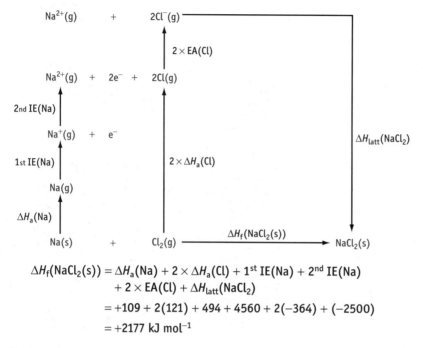

$$\Delta H_f(NaCl_2(s)) = \Delta H_a(Na) + 2 \times \Delta H_a(Cl) + 1^{st}\ IE(Na) + 2^{nd}\ IE(Na)$$
$$+ 2 \times EA(Cl) + \Delta H_{latt}(NaCl_2)$$
$$= +109 + 2(121) + 494 + 4560 + 2(-364) + (-2500)$$
$$= +2177\ \text{kJ mol}^{-1}$$

This process is very endothermic, so $NaCl_2$ is not formed.

The reason why it is so endothermic is that the extra 4560 kJ of energy, required to remove a second electron from sodium, is too great to be compensated for by the slightly higher lattice energy of the theoretical $NaCl_2$ solid. This huge jump in energy from the first to the second ionisation energy of sodium occurs because the second electron has to be removed from an inner ($2p$) shell. In this shell, the electron is screened from the 11+ nucleus by only the two $1s$-electrons. Therefore, it is held very firmly.

This concept of whether the extra energy required to remove another electron is compensated for by the higher lattice energy (or the hydration energy if the reaction is carried out in aqueous solution) is important in the chemistry of tin and lead (pp. 49–50) and in the chemistry of the transition metals (p. 187).

Melting temperatures of ionic solids

When an ionic solid melts, the lattice structure breaks down and the arrangement of ions becomes random. The average distance between neighbouring ions in the liquid is slightly greater than the interionic distance in the solid. Because the ions have to be partially separated in melting, energy is required. For 1 mol of a solid, this is ΔH_m. The value of ΔH_m depends on the lattice energy. The relationship between lattice energies, ΔH_{latt}, ΔH_m values and the melting temperatures of some ionic compounds is shown in Table 1.6.

Substance	$\Delta H_{latt}/kJ\ mol^{-1}$	$\Delta H_m/kJ\ mol^{-1}$	Melting temperature/°C
NaCl	−771	+29	801
KCl	−701	+25	770
MgO	−3890	+137	2852
CaO	−3513	+126	2614

Table 1.6 Lattice energies, melting enthalpies and melting temperatures of ionic compounds

Magnesium oxide has a high melting temperature. It is used to make the lining bricks of furnaces.

Solubility of ionic compounds

When an ionic solid dissolves in water, the lattice breaks down and the ions are separated. This is very endothermic, so you might expect that ionic solids would not dissolve in water. To explain this apparent paradox, you must think about what happens to the ions as the solid dissolves.

A furnace glowing almost white-hot

Cations become surrounded by water molecules. Strong ion–dipole forces act between the positive cations and the δ^- oxygen atoms in the water. Similarly, the anions become surrounded by water molecules with the δ^+ hydrogen atoms of the water molecules being strongly attracted to the negative anions. This process is called **hydration**. It is the highly exothermic nature of hydration that compensates for the endothermic break-up of the lattice.

Figure 1.2 An ionic solid dissolving

Surface of solid

The enthalpy of solution of a solid, ΔH_{soln}, is the enthalpy change when *1 mol* of the solid is dissolved in sufficient solvent to give an infinitely dilute solution.

The hydration enthalpy of an ion, ΔH_{hyd}, is the enthalpy change when *1 mol* of *gaseous* ions is completely surrounded by water molecules.

ⓔ An infinitely dilute solution can be thought of as one in which further dilution does not cause a heat change.

Dissolving can be regarded as a two-step process. Step 1 is to separate the ions in the solid into gaseous ions. Step 2 is the hydration of the gaseous cations and anions.

Step 1:
$$NaCl(s) \rightarrow Na^+(g) + Cl^-(g) \quad \Delta H = -\Delta H_{latt}$$

Step 2:
$$Na^+(g) \xrightarrow{H_2O} Na^+(aq) \quad \Delta H = \Delta H_{hyd}(Na^+)$$

$$Cl^-(g) \xrightarrow{H_2O} Cl^-(aq) \quad \Delta H = \Delta H_{hyd}(Cl^-)$$

On addition, the gaseous ions cancel, giving:

$$NaCl(s) \xrightarrow{H_2O} Na^+(aq) + Cl^-(aq) \quad \Delta H_{soln} = -\Delta H_{latt} + \Delta H_{hyd}(Na^+) + \Delta H_{hyd}(Cl^-)$$

This can be shown as a Hess's law cycle:

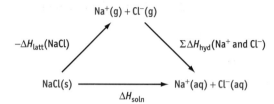

$$\Delta H_{soln} = -\Delta H_{latt} + \Delta H_{hyd}(Na^+) + \Delta H_{hyd}(Cl^-)$$

From this equation, it can be seen that:
- the more exothermic the lattice energy, the more endothermic the enthalpy of solution
- the more exothermic either of the hydration enthalpies, the more exothermic the enthalpy of solution

As exothermic changes are more likely to be spontaneous (see p. 19), solubility is lower for a large lattice energy and higher for large hydration enthalpies. Solubility depends upon the *relative* magnitudes of these quantities.

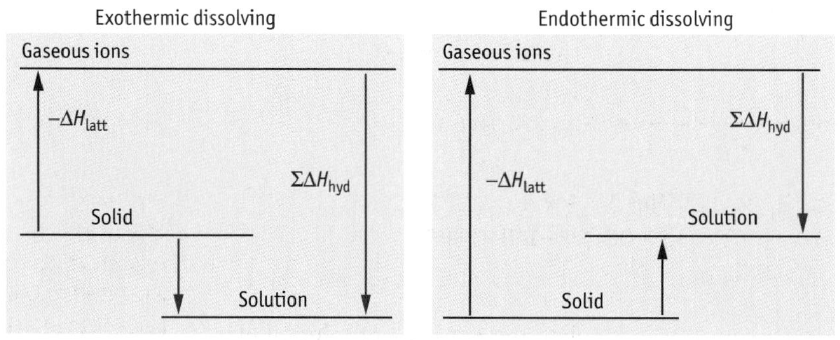

Exothermic dissolving | Endothermic dissolving

Gaseous ions

$-\Delta H_{latt}$

$\Sigma\Delta H_{hyd}$

Solid

Solution

Gaseous ions

$\Sigma\Delta H_{hyd}$

$-\Delta H_{latt}$

Solution

Solid

If the magnitude of the lattice enthalpy (blue arrow) is *less* than the sum of the hydration enthalpies of the two ions (red arrow), dissolving will be exothermic.

If the magnitude of the lattice enthalpy is *greater* than the sum of the hydration enthalpies of the two ions, dissolving will be endothermic.

A general relationship can be deduced from the energy-level diagrams above:

$\Delta H_{soln} = -$lattice energy + the sum of the hydration energies of all the ions

Cation	ΔH_{hyd}/kJ mol^{-1}	Anion	ΔH_{hyd}/kJ mol^{-1}
Li$^+$	-519	F$^-$	-506
Na$^+$	-406	Cl$^-$	-364
K$^+$	-322	Br$^-$	-335
Mg^{2+}	-1920	I$^-$	-293
Ca^{2+}	-1650	OH$^-$	-460
Sr^{2+}	-1480		
Ba^{2+}	-1360		

Table 1.7 Hydration enthalpies of ions

> **Worked example**
> Use data from Tables 1.5 and 1.7 to predict the enthalpy of solution of sodium chloride.
>
> **Answer**
> $\Delta H_{soln} = -\Delta H_{latt} + \Delta H_{hyd}(Na^+) + \Delta H_{hyd}(Cl^-)$
> $= -(-771) + (-406) + (-364) = +1$ kJ mol^{-1}

Using lattice energies and hydration energies to predict the enthalpy of solution may be inaccurate, because slight errors in any of the quantities could result in an answer with the wrong sign. For example, if the data in the above worked example had been taken from a different source, the calculation could have been:

$\Delta H_{soln} = -\Delta H_{latt} + \Delta H_{hyd}(Na^+) + \Delta H_{hyd}(Cl^-)$
$= -(-780) + (-444) + (-340) = -4$ kJ mol^{-1}

The true value of ΔH_{soln} of NaCl(s) is +3.9 kJ mol^{-1}.

Extra care must be taken with ionic compounds of formula MX$_2$. This can be illustrated using a Hess's law cycle:

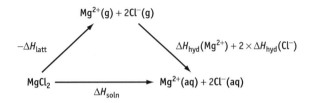

$\Delta H_{soln} = -\Delta H_{latt}(MgCl_2) + \Delta H_{hyd}(Mg^{2+}) + 2 \times \Delta H_{hyd}(Cl^-)$
$= -(-2500) + (-1920) + 2(-364) = -148$ kJ mol^{-1}

> **Worked example**
> Use data from Tables 1.5 and 1.7 to calculate the enthalpy of solution of magnesium hydroxide and calcium hydroxide. Suggest which compound is more soluble.

◀ The hydration enthalpy of the chloride ion must be multiplied by two, because there are two Cl$^-$ ions in the equation.

Answer

For magnesium hydroxide:

$$\Delta H_{soln}(Mg(OH)_2) = -\Delta H_{latt}(Mg(OH)_2) + \Delta H_{hyd}(Mg^{2+}) + 2 \times \Delta H_{hyd}(OH^-)$$
$$= -(-2842) + (-1920) + 2(-460) = +2 \text{ kJ mol}^{-1}$$

For calcium hydroxide:

$$\Delta H_{soln}(Ca(OH)_2) = -\Delta H_{latt}(Ca(OH)_2) + \Delta H_{hyd}(Ca^{2+}) + 2 \times \Delta H_{hyd}(OH^-)$$
$$= -(-2553) + (-1650) + 2(-460) = -17 \text{ kJ mol}^{-1}$$

The substances have similar formulae, but the enthalpy of solution of calcium hydroxide is more exothermic than that of magnesium hydroxide. Therefore, calcium hydroxide should be more soluble.

Table 1.8 Enthalpies (kJ mol⁻¹) of solution of anhydrous compounds at 25°C

Cation	Anion							
	F^-	Cl^-	Br^-	I^-	OH^-	CO_3^{2-}	NO_3^-	SO_4^{2-}
Li^+	+4.9**	−37	−49	−63	−24	−18	−3	−30
Na^+	+1.9	+3.9	−0.6	−7.5	−45	−27	+21	−2.4
K^+	−18	+17	+20	+20	−57	−31	+35	+24
NH_4^+	−1.2	+15	+16	+14	–	–	+26	+6.6
Ag^+	−23	+66*	+84*	+112*	–	+42*	+23	+18
Mg^{2+}	−18*	−160	−186	−213	+2.3*	−25.3*	−91	−91
Ca^{2+}	+12*	−81	−103	−120	−16.7**	−13*	−19	−18**
Al^{3+}	−27**	−330	−370	−390	*	–	–	−350

* insoluble
** slightly soluble

As can be seen from Table 1.8, many ionic solids have endothermic enthalpies of solution and are still soluble. Others have exothermic enthalpies of solution and are insoluble. The concept that exothermic changes will take place spontaneously and endothermic changes will not is an oversimplification. The criteria for spontaneity include the **entropy** change of the system (p. 17).

The conclusions that can be drawn are that:

- The enthalpy of solution of an ionic solid is a balance between the lattice energy and the sum of the hydration enthalpies of its ions.
- When comparing compounds of similar formulae, the one with the more exothermic (or less endothermic) enthalpy of solution is likely to be more soluble.
- Most soluble substances dissolve exothermically or have endothermic ΔH_{soln} values of less than 40 kJ mol⁻¹.

Solubility of the group 2 hydroxides

Solubility is a balance between the lattice energy and the sum of the hydration energies of the ions:

$$\Delta H_{soln} = -\text{lattice energy} + \text{sum of the hydration energies of the ions}$$

In any group of the periodic table, for example group 2, the lattice energies of the hydroxides are less exothermic as the group is descended. The hydration energies of the cations also become less exothermic down the group. Therefore, solubility down the group is determined by which quantity shows the *greater decrease*.

If the lattice energy decreases more than the hydration energy, the process of dissolving is more exothermic (less endothermic), so the solid is more soluble.

Substance	Lattice energy/ kJ mol^{-1}	Difference in lattice energy	Hydration enthalpy of cation/kJ mol^{-1}	Difference in hydration enthalpy
Mg(OH)$_2$	−2842		−1920	
		289		270
Ca(OH)$_2$	−2553		−1650	
		199		170
Sr(OH)$_2$	−2354		−1480	
		126		120
Ba(OH)$_2$	−2228		−1360	

Table 1.9 Differences in lattice energy and hydration enthalpy in group 2 hydroxides

It can be seen from Table 1.9 that on descending the group there is a greater change in lattice energy than there is in hydration enthalpy. This results in the enthalpy of solution becoming steadily more exothermic. Therefore, going down the group the hydroxides become increasingly soluble.

Substance	ΔH_{soln}/kJ mol^{-1}	Solubility/mol per 100 g water
Mg(OH)$_2$	+2.3	0.02×10^{-3}
Ca(OH)$_2$	−16.7	1.5×10^{-3}
Sr(OH)$_2$	−46	3.4×10^{-3}
Ba(OH)$_2$	−52	15.0×10^{-3}

Table 1.10 Solubilities and enthalpies of solution of the group 2 hydroxides

The reason why the lattice energy changes more than the hydration enthalpy is because of the way in which the two factors depend on the ionic radius:

■ The hydration energy of a cation depends upon its charge density — the charge divided by the radius.
■ The lattice energy depends upon the charges of the two ions multiplied together divided by the sum of the two ionic radii — {r(+) + (r(−)}.

The OH$^-$ ion is a small anion, similar in size to the group 2 cations. Therefore, the value of {r(+) + r(−)} increases considerably as the value of the radius of the cation, r(+), increases.

Solubility of the group 2 sulphates

The solubility of the group 2 sulphates decreases down the group as the enthalpy of solution becomes less exothermic. This is shown in Table 1.11.

Substance	ΔH_{soln}/kJ mol^{-1}	Solubility/mol per 100 g water
MgSO$_4$	−91	2×10^{-1}
CaSO$_4$	−18	5×10^{-3}
SrSO$_4$	−8.7	5×10^{-5}
BaSO$_4$	+19	9×10^{-7}

Table 1.11 Solubilities and enthalpies of solution of the group 2 sulphates

As was seen above, the lattice energy depends inversely upon the *sum* of the two ionic radii, but the hydration enthalpy of the cation depends inversely upon its radius and is *independent* of the radius of the anion.

The sulphate ion is much larger than any of the group 2 cations. Therefore, as $r(-) \gg r(+)$, the value of $\{r(+) + (r-)\}$ changes by only a small amount as the group is descended. This means that the lattice energy becomes only *slightly* smaller, whereas the hydration energy becomes *very much* smaller as the group is descended. This makes the enthalpy of solution less and less exothermic, so the solubility of the sulphates decreases.

> **e** Consider two quantities, A and B. If the value of B alters by 10%, the change in the sum of (A + B) depends upon the relative values of A and B. For example, if both have the same value of 50, an increase of 10% in the value of B results in (A + B) changing from (50 + 50) = 100 to (50 + 55) = 105. However, if B is 1, a 10% increase in the value of B results in (A + B) changing from (50 + 1) = 51 to (50 + 1.1) = 51.1. This is a much smaller change than when the values of A and B are similar.

Summary

- Solubility is a balance between the energy required to break up the lattice $(-\Delta H_{latt})$ and the hydration enthalpies of the cation and anion.
- Cations are smaller than the neutral atoms from which they are formed.
- Anions are larger than their parent atoms.
- If the anion is small and of a similar size to the cations in group 2, the decrease in lattice energy down the group is more than the decrease in hydration energy. Thus, the enthalpy of solution becomes *more* exothermic. This causes solubility to *increase* down the group.
- If the anion is large and much larger than the cations in group 2, the decrease in lattice energy down the group is less than the decrease in hydration energy. Thus, the enthalpy of solution becomes *less* exothermic. This causes the solubility to *decrease* down the group.

Entropy

It is often assumed that exothermic reactions will take place and endothermic reactions will not. This is an oversimplification, as can be seen by studying the solubilities and the enthalpies of solution of many salts. For example:
- ΔH_{soln} of ammonium nitrate is endothermic, yet it is very soluble in water.
- ΔH_{soln} of calcium carbonate is exothermic, yet it is insoluble in water.

During an exothermic process, the energy of the chemicals decreases (ΔH is negative). However, the energy of the surroundings increases by exactly the same amount. In an endothermic reaction, the chemicals gain energy (ΔH is positive) and the surroundings lose an equal quantity of energy. So what is the driving force of spontaneous change?

The answer lies in the simple concept that **energy and matter tend to spread out or disperse**.

When a highly ordered crystalline solid dissolves in water, the solid becomes dispersed throughout the liquid. When the denser gas carbon dioxide is added to air, it does not form a lower layer, but spreads throughout the air. The same happens with energy. If a hot piece of iron is placed in a beaker of water, the heat from the iron disperses into the water until both the iron and the water are at the same temperature. You cannot boil a kettle of water by putting it on a block of ice and expect the ice to become colder as the water heats up. Such a change would not break the first law of thermodynamics (the conservation of energy), but experience tells us that it never happens. Heat spontaneously flows from a hotter body to a colder body.

The spreading out of a solute into water, the spontaneous mixing of carbon dioxide and air, the heat transfer from the hot iron to the colder water are all examples of an increase in disorder. The scientific term for disorder is **entropy**.

The second law of thermodynamics states that spontaneous changes result in an increase in disorder or entropy.

The second law of thermodynamics determines:
- whether a physical or chemical change is likely to happen at a particular temperature
- whether redox reactions will take place
- equilibrium position

It can be said that the second law explains all of chemistry.

Care must be taken to include not only the entropy change of the chemicals (ΔS_{system}) but also the entropy change of the surroundings (ΔS_{surr}). For example, when solid sodium hydroxide is added to water, the mixture of the two chemicals is called the system. The test tube and the air in the room are regarded as the surroundings. For a change to happen spontaneously, ΔS_{total} must be positive:

$$\Delta S_{total} = \Delta S_{system} + \Delta S_{surr}$$

Entropy change of the system

A solid is much more ordered (or less disordered) than a liquid, which in turn is more ordered than a gas. So gaseous water is more disordered and has a larger entropy than liquid water, which has a greater entropy than ice. In general, this can be expressed as:

$$S_{solid} < S_{liquid} < S_{gas}$$

In the combustion of phosphorus, the reaction goes from a solid plus a gas to a solid:

$$P_4(s) + 5O_2(g) \rightarrow P_4O_{10}(s)$$

The disorder of a gas is replaced by the order of a solid. Therefore, the extent of disorder decreases and ΔS_{system} is negative.

When dilute hydrochloric acid is added to solid calcium carbonate, carbon dioxide gas is produced:

$$CaCO_3(s) + 2HCl(aq) \rightarrow CaCl_2(aq) + H_2O(l) + CO_2(g)$$
solid + solution → solution + gas

The disorder increases, so ΔS_{system} is positive.

The entropy change of the system can be calculated from the formula:

$$\Delta S^{\ominus}_{system} = \Sigma\, nS^{\circ}(\text{products}) - \Sigma\, nS^{\circ}(\text{reactants})$$

In this equation, n represents the stoichiometric numbers in the chemical equation.

> **e** Note the similarity between this expression and the one used to find ΔH_r from enthalpy of formation data:
>
> $$\Delta H_r = \Sigma\, n\Delta H_f(\text{products}) - \Sigma\, n\Delta H_f(\text{reactants})$$

As can be seen from Table 1.12, the entropy of a substance, for example water, decreases as it changes from gas to liquid and then to solid.

Gas	Entropy S°/ J K^{-1} mol^{-1}	Liquid	Entropy S°/ J K^{-1} mol^{-1}	Solid	Entropy S°/ J K^{-1} mol^{-1}
H_2	131	C_2H_5OH	161	P_4	164
O_2	205	CCl_4	216	P_4O_{10}	229
N_2	192	C_6H_6	174	C	5.7
$H_2O(g)$	189	$H_2O(l)$	70	$H_2O(s)$	43
CO_2	214			CaO	40
NH_3	192			$CaCO_3$	93
CH_4	186				
C_2H_6	230				

Table 1.12 Standard entropies of some elements and compounds at 25°C

Another trend is that entropy increases as substance complexity increases. For example, the entropy of ethane is greater than that of methane; the entropy of calcium carbonate is greater than that of calcium oxide.

> **Worked example**
> Use data from Table 1.12 to calculate the standard entropy change of the system for the reaction between phosphorus and oxygen:
>
> $$P_4(s) + 5O_2(g) \rightarrow P_4O_{10}(s)$$
>
> **Answer**
> $$\Delta S^{\ominus}_{system} = \Sigma\, nS^{\circ}(\text{products}) - \Sigma\, nS^{\circ}(\text{reactants})$$
> $$= 229 - (164 + 5 \times 205) = -960\ \text{J K}^{-1}\text{mol}^{-1}$$

e Note that S has joules in the units, whereas ΔH has kilojoules.

At first sight you might think that the reaction in the worked example should not take place because the entropy decreases. However, this is only the entropy change of the *system*. Both this reaction (negative ΔS value) and the reaction of acid with calcium carbonate (positive ΔS value) take place spontaneously. What has not been taken into account is the entropy change of the surroundings (the reactions are exothermic).

Entropy change of the surroundings

When an exothermic reaction takes place, heat energy is transferred to the surrounding air, causing an increase in disorder of the air molecules. This can be seen from the Maxwell–Boltzmann distribution of energies at two temperatures.

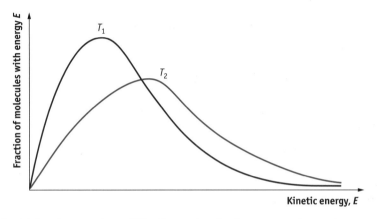

Figure 1.3
Maxwell–Boltzmann distribution of molecular energies at two temperatures (T₂ > T₁)

At the higher temperature (T_2), the molecules have a much greater range of energy and so are more random or disordered. This leads to the important conclusions:

- $\Delta S^{\ominus}_{surr}$ is positive for all exothermic reactions.
- $\Delta S^{\ominus}_{surr}$ is negative for all endothermic reactions.

This is shown pictorially in Figure 1.4.

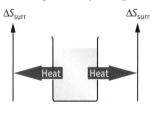
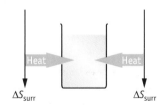

Exothermic reaction   Endothermic reaction

Figure 1.4 $\Delta S^{\ominus}_{surr}$ and exothermic and endothermic reactions

If the surroundings are hot, the entropy increase is small because the molecules have high entropy and are in chaotic motion. Conversely, if the surroundings are cold, the entropy change is much greater. The entropy change in the surroundings, caused by transfer of heat, is inversely proportional to the temperature of the surroundings — the heat change of the surroundings is the negative of the enthalpy change of the system:

$$\Delta S^{\ominus}_{surr} = \frac{-\Delta H^{\ominus}}{T}$$

e If the system is exothermic, it loses enthalpy which is transferred as heat to the surroundings.

The temperature is given in kelvin (K = °C + 273).

Total entropy change

The total entropy change (sometimes called the entropy change of the universe) is the sum of the entropy changes of the system and the surroundings:

$$\Delta S^{\ominus}_{total} = \Delta S^{\ominus}_{system} + \Delta S^{\ominus}_{surr}$$

> **Worked example**
>
> Calculate the total entropy change for the combustion of phosphorus. The entropy change of the *system* is $-960 \text{ J K}^{-1} \text{ mol}^{-1}$ and the entropy change of the *surroundings* is $+10\,000 \text{ J K}^{-1} \text{ mol}^{-1}$.
>
> **Answer**
>
> $$\Delta S^{\ominus}_{total} = \Delta S^{\ominus}_{system} + \Delta S^{\ominus}_{surr} = -960 + (+10\,000)$$
>
> $$= +9040 \text{ J K}^{-1} \text{ mol}^{-1}$$

Changes are thermodynamically feasible if the *total* entropy change is positive.

This means that an unfavourable (negative) entropy change of the system can be compensated for by a favourable (positive) entropy change of the surroundings.

$\Delta S^{\ominus}_{system}$	$\Delta S^{\ominus}_{surr}$	Feasible
Positive	Positive (exothermic reaction)	Always
Negative	Negative (endothermic reaction)	Never
Negative	Positive (exothermic reaction)	If the value of $\Delta H/T > \Delta S^{\ominus}_{system}$ (more likely at low temperatures)
Positive	Negative (endothermic reaction)	If the value $\Delta S^{\ominus}_{system} > \Delta H/T$ (more likely at high temperatures)

Table 1.13 Entropy changes and feasibility

> **Worked example 1**
>
> Comment on the feasibility of the following reaction occurring at a temperature of 298 K:
>
> $$C_2H_5OH(l) + PCl_5(s) \rightarrow C_2H_5Cl(g) + HCl(g) + POCl_3(l)$$
>
> $$\Delta H = -107 \text{ kJ mol}^{-1}; \Delta S_{system} = +368 \text{ J K}^{-1} \text{ mol}^{-1}$$

e As with ΔH calculations, you should always include a sign in the answer for ΔS.

ΔS_{system} is positive because the reaction involves liquid + solid → two gases + liquid (getting more random).

Answer

As ΔH is negative, ΔS_{surr} will be positive. Both ΔS_{surr} and ΔS_{system} are favourable (positive), so the reaction is thermodynamically feasible at all temperatures.

e The reaction may be too slow (reactants kinetically stable) at low temperatures.

Worked example 2

Comment on the feasibility of the following reaction occurring at a temperature of 298 K:

$$2C(s) + 2H_2(g) \rightarrow CH_2{=}CH_2(g)$$
$$\Delta H = +52.2 \text{ kJ mol}^{-1}; \quad \Delta S_{system} = -184 \text{ J K}^{-1} \text{ mol}^{-1}$$

Answer

Both ΔH and ΔS_{system} are unfavourable, so the reaction will not take place. The carbon and hydrogen are thermodynamically stable relative to ethene at all temperatures.

Worked example 3

Comment on the feasibility of the following reaction occurring at a temperature of 298 K:

$$H_2(g) + \tfrac{1}{2}O_2(g) \rightarrow H_2O(l)$$
$$\Delta H = -286 \text{ kJ mol}^{-1}; \quad \Delta S_{system} = -45 \text{ J K}^{-1} \text{ mol}^{-1}$$

Answer

ΔH is favourable (exothermic) but ΔS_{system} is unfavourable (negative). The reaction will take place only if $\Delta H/T$ is greater than ΔS_{system}. At low or moderate temperatures this reaction is thermodynamically feasible. Very high temperatures prevent it from taking place.

This reaction mixture is kinetically stable at room temperature. Either a catalyst or a spark is needed for reaction to occur. Water decomposes into its elements only at very high temperatures.

Worked example 4

Comment on the feasibility of the following reaction occurring at a temperature of 298 K:

$$CaCO_3(s) \rightarrow CaO(s) + CO_2(g)$$
$$\Delta H = +178 \text{ kJ mol}^{-1}; \quad \Delta S_{system} = +164 \text{ J K}^{-1} \text{ mol}^{-1}$$

Answer

ΔH is unfavourable (endothermic), but ΔS_{system} is favourable (positive). Therefore, the reaction will be thermodynamically feasible when ΔS_{system} is greater than $\Delta H/T$. This occurs at high temperatures. Thus, calcium carbonate is both thermodynamically and kinetically stable at room temperature.

e Calcium carbonate is kinetically stable as the activation energy for its decomposition is high.

e The thermodynamic stability of reactants is measured by the sign of ΔS_{total} (which must be positive), and *not* just by the sign of ΔH_r as is the reason often given at A-level.

e Thermodynamics gives no information about reaction rate. A thermodynamically feasible reaction might have such a high activation energy that it does not proceed at room temperature.

Solubility

Dissolving a gas always results in a negative $\Delta S^{\ominus}_{\text{system}}$ because the system becomes more ordered. Therefore, for a gas to be soluble it must always dissolve exothermically (the surroundings become more disordered). This means that the equilibrium:

$$X(g) \rightleftharpoons X(aq)$$

is driven to the left by an increase in temperature. Gases are less soluble in hot water than in cold water.

Dissolving solids always results in a positive $\Delta S^{\ominus}_{\text{system}}$ (the system becomes more disordered). This means that $\Delta H^{\ominus}_{\text{soln}}$ can be either negative (the surroundings also become more disordered) or slightly positive (the surroundings become slightly less disordered). The equilibrium:

$$X(s) \rightleftharpoons X(aq)$$

is driven to the left (less soluble) if $\Delta H^{\ominus}_{\text{soln}}$ is exothermic and to the right (more soluble) if $\Delta H^{\ominus}_{\text{soln}}$ is endothermic.

Melting and boiling points

At equilibrium, the value of ΔS_{total} is zero. At 0°C, there is equilibrium between ice and water. The ice does not melt, nor does the water freeze, unless heat is added to or taken from the system. Neither direction is thermodynamically feasible, so the two forms of water remain in equilibrium:

$$\Delta S_{\text{total}} = \Delta S_{\text{system}} + \Delta S_{\text{surr}}$$

$$= \Delta S_{\text{system}} - \frac{\Delta H}{T} = 0$$

$$\Delta S_{\text{system}} = \frac{\Delta H}{T} \quad \text{or} \quad T = \frac{\Delta H}{\Delta S_{\text{system}}}$$

ΔH for ice melting = +6012 J mol^{-1}

$\Delta S_{\text{system}} = S(\text{water}) - S(\text{ice}) = +22$ J K^{-1} mol^{-1}

melting temperature of ice $= \dfrac{6012}{22} = 273$ K $= 0°C$

ΔH for water boiling = +40 700 J mol^{-1}

$\Delta S_{\text{system}} = S(\text{steam}) - S(\text{water}) = +109$ J K^{-1} mol^{-1}

boiling temperature of water $= \dfrac{40\,700}{109} = 373$ K $= 100°C$

It can be seen from the expression $T = \Delta H/\Delta S$, that the melting or boiling temperature depends upon the amount of energy required for the change of state. This explains why boiling and melting temperatures depend on the strength of the forces between the particles:

strong force = large amount of energy needed to separate the particles = high melting or boiling temperature

e The entropy values used must be those at the melting temperature, not those at 25°C.

Summary

- The reactants are thermodynamically unstable relative to the products if ΔS_{total} for the change is positive. This means that the reaction is thermodynamically feasible.
- Endothermic reactions can happen only if the entropy change of the system is positive.
- Endothermic reactions are more likely to take place at higher temperatures.
- Exothermic reactions are always thermodynamically favourable if the entropy change of the system is positive.
- Exothermic reactions are thermodynamically favourable even when the entropy of the system is negative, if the entropy change of the surroundings outweighs the entropy change of the system.

Questions

Questions 1–4 are revision questions on the energetics required for AS. The data required to answer these questions are given in the tables below.

Substance	ΔH_f/kJ mol^{-1}
$C_2H_6(g)$	−85
$CO_2(g)$	−394
$H_2O(g)$	−242
$CO(g)$	−111

Substance	ΔH_c/kJ mol^{-1}
$C_2H_6(g)$	−1560
$C_2H_4(g)$	−1409
$C_2H_5OH(l)$	−1371
$C(s)$	−394
$H_2(g)$	−286

Bond	ΔH_{BE}/kJ mol^{-1}
C–C	+348
C=C	+612
C–H	+412
C–Br	+276
H–Br	+366

1 Using enthalpy of formation data, calculate the enthalpy of the reaction:

$$C_2H_6(g) + 2H_2O(g) \rightarrow 2CO(g) + 5H_2(g)$$

2 Using enthalpy of combustion data, calculate the enthalpy of formation of ethanol.

3 Using bond enthalpy data, calculate the enthalpy of the reaction:

$$CH_2{=}CH{-}CH{=}CH_2 + 2HBr \rightarrow CH_3{-}CHBr{-}CHBr{-}CH_3$$

4 Draw a Hess's law cycle and use it, together with the enthalpy of combustion data in the table above, to find the enthalpy of the reaction:

$$C_2H_4(g) + H_2(g) \rightarrow C_2H_6(g)$$

Use the data in the table below to answer questions 5 and 6.

	Enthalpy change/kJ mol^{-1}
ΔH_f AlF$_3$(s)	−1301
1st IE aluminium	+577
2nd IE aluminium	+1820
3rd IE aluminium	+2740
ΔH_a aluminium	+314
ΔH_a fluorine	+79
EA fluorine	−348
ΔH_f Na$_2$O(s)	−416
1st IE sodium	+494
1st EA oxygen	−142
ΔH_a sodium	+109
ΔH_a oxygen	+248
Lattice energy Na$_2$O(s)	−2478

5 Draw a Born–Haber cycle for aluminium fluoride, AlF$_3$(s). Use it and the data above to calculate the lattice energy of solid aluminium fluoride.

6 Draw a Born–Haber cycle for sodium oxide, Na$_2$O(s). Use it and the data in the table above to calculate the *second* electron affinity of oxygen.

7 Draw a Hess's law diagram, and use it together with the data below, to calculate ΔH_{soln} of lithium fluoride, LiF.

	Enthalpy change/kJ mol^{-1}
$\Delta H_{hyd}(Li^+(g))$	−519
$\Delta H_{hyd}(F^-(g))$	−506
$\Delta H_{latt}(LiF(s))$	−1022

Comment on the likely solubility of lithium fluoride in water.

8 Draw a Hess's law diagram for dissolving calcium chloride. Use it and the data below to calculate ΔH_{hyd} of a chloride ion, Cl^-.

	Enthalpy change/kJ mol^{-1}
$\Delta H_{hyd}(Ca^{2+}(g))$	−1650
$\Delta H_{latt}(CaCl_2(s))$	−2237
$\Delta H_{soln}(CaCl_2(s))$	−83

9 Given the ionic radii of the ions M^{2+} and Q^{3+}, explain which ion would have a higher hydration enthalpy.

Ion	Ionic radius/nm
M^{2+}	0.031
Q^{3+}	0.095

10 Suggest and explain the trend in solubility of the group 2 fluorides, MgF_2 to BaF_2.

11 Suggest and explain the trend in solubility of the group 2 carbonates, $MgCO_3$ to $BaCO_3$.

12 State and explain:

a whether $H_2O(l)$ at 25 °C has a higher or lower entropy than $H_2O(l)$ at 35 °C

b whether $H_2O(l)$ at 100 °C has a higher or lower entropy than $H_2O(g)$ at 100 °C

13 Use the following equations to state and explain whether the reactions result in an increase or decrease in the entropy of the systems:

a $NH_4NO_3(s) \rightarrow NH_4^+(aq) + NO_3^-(aq)$

b $NH_4Cl(s) + OH^-(aq) \rightarrow NH_3(g) + Cl^-(aq) + H_2O(l)$

c $CaCO_3(s) \rightarrow CaO(s) + CO_2(g)$

14 a Calculate ΔS_{system} for the following reaction at 85 °C:

$$N_2O_4(g) \rightarrow 2NO_2(g) \quad \Delta H = +57.4 \text{ kJ mol}^{-1}$$

Compound	Entropy, S, at 85 °C/J K^{-1} mol^{-1}
$N_2O_4(g)$	325
$NO_2(g)$	256

b Calculate ΔS_{total} for the reaction at 85 °C.

c Comment on the feasibility of this reaction.

d Explain the term **thermodynamic stability** with reference to this reaction.

15 a Predict which of the following changes, W to Z, will take place at a temperature of 298 K.

Change	ΔH/kJ mol^{-1}	ΔS_{system}/J K^{-1} mol^{-1}
W	−170	+500
X	−170	−500
Y	+170	−500
Z	+170	+500

b Which of the changes W to Z will become more favourable when he temperature is increased?

16 Ludwig Boltzmann could be described as the 'father of entropy'. Refer to the web and write a few lines about him. What was written on his tombstone?

The periodic table

Chapter 2

Introduction

The periodic table is divided into vertical columns, called **groups**, and horizontal rows, called **periods**.

Elements in the same group have the same **electron configuration** in their outer orbits. For example, all the elements in group 2 have the configuration ns^2; all the elements in group 4 have the configuration $ns^2 \, np^2$.

All the elements in a period have the same number of orbits occupied. For example, all the elements in the third period have electrons in the first, second and third orbits.

The periodic table can also be divided into **blocks**, depending on the **orbital** that the last electron entered:

- Groups 1 and 2 are in the s-block.
- Groups 3 to 7 and Group 0 (the noble gases) are in the p-block.
- The elements scandium (Sc) to zinc (Zn) and the two rows below them, plus actinium (Ac), are in the d-block.
- The elements cerium (Ce) to lutetium (Lu) and the radioactive elements thorium (Th) to lawrencium (Lr) are in the f-block.

> **e** The definition of an s-block element is one in which the highest energy electron is in an s-orbital. Similarly, for the p-block, the highest energy electron is in a p-orbital. This definition breaks down for the d-block elements, which are defined in terms of their positions in the periodic table.

Trends in a period

A period is a horizontal row of elements in the periodic table, starting with an alkali metal (except in the first period) and finishing with a noble gas.

- The first period is H and He.
- The second period is Li, Be, B, C, N, O, F, Ne.
- The third period is Na, Mg, Al, Si, P, S, Cl, Ar.
- The fourth period includes the d-block elements Sc to Zn.

Electron configuration

Electrons are added to the same shell or orbit. The elements in groups 1 and 2 have their outer electrons in an s-orbital. The elements in groups 3 to 7 and group 0 have their outer electrons in p-orbitals.

> **e** Do not confuse orbits (first, second, third etc.) with orbitals (s, p, d and f). Orbits are sometimes called shells; orbitals are sometimes called sub-shells.

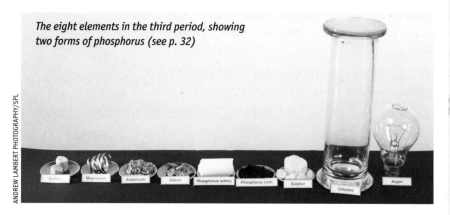

The eight elements in the third period, showing two forms of phosphorus (see p. 32)

(see p. 32)

The electron configurations of the elements in the third period are given in Table 2.1.

ANDREW LAMBERT PHOTOGRAPHY/SPL

Element	Electron configuration
Na	$1s^2\,2s^2\,2p^6\,3s^1$
Mg	$1s^2\,2s^2\,2p^6\,3s^2$
Al	$1s^2\,2s^2\,2p^6\,3s^2\,3p^1$
Si	$1s^2\,2s^2\,2p^6\,3s^2\,3p^2$
P	$1s^2\,2s^2\,2p^6\,3s^2\,3p^3$
S	$1s^2\,2s^2\,2p^6\,3s^2\,3p^4$
Cl	$1s^2\,2s^2\,2p^6\,3s^2\,3p^5$
Ar	$1s^2\,2s^2\,2p^6\,3s^2\,3p^6$

Table 2.1 Electron configurations of elements in the third period

The inner shells containing $1s^2\,2s^2\,2p^6$ can be written as [Ne]. Hence, the electronic configuration of sulphur can be given as [Ne] $3s^2\,3p^4$.

Valence electrons

Valence electrons are those that can be used to form ionic or covalent bonds.

- For the elements in the third period (apart from argon), the number of valence electrons is equal to the number of electrons in the third orbit. Argon has no valence electrons as it does not form any bonds.
- If an element has six valence electrons that are all used in bonding with a more electronegative element, the element has an oxidation number of +6.
- If only four valence electrons are used when bonding to a more electronegative element, the element has an oxidation number of +4.

The common oxidation numbers of the elements in the third period are shown in Figure 2.1.

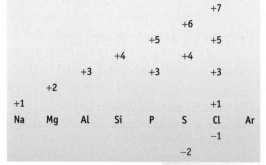

Figure 2.1 Oxidation numbers of the elements in the third period

Expansion of the octet

The third orbit can hold a maximum of 18 electrons. This is because this orbit is divided into three different types of orbitals:

- a single 3s-orbital, which can hold two electrons

- three 3p-orbitals, which can hold two electrons each, making a total of six
- five 3d-orbitals, which can hold two electrons each, making a total of ten

Silicon

Silicon has four valence electrons and so will form four covalent bonds, as in SiO_2 and $SiCl_4$. It can also accept pairs of electrons into its empty d-orbitals, as in the SiF_6^{2-} ion.

Phosphorus

Phosphorus has five valence electrons. When it forms three covalent bonds, as in PCl_3, it has the electron structure of the noble gas argon.

This compound has three bond pairs of electrons and one lone pair. These electron pairs repel each other to a position of maximum separation. Therefore, its shape is pyramidal. The Cl–P–Cl bond angle is less than the tetrahedral angle of 109.5° because the lone pair/bond pair repulsion is stronger than the bond pair/bond pair repulsion.

However, in phosphorus one electron can be promoted, by an endothermic process, to an empty 3d-orbital:

$$[Ne]\ 3s^2\ 3p_x{}^1\ 3p_y{}^1\ 3p_z{}^1 \rightarrow [Ne]\ 3s^1\ 3p_x{}^1\ 3p_y{}^1\ 3p_z{}^1\ 3d^1$$

This gives the phosphorus atom five unpaired electrons. Therefore, five covalent bonds can be formed, as in PCl_5:

PCl_5 has five bond pairs and no lone pairs. The five bond pairs repel each other to a position of maximum separation (minimum repulsion or a position of minimum potential energy), so the molecule has a trigonal bipyramidal shape.

The energy required to promote an electron (and break an extra Cl–Cl bond) is obtained from the bond energies of the two additional P–Cl bonds. With iodine, however, formation of the weaker P–I covalent bond is not sufficiently exothermic to compensate for the energy required to promote a 3s-electron into an empty 3d-orbital, so PI_5 does not exist.

Sulphur

Sulphur has the electronic configuration $[Ne]\ 3s^2\ 3p_x{}^2\ 3p_y{}^1\ 3p_z{}^1\ 3d^0$. Therefore, it can form two covalent bonds, as in H_2S, thus attaining the electron configuration of argon:

Also, one of the $3p_x$-electrons of sulphur can be promoted into an empty 3d-orbital:

$$[Ne]\ 3s^2\ 3p_x{}^2\ 3p_y{}^1\ 3p_z{}^1 \rightarrow [Ne]\ 3s^2\ 3p_x{}^1\ 3p_y{}^1\ 3p_z{}^1\ 3d^1$$

SiCl₄

PCl₃

Shape of PCl₃

PCl₅

Shape of PCl₅

ⓔ At room temperature, PCl_5 is thermodynamically stable compared with PCl_3 and Cl_2. Therefore, the reaction $PCl_3 + Cl_2 \rightarrow PCl_5$ is energetically feasible.

This gives the sulphur atom four unpaired electrons. Therefore, four covalent bonds can be formed, as in SO_2:

SO_2 has two σ-bonds (and two π-bonds) plus one lone pair. Therefore, the shape of the molecule is bent (non-linear).

Further, one of the $3p_x$-electrons and one of the $3s$-electrons can be promoted into two different $3d$-orbitals:

$$[Ne]\ 3s^2\ 3p_x^2\ 3p_y^1\ 3p_z^1 \rightarrow [Ne]\ 3s^1\ 3p_x^1\ 3p_y^1\ 3p_z^1\ 3d^1\ 3d^1$$

This gives the sulphur atom six unpaired electrons. Therefore, six covalent bonds can be formed:

- six σ-bonds, as in SF_6
- three σ- and three π-bonds, as in SO_3
- four σ- and two π-bonds, as in H_2SO_4

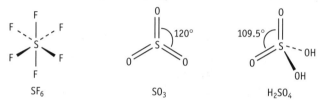

Chlorine

Chlorine has the electron configuration $[Ne]\ 3s^2\ 3p_x^2\ 3p_y^2\ 3p_z^1$. It has one unpaired electron and so forms one covalent bond, as in HCl.

Also, electrons can be promoted into empty $3d$-orbitals. If one of the $3p_y$-electrons is promoted, the chlorine atom has three unpaired electrons. Therefore, three covalent bonds can be formed, as in ClF_3.

If two electrons are promoted (one $3p_y$-electron and one $3p_x$-electron), the chlorine atom has five unpaired electrons. Five covalent bonds can be formed, as in the ClO_3^- ion:

$$^-O \longrightarrow \overset{\cdot\cdot}{Cl} \diagdown\diagup O$$

ClO_3^-

One of the $3s$-electrons can also be promoted, giving seven unpaired electrons and forming seven covalent bonds, as in $HClO_4$.

Argon

Although argon has empty $3d$-orbitals, the energy required to promote an electron would not be compensated for by any bond energy released. Krypton does form compounds. This is because the energy required to promote a $4p$-electron into an empty $4d$-orbital is considerably less than that required to promote a $3p$-electron into a $3d$-orbital. The same applies to xenon, which forms XeF_4. This involves promoting two $5p$ electrons into empty $5d$-orbitals.

Atomic radius

Atomic radius *decreases* across a period.

Element	Na	Mg	Al	Si	P	S	Cl
Radius/nm	0.16	0.14	0.13	0.12	0.11	0.10	0.099

Table 2.2 Atomic radii of the elements in period 3

The atomic radius decreases across a period because the nuclear charge increases without there being an increase in the number of electron shells. The force between the nucleus and the electrons increases as the atomic number increases, drawing the electrons closer to the nucleus and, therefore, reducing the atomic radius.

First ionisation energy

The first ionisation energy is defined as the energy change *per mol* for the process:

$$E(g) \rightarrow E^+(g) + e^-$$

For chlorine, it is the energy change per mol for the process:

$$Cl(g) \rightarrow Cl^+(g) + e^-$$

The general trend across a period is for the first ionisation energy to increase. This is because the number of protons increases without an increase in the number of inner electron shells. The effective nuclear charge increases and the radius of the atom decreases. Together, these result in an increase in the first ionisation energy.

There are two interruptions to this trend:
- The first ionisation energy of aluminium is less than that of magnesium.
- The first ionisation energy of sulphur is less than that of phosphorus.

The electron removed from aluminium is the single $3p$-electron, whereas the electron removed from magnesium is one of the two $3s$-electrons. The $3p$-electron in aluminium is slightly shielded by the $3s$-electrons and so is easier to remove, in spite of the increased nuclear charge and smaller size of the aluminium atom compared with magnesium.

The $3p$-electron is in a higher energy level, so less energy is needed to remove it. An analogy would be that it takes more energy to remove a spacecraft from the surface of the Earth than from an orbiting space station, which is at a much higher potential-energy level.

> **e** Do not explain this effect in terms of the 'stability' of the full s-orbital in magnesium. There is no evidence that this is a stable state, as is shown by the high reactivity of magnesium, [Ne] $3s^2$, and the lower reactivity of aluminium, [Ne] $3s^2\ 3p^1$.

Half-filled and fully filled p-orbitals are slightly stabilised (are at a lower energy level) for a complex reason called exchange energy. It arises from the number of different ways in which two electrons within the same energy level and with parallel spins can be arranged. This concept is beyond A-level.

> **e** The element must be gaseous and the electron must be removed from an *atom* to form a gaseous unipositive ion.

The electron removed from sulphur is from a doubly occupied $3p_x$-orbital, whereas the electron removed from phosphorus is from a singly occupied p-orbital.

The two electrons in the $3p_x$-orbital repel each other, making it easier to remove one of them, in spite of the increased nuclear charge.

Sulphur: [Ne] $3s^2\ 3p_x^2\ 3p_y^1\ 3p_z^1$

Phosphorus: [Ne] $3s^2\ 3p_x^1\ 3p_y^1\ 3p_z^1$

Metallic character

The metallic character of the elements decreases across the period as the atomic number of the element increases.

Typical properties of the metals are:
- They exist as metallic lattices in which the positive ions are arranged in a regular pattern and are surrounded by a 'sea' of delocalised electrons.
- They conduct electricity in the solid state; this is caused by the mobile delocalised electrons.
- They are malleable and ductile.
- They form positive ions (e.g. Na^+, Mg^{2+} and Al^{3+}).
- They have low ionisation energies.
- They react with oxygen to form basic oxides.
- They react with water to form hydrogen gas.
- They react with halogens to form ionic halides.

Typical properties of the non-metal are:
- They exist as simple molecules (e.g. Cl_2 and P_4) or as giant covalent lattices such as graphite, diamond and silicon.
- Apart from graphite, they do not conduct electricity.
- They are brittle (graphite and diamond are exceptions).
- They form negative ions, either monatomic anions (e.g. Cl^-) or polyatomic oxygen-containing anions (e.g. SO_4^{2-}).
- They form covalent bonds.
- They have high ionisation energies.
- They react with oxygen to form acidic oxides.
- Apart from fluorine and chlorine, they are unreactive with water.
- They react with halogens to form covalent halides.

Reactions of the period 3 elements and their compounds

The elements in the third period are:

sodium	magnesium	aluminium	silicon	phosphorus	sulphur	chlorine	argon
Na	Mg	Al	Si	P	S	Cl	Ar

Argon is chemically inert and does not react.

Reaction with oxygen

Apart from sodium, which forms a peroxide, and chlorine, which does not react, the elements in period 3 react with oxygen in air to form oxides.

Sodium

When heated in air, sodium burns with a yellow flame and produces sodium peroxide:

$$2Na + O_2 \rightarrow Na_2O_2$$

Sodium peroxide is an ionic compound containing the O_2^{2-} ion, $^-O\text{–}O^-$.

Under these conditions, sodium does not form an oxide because the sodium ion is singly charged and the lattice energy of sodium oxide is not sufficient to compensate for breaking both the bonds in the O=O molecule.

Magnesium

Magnesium burns in air with a bright white flame:

$$2Mg + O_2 \rightarrow 2MgO$$

It is because of this that magnesium is used in the manufacture of flares and fireworks. Magnesium oxide is a white solid that is basic.

The above reaction is an example of a simple redox reaction. The magnesium atoms lose two electrons and so are oxidised:

$$Mg \rightarrow Mg^{2+} + 2e^-$$

The oxygen atoms each gain two electrons and so are reduced:

$$O_2 + 4e^- \rightarrow 2O^{2-}$$

The oxidation number of sodium goes up from 0 to +2; that of oxygen goes down from 0 to –2.

Aluminium

Aluminium is usually coated in a protective layer of oxide and so does not corrode in air. The high lattice energy of aluminium oxide is the reason for this protection.

If oxide-coated aluminium is heated strongly in air, the Al_2O_3 lattice breaks down and then the aluminium burns brightly, with the evolution of a huge amount of heat:

$$4Al + 3O_2 \rightarrow 2Al_2O_3$$

Aluminium oxide is amphoteric (p. 34). However, it is completely insoluble in water and an aqueous suspension of it has a pH of 7.

Silicon

Silicon exists as a giant covalent lattice similar to diamond. It will react with air, but only when strongly heated, because strong covalent bonds have to be broken in both the silicon lattice and in the oxygen molecules. Silicon dioxide, a hard white solid, is formed:

$$Si + 2O_2 \rightarrow SiO_2$$

Silicon dioxide is insoluble, so a mixture of it and water is pH 7. Silicon dioxide is weakly acidic and reacts with molten or concentrated sodium hydroxide.

◀ The lithium ion is smaller than Na^+ and so the lattice energy of its oxide, Li_2O, is exothermic enough for both covalent bonds in the O_2 molecule to break and form two O^{2-} ions. Magnesium ions are 2+ and smaller than Na^+, so the lattice energy of MgO is also large enough to allow O^{2-} ions to form.

ⓔ Oxidation is loss of electrons.

ⓔ Reduction is gain of electrons.

◀ Other amphoteric oxides, such as zinc oxide, lead(II) oxide and tin(II) oxide, are insoluble in water.

Phosphorus

Phosphorus exists in two common forms (**allotropes**). White phosphorus consists of P_4 molecules and burns in air when gently heated:

$$P_4 + 5O_2 \rightarrow P_4O_{10}$$

It must not be handled — body heat causes it to catch fire.

White phosphorus burns with a yellow-white flame and produces clouds of poisonous white phosphorus(V) oxide. The formula of this compound is sometimes simplified to P_2O_5, but it consists of P_4O_{10} molecules.

White phosphorus is stored under water. If a piece of phosphorus is left exposed to the air, it dries out and then catches fire because the gradual oxidation process produces enough heat to ignite it.

The other form of phosphorus, called red phosphorus, has a more complex structure than the white allotrope. It needs stronger heating to burn in air to form phosphorus(V) oxide.

Phosphorus(V) oxide is an acidic oxide that reacts with water to form a solution of phosphoric(V) acid, H_3PO_4:

$$P_2O_5 + 3H_2O \rightarrow 2H_3PO_4$$

Phosphoric(V) acid forms a solution of $H^+(aq)$ and $H_2PO_4^-(aq)$ ions that has a pH of ≈ 1:

$$H_3PO_4(aq) \rightleftharpoons H^+(aq) + H_2PO_4^-(aq)$$

Sulphur

Sulphur is a yellow solid that burns in air with a blue flame to produce sulphur dioxide:

$$S + O_2 \rightarrow SO_2$$

Sulphur is in the +4 oxidation state in SO_2. Sulphur dioxide is acidic, reacting with water to form a solution of sulphuric(IV) acid (also called sulphurous acid):

$$SO_2 + H_2O \rightarrow H_2SO_3$$

Sulphuric(IV) acid partially ionises into H^+ ions and hydrogensulphate(IV) ions and the solution has a pH ≈ 2.

$$H_2SO_3(aq) \rightleftharpoons H^+(aq) + HSO_3^-(aq)$$

ZAHOOR UL-HAQ

Sodium (left), phosphorus (centre) and sulphur (right) burning in oxygen

e The formula of white phosphorus is often written as P rather than as P_4.

Chlorine
Chlorine does not react directly with oxygen.

Acid–base character of the oxides and hydroxides

The trend across the period is for the elements to change from metallic (sodium) to non-metallic (chlorine). Therefore, the oxides go from being strongly basic to strongly acidic.

Element	Na	Mg	Al	Si	P	S	Cl
Oxide	Na_2O	MgO	Al_2O_3	SiO_2	P_4O_6 P_4O_{10}	SO_2 SO_3	Cl_2O Cl_2O_5 Cl_2O_7
Acid–base	Basic	Basic	Amphoteric	Weakly acidic	Acidic	Acidic	Acidic
Hydroxide	NaOH	$Mg(OH)_2$	$Al(OH)_3$				
Acid–base character	Alkaline	Alkaline	Amphoteric				

Table 2.3 Acid–base character of the oxides and hydroxides of the period 3 elements

◀ The solubility in water of basic oxides decreases across a period and that of the acidic oxides increases. The two oxides in the middle, Al_2O_3 and SiO_2, are insoluble.

A base is a substance that accepts a proton from an acid. Therefore, it reacts with an acid to form a cation and water.

An alkali is a base that is soluble in water and produces $OH^-(aq)$ ions in solution.

An amphoteric substance can react as either a base or an acid.

An acid is a substance that gives a proton to a base. Therefore, it reacts with a base to form an anion and water.

An acidic substance produces $H^+(aq)$ ions in water.

Sodium oxide and hydroxide

Sodium oxide
Sodium oxide is a basic oxide. It is an ionic solid consisting of a regular array of Na^+ and O^{2-} ions. It removes protons from water, forming an alkaline solution of sodium hydroxide (pH ≈ 14):

$$Na_2O + H_2O \rightarrow 2NaOH$$

It reacts with an acid to form a salt and water. For example, it reacts with dilute sulphuric acid to form sodium sulphate:

$$Na_2O + H_2SO_4 \rightarrow Na_2SO_4 + H_2O$$

The ionic equation for the reaction of sodium oxide with an acid is:

$$Na_2O(s) + 2H^+(aq) \rightarrow 2Na^+(aq) + H_2O(l)$$

Sodium hydroxide
Sodium hydroxide is an alkali:

$$NaOH + aq \rightarrow Na^+(aq) + OH^-(aq)$$

Magnesium oxide and hydroxide

Magnesium oxide
Magnesium oxide is a basic oxide. It is ionic, containing the O^{2-} ion.

ℯ Sodium peroxide, Na_2O_2, is also a base. It reacts with water to form an alkaline solution of sodium hydroxide and hydrogen peroxide:

$Na_2O_2 + 2H_2O \rightarrow$ $2NaOH + H_2O_2$

It reacts slowly with water to form an alkaline suspension of magnesium hydroxide (pH ≈ 11):

$$MgO + H_2O \rightarrow Mg(OH)_2$$

It reacts with H^+ ions from an acid:

$$MgO(s) + 2H^+(aq) \rightarrow Mg^{2+}(aq) + H_2O(l)$$

It reacts with dilute sulphuric acid to form magnesium sulphate and water:

$$MgO + H_2SO_4 \rightarrow MgSO_4 + H_2O$$

The white solid reacts to form a colourless solution.

Magnesium hydroxide

Magnesium hydroxide is also a base and reacts with acids. For example, with dilute sulphuric acid the equation is:

$$Mg(OH)_2(s) + 2H^+(aq) \rightarrow Mg^{2+}(aq) + 2H_2O(l)$$

With dilute hydrochloric acid the equation is:

$$Mg(OH)_2 + 2HCl \rightarrow MgCl_2 + 2H_2O$$

Aluminium oxide and hydroxide

Both aluminium oxide and aluminium hydroxide are **amphoteric**. Neither is soluble in water, so suspensions in water have pH 7.

Reaction as a base

On addition of an acid, both the oxide and hydroxide act as bases. Al^{3+} ions are formed:

$$Al_2O_3(s) + 6H^+(aq) \rightarrow 2Al^{3+}(aq) + 3H_2O(l)$$
$$Al(OH)_3(s) + 3H^+(aq) \rightarrow Al^{3+}(aq) + 3H_2O(l)$$

Reaction as an acid

On addition of an alkali, both the oxide and hydroxide react to form the complex ion $[Al(OH)_6]^{3-}$:

$$Al_2O_3(s) + 6OH^-(aq) + 3H_2O(l) \rightarrow 2[Al(OH)_6)]^{3-}(aq)$$
$$Al(OH)_3(s) + 3OH^-(aq) \rightarrow [Al(OH)_6)]^{3-}(aq)$$

This ion consists of six hydroxide ions datively bonded to a central aluminium ion. The overall charge is 3–, because the six OH^- ions have a total charge of 6– and the 3+ of the aluminium ion neutralises three of these negative charges.

> **ⓔ** This reaction is fundamental to the purification of bauxite in the extraction of aluminium.
>
> Bauxite contains aluminium oxide with impurities of iron(III) oxide and titanium(IV) oxide (both basic oxides) and silicon dioxide (a weakly acidic oxide). When 10% sodium hydroxide solution is added, the amphoteric aluminium oxide reacts to form a solution. (Do not say that it 'dissolves'. A chemical reaction is taking place, *not* the physical change of dissolving.) The red basic iron(III) oxide and the white titanium(IV) oxide do not react, nor does the unreactive silicon dioxide, so these impurities can be filtered off.

ⓔ Calcium sulphate is only sparingly soluble. Therefore, the reaction between a piece of solid calcium oxide and dilute sulphuric acid soon stops, because the calcium oxide becomes coated with calcium sulphate.

When aqueous sodium hydroxide is added to a solution containing aluminium ions, a white precipitate of aluminium hydroxide is first formed:

$$Al^{3+}(aq) + 3OH^-(aq) \rightarrow Al(OH)_3(s)$$

If excess sodium hydroxide is then added, this precipitate reacts to form a colourless solution of sodium aluminate:

$$Al(OH)_3(s) + 3OH^-(aq) \rightarrow [Al(OH)_6)]^{3-}(aq)$$

The sodium ions are spectator ions and are left out of both ionic equations.

Silicon dioxide

The structure of solid silicon dioxide is a giant covalent lattice in which each silicon atom is bonded to four oxygen atoms and each oxygen atom is bonded to two silicon atoms. Sand and quartz are forms of silicon dioxide.

*The Sahara desert,
Morocco. Sand is a
form of silicon dioxide.*

Silicon dioxide is very unreactive. It is a weakly acidic oxide, but, because of its high lattice energy, it reacts only slightly with hot concentrated sodium hydroxide to form a solution of sodium silicate:

$$SiO_2 + 2NaOH \rightleftharpoons Na_2SiO_3 + H_2O$$

Phosphorus trioxide and pentoxide

Phosphorus forms two oxides: phosphorus trioxide, P_2O_3, and phosphorus pentoxide, P_2O_5. The correct formulae are P_4O_6 and P_4O_{10}, but the simpler formulae are generally used. Both oxides are strongly acidic. They react with water to form acids. For example:

$$P_2O_5 + 3H_2O \rightarrow 2H_3PO_4 \rightleftharpoons H^+ + H_2PO_4^-$$

They react with alkalis to form salts. For example:

$$P_2O_5 + 6OH^- \rightarrow 2PO_4^{3-} + 3H_2O$$

Sulphur dioxide and trioxide

Sulphur forms two oxides: **sulphur dioxide**, SO_2, and **sulphur trioxide**, SO_3. Both are acidic oxides.

Sulphur dioxide

Sulphur dioxide is a molecular substance in which the two oxygen atoms are covalently bonded to the sulphur with double bonds. There are weak van der Waals forces between the molecules and, as these are easily broken, sulphur dioxide is a gas at room temperature.

It is soluble in water, forming a solution of sulphuric(IV) acid (sulphurous acid), H_2SO_3, which has a pH $\approx$ 2:

$$SO_2 + H_2O \rightarrow H_2SO_3$$
$$H_2SO_3 \rightleftharpoons H^+ + HSO_3^-$$

It reacts with alkalis to form the sulphite anion:

$$SO_2 + 2OH^- \rightarrow SO_3^{2-} + H_2O$$

Sulphur trioxide

Sulphur trioxide is a white solid that fumes in damp air forming a mist of sulphuric acid:

$$SO_3 + H_2O \rightarrow H_2SO_4$$

In the manufacture of sulphuric acid, sulphur trioxide is adsorbed by 98% sulphuric acid forming 99.5% sulphuric acid, which is then diluted with water.

Oxides of chlorine

Chlorine forms a number of oxides in which the oxidation state of chlorine is +1, +5 or +7. They are all acidic and react with alkalis to form oxygen-containing anions, such as the chlorate(I) ion, ClO^-.

$$Cl_2O + 2OH^- \rightarrow 2ClO^- + H_2O$$

Reaction with water

The metals react with water, either in its liquid form or when heated in steam, to form hydrogen. If the reaction is with liquid water, the alkaline metal hydroxide is produced. If the reaction is with steam, the basic metal oxide is formed.

Silicon and carbon are in the same group of the periodic table. Therefore, the formula of sodium silicate will be similar to that of sodium carbonate.

Of the non-metals, only chlorine reacts. It forms a mixture of two acids.

Sodium

When a small piece of sodium is added to a beaker of water, it melts and buzzes around on the surface. The solution becomes hot, because the reaction is exothermic. Hydrogen gas and an alkaline solution of sodium hydroxide are produced.

$$2Na + 2H_2O \rightarrow 2NaOH + H_2$$

Magnesium

A very slow reaction takes place when magnesium is added to water at room temperature. Bubbles of hydrogen gradually appear and the solution becomes alkaline to litmus because of the magnesium hydroxide produced.

$$Mg + 2H_2O \rightarrow Mg(OH)_2 + H_2$$

If magnesium ribbon is heated in steam, it burns with a bright white light, forming hydrogen gas and a white residue of magnesium oxide.

$$Mg + H_2O \rightarrow MgO + H_2$$

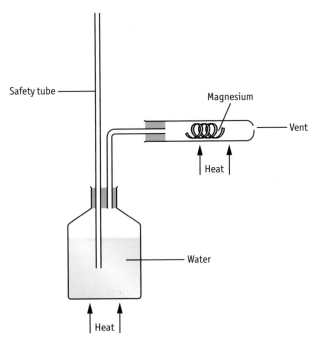

Figure 2.2 Apparatus for the reaction of magnesium with steam

Aluminium

Aluminium does not react with liquid water because it is protected by a surface layer of insoluble aluminium oxide. This is one of the most useful properties of aluminium in that it is a metal that does not corrode.

$$Al(s) + H_2O(l) \rightarrow \text{no reaction}$$

The fact that aluminium does not corrode is one of the reasons why it is used in the manufacture of Land Rover body panels and drink cans, for example. In alloys with other metals, aluminium is used in the fabrication of aeroplane wings and fuselage, where its low density is another important property.

The gearboxes of helicopters are made of an alloy of aluminium and a significant percentage of magnesium. This gives an excellent strength-to-weight ratio, which is vital for a good payload. However, the magnesium atoms in the metallic lattice disrupt the protective layer and so the alloy does corrode, especially in salt water.

If aluminium is heated strongly in steam, the protective oxide layer breaks down and the aluminium burns violently to form aluminium oxide and hydrogen:

$$2Al(s) + 3H_2O(g) \rightarrow Al_2O_3(s) + 3H_2(g)$$

This reaction was demonstrated in the Falklands War, when Exocet missiles or bombs struck Royal Navy frigates. The ships' superstructure was made of aluminium, and in the heat of the explosion caught fire. The fire could not be extinguished and the frigates were destroyed.

A burning aluminium frigate in the Falklands War

Silicon

Silicon does not react with water.

Phosphorus

Phosphorus does not react with water. It is stored under water to isolate it from oxygen in the air.

Chlorine

When chlorine is bubbled into water, a reversible reaction takes place, forming hydrochloric and chloric(I) acids.

$$Cl_2 + H_2O \rightleftharpoons HCl + HOCl$$

A solution of chlorine in water, which contains the two acids, is called chlorine water.

This is an example of a **disproportionation** reaction — one species is simultaneously oxidised and reduced. Here the chlorine is oxidised to HOCl and reduced to HCl. The oxidation number of chlorine goes from 0 in Cl_2 up to +1 in HOCl and down to −1 in HCl.

Bromine reacts with water in a similar way.

$$Br_2 + H_2O \rightleftharpoons HBr + HOBr$$

On standing in sunlight chloric(I) and bromic(I) acids decompose. The overall equation for the reaction of chlorine and water in sunlight is:

$$2Cl_2 + 2H_2O \rightarrow 4HCl + O_2$$

Reaction with chlorine

Apart from argon, all the elements in period 3 react with chlorine (and with the other halogens). Metals form ionic halides and non-metals produce covalent molecular halides.

Chloride	Sodium	Magnesium	Aluminium	Silicon	Phosphorus	Sulphur
Formula	NaCl	$MgCl_2$	$AlCl_3$*	$SiCl_4$	PCl_3 and PCl_5	S_2Cl_2
Bonding	Ionic	Ionic	Covalent	Covalent	Covalent	Covalent
Melting temperature/°C	801	714	190*	−70	PCl_3 −112 PCl_5 162	−80

Table 2.4 Properties of chlorides of the period 3 elements

* The solid is a polymeric covalent lattice structure of $AlCl_3$ units. Hydrated aluminium chloride, $AlCl_3.6H_2O$, is ionic.

Note that the melting temperature of the covalent chlorides increases as the number of electrons in the molecule increases. This is because the strength of the *intermolecular* forces (temporary induced dipole–induced dipole) depends mainly on the total number of electrons in the molecule.

Aluminium fluoride has a melting temperature of 1290°C. It is ionic because of the difference in electronegativity between aluminium and fluorine of 2.5. The difference in electronegativity between aluminium and chlorine is only 1.5. The Al^{3+} ion is highly charged and has a small radius. This makes it strongly polarising. Ionic compounds with Al^{3+} ions and large anions, such as Cl^- or I^-, cannot exist because the anions would be so polarised that the electrons would be shared and the bond would become polar covalent.

Chlorine reacts with the other halogens to form covalent compounds such as ClF, ClF_3, ICl and ICl_3.

The boiling temperatures of chlorine, bromine and two interhalogen compounds (Table 2.5) prove that the dominant intermolecular force, other than the hydrogen bond, is the induced dipole–induced dipole force. Cl_2 and Br_2 are non-polar molecules. BrF and BrCl are both polar, yet their boiling temperatures are exactly in line between those of chlorine and bromine, showing that the number of electrons in the molecule is more important than the polarity of the bonds.

Substance	Cl_2	BrF	BrCl	Br_2
Boiling temperature/K	238	253	278	332
Number of electrons in the molecule	34	44	52	70
Difference in electronegativity	0	1.2	0.2	0

Table 2.5 Effects of induced dipole–induced dipole interactions in halogens

Sodium

When chlorine gas is passed over heated sodium, a vigorous reaction takes place and sodium chloride is formed as a white ionic solid:

$$2Na + Cl_2 \rightarrow 2NaCl$$

Magnesium

On heating, magnesium reacts with chlorine, forming solid ionic magnesium chloride:

$$Mg + Cl_2 \rightarrow MgCl_2$$

The charge density of the Mg^{2+} ion is large enough, owing to its small radius and 2+ charge, to polarise the Cl^- ions. This causes the bond to become partially covalent.

Aluminium

When chlorine is passed over hot aluminium, a highly exothermic reaction takes place. A vapour of covalent aluminium chloride, Al_2Cl_6, is formed:

$$2Al(s) + 3Cl_2(g) \rightarrow Al_2Cl_6(g)$$

Figure 2.3 Laboratory preparation of anhydrous aluminium chloride

Anhydrous aluminium chloride is covalent. It is soluble in a number of organic solvents such as benzene, C_6H_6.

The solid is a polymeric lattice structure of $AlCl_3$ units. When heated it sublimes to give a vapour that contains covalent Al_2Cl_6 molecules. Each aluminium atom is covalently bonded to three chlorine atoms and datively bonded to a fourth. It can be regarded as a structure formed from two covalent $AlCl_3$ molecules joined by dative bonds between the lone pair of electrons on a chlorine atom in one $AlCl_3$ molecule and the empty orbital in the aluminium atom of the other $AlCl_3$ molecule.

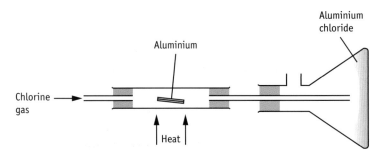

Bonding in Al_2Cl_6 Shape of molecule

In the Al_2Cl_6 molecule, the aluminium atoms are surrounded by four bond pairs and no lone pairs. The bond pairs repel each other to a position of maximum separation, causing the chlorine atoms to be arranged tetrahedrally around each aluminium atom.

There is no Al–Al bond in Al_2Cl_6.

Hydrated aluminium chloride has the formula $AlCl_3.6H_2O$. It is prepared by reacting solid aluminium hydroxide with dilute hydrochloric acid and carefully evaporating the solution.

Hydrated aluminium chloride is an ionic solid consisting of $[Al(H_2O)_6]^{3+}$ and Cl^- ions. Each of the water molecules is bonded with a dative bond from the oxygen to an empty orbital in the aluminium ion. The six water molecules are arranged octahedrally around the aluminium ion.

Silicon

On heating in chlorine, silicon forms silicon tetrachloride, which is a volatile covalent liquid.

$$Si + 2Cl_2 \rightarrow SiCl_4$$

Phosphorus

Phosphorus reacts vigorously with chlorine. If phosphorus is in excess, the trichloride is formed:

$$2P + 3Cl_2 \rightarrow 2PCl_3$$

If chlorine is in excess, the pentachloride is formed:

$$2P + 5Cl_2 \rightarrow 2PCl_5$$

This is a redox reaction. The phosphorus has been oxidised — its oxidation number has gone up from 0 to +5. The chlorine has been reduced — its oxidation number has gone down from 0 to –1.

Solid phosphorus pentachloride is ionic, consisting of a lattice of alternating tetrahedral PCl_4^+ and octahedral PCl_6^- ions. When heated it sublimes, giving gaseous covalent PCl_5 molecules, which are trigonal pyramidal in shape because the phosphorus atom has five bond pairs and no lone pairs.

Sulphur

When chlorine is bubbled into molten sulphur, a foul-smelling orange liquid is formed. This is sulphur(I) chloride, S_2Cl_2. The structure is shown below:

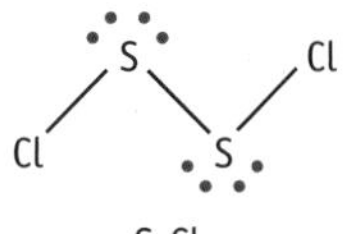

S_2Cl_2

The shape of this molecule is bent around the sulphur atoms and twisted out of a plane. Each sulphur atom has two bond pairs and two lone pairs, so the Cl–S–S angle is about 105°.

The sulphur atom is in the +1 oxidation state. (Each chlorine is –1, making a total of –2. As there are two sulphur atoms, each will be +2/2 = +1.)

Sulphur reacts with fluorine to form sulphur hexafluoride, SF_6. In the sulphur atom two electrons are promoted from the $[Ne]\ 3s^2\ 3p_x^2\ 3p_y^1\ 3p_z^1$ state. The result is $[Ne]\ 3s^1\ 3p_x^1\ 3p_y^1\ 3p_z^1\ 3d^1\ 3d^1$, which has six unpaired electrons and hence can form six covalent bonds. The SF_6 molecule is unusual in that it is almost totally unreactive and is insoluble in water.

Reactions of the chlorides

- Ionic chlorides dissolve in water to form hydrated cations and chloride anions.
- Covalent chlorides react with water, liberating hydrogen chloride, which makes the solution acidic.

Sodium chloride

Sodium chloride dissolves in water to form hydrated sodium ions and chloride ions:

$$NaCl(s) + aq \rightarrow Na^+(aq) + Cl^-(aq)$$

The exothermic hydration energies of the two ions compensates for the endothermic break-up of the ionic lattice (minus the lattice energy, hence a positive value). Each sodium ion is surrounded by a number of water molecules, with the δ^- oxygen atoms being attracted to the positive Na^+ ion. The solution is pH 7.

ⓔ Note that sodium chloride does *not* react with water to form sodium hydroxide and hydrochloric acid.

Magnesium chloride

Magnesium chloride dissolves in water to give hydrated ions:

$$MgCl_2(s) + aq \rightarrow Mg^{2+}(aq) + 2Cl^-(aq)$$

Each magnesium ion is surrounded by six water molecules, forming an $[Mg(H_2O)_6]^{2+}$ ion. The charge density (charge divided by the square of the radius) of the Mg^{2+} ion is just sufficient for one of these water molecules to be deprotonated by the solvent:

$$[Mg(H_2O)_6]^{2+}(aq) + H_2O(l) \rightleftharpoons [Mg(H_2O)_5OH]^+(aq) + H_3O^+(aq)$$

The formation of H_3O^+ ions makes the solution acidic, with pH $\approx$ 5.

When a solution of an alkali, such as sodium hydroxide, is added to magnesium salts, the equilibrium above is driven to the right because of the removal of the H_3O^+ ions:

$$H_3O^+ + OH^- \rightarrow 2H_2O$$

The result is a precipitate of magnesium hydroxide, as two protons in total are removed:

$$[Mg(H_2O)_6]^{2+}(aq) + 2OH^-(aq) \rightarrow Mg(OH)_2(s) + 6H_2O(l)$$

The addition of ammonia solution also causes the production of a precipitate of magnesium hydroxide because the ammonia molecules remove a proton from the water surrounding the magnesium ion:

$$[Mg(H_2O)_6]^{2+}(aq) + 2NH_3(aq) \rightarrow Mg(OH)_2(s) + 2NH_4^+(aq) + 4H_2O(l)$$

A pH of at least 10 is required for this precipitation to occur.

ⓔ The exact formulae of precipitated metal hydroxides are not known, but it is traditional to write them either as simple hydroxides of formula $M(OH)_x$ or as hydrated hydroxides of formula $M(OH)_x(H_2O)_y$ where $x + y = 6$.

Aluminium chloride

Anhydrous aluminium chloride

- Anhydrous aluminium chloride is covalent.
- It is soluble in benzene and ether.
- In a limited amount of water, it is hydrolysed to solid aluminium oxide and steamy fumes of hydrogen chloride:

$$2AlCl_3(s) + 3H_2O(l) \rightarrow Al_2O_3(s) + 6HCl(g)$$

- With excess water, aluminium hydroxide and a highly acidic solution (pH ≈ 1) are formed:

$$AlCl_3(s) + 3H_2O(l) \rightarrow Al(OH)_3(s) + 3H^+(aq) + 3Cl^-(aq)$$

This reaction happens in steps. Each chlorine atom is replaced in turn by an −OH group.

- Anhydrous aluminium chloride is used as a catalyst in the Friedel–Crafts reaction (p. 238).

Hydrated aluminium chloride

- Hydrated aluminium chloride is an ionic solid. Its formula is $[Al(H_2O)_6]Cl_3$, usually written as $AlCl_3.6H_2O$. The lattice is made up of a regular arrangement of aluminium ions, each surrounded by six water molecules and by chloride ions.

- When water is added to hydrated aluminium chloride it first dissolves:

$$AlCl_3.6H_2O(s) + aq \rightarrow [Al(H_2O)_6]^{3+}(aq) + 3Cl^-(aq)$$

The hydrated aluminium ions are partially deprotonated by water molecules:

$$[Al(H_2O)_6]^{3+}(aq) + H_2O(l) \rightleftharpoons [Al(H_2O)_5OH]^{2+}(aq) + H_3O^+(aq)$$

The formation of the H_3O^+ ions makes the solution acidic (pH ≈ 3).

This first deprotonation is over 50% complete and further deprotonation occurs:

$$[Al(H_2O)_5OH]^{2+}(aq) + H_2O(l) \rightleftharpoons [Al(H_2O)_4(OH)_2]^+(aq) + H_3O^+(aq)$$

- If alkali is added to a solution containing hydrated aluminium ions, the equilibrium is driven completely to the right, a third proton is removed and a white precipitate of hydrated aluminium hydroxide is formed:

$$[Al(H_2O)_6]^{3+}(aq) + 3OH^-(aq) \rightarrow [Al(H_2O)_3(OH)_3](s) + 3H_2O(l)$$

In excess strong alkali, this precipitate 'dissolves' (in fact, it reacts to form a solution) because aluminium hydroxide is amphoteric:

$$[Al(H_2O)_3(OH)_3](s) + 3OH^-(aq) \rightarrow [Al(OH)_6]^{3-}(aq) + 3H_2O(l)$$

- On heating, solid hydrated aluminium chloride gives off hydrogen chloride vapour:

$$[Al(H_2O)_6]Cl_3(s) \rightarrow Al(OH)_3(s) + 3HCl(g)$$

In this reaction it is the chloride ions that deprotonate the hydrated ion.

The high charge density of the small Al^{3+} ion draws the electrons in the dative bond towards the Al^{3+} ion. This makes the H atom of the H_2O more δ^+ and therefore more easily removed in a deprotonation reaction.

Silicon tetrachloride (silicon(IV) chloride)

Silicon tetrachloride is a covalent liquid consisting of simple $SiCl_4$ molecules with covalent bonds between the silicon and the chlorine atoms within the molecule and weak induced dipole–induced dipole forces between molecules. The $SiCl_4$ molecule is tetrahedral as the central silicon atom has four bond pairs and no lone pairs. Although the bonds are polar, the polarities cancel out because the molecule is symmetrical.

Silicon tetrachloride is rapidly hydrolysed by water, forming a precipitate of silicon dioxide and an acidic solution of hydrochloric acid:

$$SiCl_4 + 2H_2O \rightarrow SiO_2 + 4HCl$$

The lone pair of electrons on the oxygen atom in a water molecule forms a bond with an empty $3d$-orbital on the silicon atom. The energy released by formation of this bond causes a silicon–chlorine bond to break.

Phosphorus trichloride (phosphorus(III) chloride)

Phosphorus trichloride is a covalent liquid. The central phosphorus atom has empty $3d$-orbitals that can accept a pair of electrons from the oxygen in a water molecule. This results in a rapid reaction, forming phosphorus(III) acid and hydrochloric acid:

$$PCl_3 + 3H_2O \rightarrow H_3PO_3 + 3HCl$$

Phosphorus(III) acid ionises slightly and hydrochloric acid ionises fully to form H^+ ions. Therefore, the solution is highly acidic.

Phosphorus pentachloride (phosphorus(V) chloride)

- Phosphorus pentachloride behaves as a covalent chloride.
- It is rapidly hydrolysed by water, forming a solution containing phosphoric(V) acid and hydrochloric acid:

$$PCl_5 + 4H_2O \rightarrow H_3PO_4 + 5HCl$$

  Both phosphoric(V) acid and hydrochloric acid are strong acids. The resulting solution has a pH $\approx$ 1, mainly owing to the complete ionisation of HCl.
- Phosphorus pentachloride reacts with organic compounds containing an –OH group. It reacts with alcohols and carboxylic acids liberating steamy fumes of hydrogen chloride:

$$PCl_5 + C_2H_5OH \rightarrow POCl_3 + C_2H_5Cl + HCl$$
$$PCl_5 + CH_3COOH \rightarrow POCl_3 + CH_3COCl + HCl$$

The organic substance must be dry, otherwise the phosphorus pentachloride reacts preferentially with the water.

Solubility of common compounds of elements in period 3

- **Sodium** — all sodium compounds are soluble in water.
- **Magnesium** — the sulphate, nitrate, chloride, bromide and iodide are soluble. Magnesium hydroxide and carbonate are only very slightly soluble.
- **Aluminium** — the sulphate, nitrate, chloride, bromide and iodide are soluble. Aluminium hydroxide is insoluble.
- **Silicon** — all covalent silicon compounds are insoluble in water. Sodium silicate, Na_2SiO_3, is ionic and soluble.
- **Phosphorus** — phosphoric acid, H_3PO_4, and group 1 phosphates such as sodium phosphate, Na_3PO_4, are soluble in water. Other phosphates are insoluble.
- **Sulphur** — sulphur dioxide and sulphur trioxide react with water to form solutions of sulphurous and sulphuric acids.

Group 1 sulphites are soluble in water. Sulphites of other elements (e.g. barium in group 2) are insoluble. The precipitate, obtained when aqueous barium chloride is added to a solution of an unknown, could be caused by either sulphite or sulphate ions. Solid barium sulphite reacts with hydrochloric acid to form

e Ionic chlorides dissolve in water; covalent chlorides are hydrolysed, forming an oxide or oxyacid and hydrochloric acid.

e Aluminium carbonate decomposes at room temperature, so if a solution containing carbonate ions is added to a solution of an aluminium salt, the precipitate is aluminium hydroxide and carbon dioxide gas is evolved.

barium chloride and sulphur dioxide and so the precipitate 'dissolves':

$$BaSO_3(s) + 2HCl(aq) \rightarrow BaCl_2(aq) + H_2O(l) + SO_2(aq)$$

All sulphates are soluble, apart from barium sulphate, strontium sulphate and lead sulphate. Calcium sulphate is only sparingly soluble.

The ionic equation for the reaction of aqueous barium chloride with a solution of a sulphate is:

$$Ba^{2+}(aq) + SO_4^{2-}(aq) \rightarrow BaSO_4(s)$$

- **Chlorine** — all ionic chlorides are soluble in water, apart from silver chloride, mercury(I) chloride and copper(I) chloride. Lead(II) chloride is insoluble in cold water, but dissolves in hot water.

Silver chloride is a white solid that slowly turns blue-black in light as it is decomposed to silver metal. It dissolves in excess dilute ammonia.

The ionic equation for the precipitation reaction when aqueous silver nitrate is added to a solution of a chloride is:

$$Ag^+(aq) + Cl^-(aq) \rightarrow AgCl(s)$$

Summary

Some properties of the oxides and chlorides of elements in period 3 are given in Table 2.6.

Element	Na and Mg	Al	Si, P, S and Cl
	Metallic	Metallic	Non-metallic
Oxide	Ionic	Ionic	Covalent
	Basic	Amphoteric	Acidic
	React with acids	Reacts with acids and with alkalis	React with alkalis
Chloride	Ionic	Anhydrous: covalent Hydrated: ionic	Covalent
	Dissolve in water	Anhydrous: reacts with water to form HCl Hydrated: dissolves	React with water to form HCl

Table 2.6 Properties of the oxides and chlorides of the elements of period 3

Group 4: carbon to lead

All the elements in a group have the same number of electrons in their outer shells.

The character of the elements and their compounds changes down the group as the atomic number increases:
- Atomic radius increases.
- First ionisation energy decreases.
- Covalent bond strength decreases.
- Hydration energy of the cation decreases.
- Metallic character increases.
- Oxides become less acidic and more basic.

The elements in group 4 are shown in Table 2.7.

Table 2.7 Group 4 elements

Element	Symbol	Atomic number	Comment
Carbon	C	6	The basis of organic chemistry
Silicon	Si	14	The second most abundant element in the Earth's crust
Germanium	Ge	32	Named after Germany
Tin	Sn	50	Symbol based on the Latin 'stannum' — tin
Lead	Pb	82	Symbol based on the Latin 'plumbum' — lead

Germanium was not known at the time that Mendeleev produced his form of the periodic table. He left a gap for an element that he called 'eka-silicon' and predicted its properties. The element (germanium) was soon discovered and its properties were found to be as Mendeleev had suggested.

Electron structure

All the elements in group 4 have four valence electrons, arranged $ns^2\ np_x^1\ np_y^1$. When four covalent bonds are formed, one of the outer s-electrons is promoted into the empty p_z-orbital, so that there are four unpaired electrons. All the group 4 elements form compounds in which the element is in the +4 oxidation state.

Atomic radius

Atomic radius increases down the group (Table 2.8) as the number of electron shells increases.

Carbon has two shells (orbits) occupied. Silicon has three, germanium has four, tin has five and lead has six occupied orbits.

First ionisation energy

First ionisation energy decreases down the group. The nuclear charge increases, but this is matched by a similar increase in the number of inner shielding electrons. The result is that the effective nuclear charge (number of protons minus the number of inner electrons) remains almost constant. However, as the atomic radius increases, the outer electron is further away from the nucleus and less energy is required to remove it.

Covalent bond strength

Covalent bond strength is measured by bond enthalpy. The covalent bond enthalpy of the group 4 elements decreases down the group, although the C–Cl bond is weaker than the Si–Cl bond.

e The reactions of germanium and its compounds are not included in this book. If they were to be asked for in an A-level question, you should assume that the reaction characteristics fall between those of silicon and tin.

Table 2.8 Atomic radii and bond enthalpies of group 4 elements

| | Atomic radius/nm | Bond enthalpy/kJ mol^{-1} | | |
		Bond with self	Bond with hydrogen	Bond with chlorine
Carbon	0.077	348	412	338
Silicon	0.117	220	323	390
Germanium	0.122	200	290	356
Tin	0.140	110	252	344

The main reason why there is a *general* trend of decreasing bond strength down the group is that the bond strength depends on the sum of the covalent radii of the two atoms involved.

Another factor is the difference in electronegativity of the two elements forming the bond. A large difference results in a stronger covalent bond. This is the reason why the bond enthalpy of the Si–Cl bond is greater than that of the C–Cl bond. The difference in electronegativity between carbon and chlorine is only 0.5; between silicon and chlorine it is 1.2.

Hydration enthalpy of the cations

Tin and lead are the only group 4 elements that form cations with a charge of +2. The hydration enthalpy of Pb^{2+} ions is approximately -1500 kJ mol^{-1} and that of the smaller Sn^{2+} ion is approximately -1600 kJ mol^{-1}.

There is no evidence for the existence of truly ionic compounds containing Sn^{4+} or Pb^{4+} ions, although equations containing these species are sometimes seen.

Metallic character

- Metallic character increases down the group.
- Carbon in the form of graphite conducts electricity because of the delocalised electrons above and below the planes of interlocking carbon atoms. Generally, the electrical conductivity for the group 4 elements increases down the group:
  - Carbon — diamond is an insulator; graphite conducts.
  - Silicon — when pure, silicon is a non-conductor. When 'doped' with traces of a group 3 or group 5 element, it becomes a semi-conductor.
  - Tin — this is a good conductor (except in its grey allotropic form).
  - Lead — this is a very good conductor.
- Tin and lead are malleable. The non-metallic elements are not.
- Tin and lead form monatomic cations. The other group 4 elements do not.

Acid–base character of the oxides

Carbon dioxide

- Carbon dioxide is acidic. It dissolves in water to form carbonic acid, which is a weak acid:

  $$H_2O + CO_2 \rightleftharpoons H_2CO_3$$

Aqueous solutions of carbon dioxide have pH 5.

- It reacts with bases, such as sodium hydroxide to form a salt:

  $$CO_2 + 2NaOH \rightarrow Na_2CO_3 + H_2O$$

Silicon dioxide

- Silicon dioxide exists as a giant atomic lattice, with each silicon atom singly bonded to four oxygen atoms. Therefore, all its reactions have extremely high activation energies.
- It is weakly acidic.
- It does not dissolve in water.

e The ability of carbon to form millions of organic compounds arises from the strength of the C–C bond, which is much stronger than the Si–Si bond. This is why there is no analogous 'organic silicon chemistry'.

- It does not react with dilute alkali.
- It reacts slowly with hot concentrated sodium hydroxide to form a solution of sodium silicate:

$$SiO_2 + 2NaOH \rightarrow Na_2SiO_3 + H_2O$$

> **e** Carbon dioxide is a simple molecular substance in which the carbon atom in the CO_2 molecule is doubly bonded to each oxygen atom. The bond enthalpy of the C=O bond is high enough for this arrangement to be more energetically favourable than forming a giant atomic lattice (as does silicon dioxide).
>
> Silicon is a much bigger atom than carbon, so there is less overlap in a π-bond and hence lower bond enthalpy than with the π-bond between carbon and oxygen atoms. The C=O bond enthalpy is -743 kJ mol^{-1}, whereas that of Si=O is only -640 kJ mol^{-1}. It is energetically preferable for silicon to form a lattice with the silicon and oxygen atoms joined by four single bonds, rather than existing as a simple molecule with two double bonds.

Tin oxides

Tin forms two oxides: tin(II) oxide, SnO, and tin(IV) oxide, SnO_2. Both are **amphoteric** — they react with acids and with bases.

Tin(II) oxide reacts with dilute hydrochloric acid to form tin(II) chloride:

$$SnO + 2HCl \rightarrow SnCl_2 + H_2O$$

It reacts with aqueous sodium hydroxide to form a solution of sodium stannate(II):

$$SnO(s) + 2OH^-(aq) + H_2O(l) \rightarrow [Sn(OH)_4]^{2-}(aq)$$

Tin(IV) oxide reacts with concentrated hydrochloric acid to form tin(IV) chloride:

$$SnO_2 + 4HCl \rightarrow SnCl_4 + 2H_2O$$

It reacts with aqueous alkali to form soluble stannate(IV) ions:

$$SnO_2(s) + 2OH^-(aq) + 2H_2O(l) \rightarrow [Sn(OH)_6]^{2-}(aq)$$

Lead oxides

Lead also forms two amphoteric oxides.

Lead(II) oxide, PbO, reacts with dilute nitric acid (lead chloride is insoluble in water) to form a solution of lead(II) nitrate:

$$PbO + 2HNO_3 \rightarrow Pb(NO_3)_2 + H_2O$$

It reacts with aqueous alkali to form plumbate(II) ions:

$$PbO(s) + 2OH^-(aq) + H_2O(l) \rightarrow [Pb(OH)_4]^{2-}(aq)$$

Lead(IV) oxide reacts with concentrated hydrochloric acid in a similar way to tin(IV) oxide. Lead(IV) chloride is formed:

$$PbO_2 + 4HCl \rightarrow PbCl_4 + 2H_2O$$

It reacts with aqueous alkali to form plumbate(IV) ions:

$$PbO_2(s) + 2OH^-(aq) + 2H_2O(l) \rightarrow [Pb(OH)_6]^{2-}(aq)$$

+2 and +4 oxidation states

Carbon

Carbon has an oxidation state of +4 in CO_2 and in other compounds in which it is bonded to a more electronegative element.

> **e** Lead also forms a 'mixed' oxide, Pb_3O_4, which is red. It behaves as a mixture of $2PbO$ and PbO_2. 'Red lead' was used for rust prevention of iron structures. However, it has now been banned because of its toxicity.

Carbon monoxide is an exception. Here, carbon has an oxidation state of +2, but the molecule is not C=O. There is a double covalent bond between the two atoms and also a dative bond. A lone pair of electrons on the oxygen forms a bond with an empty orbital in the carbon.

The bond enthalpy in carbon monoxide is -1077 kJ mol^{-1}. The C=O bond enthalpy in carbon dioxide is -805 kJ mol^{-1} and the average C–O bond enthalpy is -358 kJ mol^{-1}. This implies that there are three bonds between the carbon and the oxygen in a carbon monoxide molecule.

Silicon

Silicon has no stable compounds in the +2 oxidation state. Compounds in the +4 oxidation state include silicon dioxide and silicon tetrachloride.

Tin

Tin(II) compounds

Tin(II) fluoride is a sparingly soluble ionic solid that is added to toothpaste to protect tooth enamel from decay

Tin(II) chloride is an ionic solid, which is soluble in dilute hydrochloric acid. It is strongly reducing and is easily oxidised to tin(IV) chloride. It reduces iron(III) compounds to iron(II), for example:

$$2FeCl_3 + SnCl_2 \rightarrow 2FeCl_2 + SnCl_4$$

This equation is often written ionically, even though the existence of simple hydrated Sn^{4+} ions is doubtful. The two half-equations are:

$Fe^{3+}(aq) + e^- \rightarrow Fe^{2+}(aq)$ electron added, so reduction
$Sn^{2+}(aq) \rightarrow Sn^{4+}(aq) + 2e^-$ electrons lost, so oxidation

The overall equation is:

$$2Fe^{3+}(aq) + Sn^{2+}(aq) \rightarrow 2Fe^{2+}(aq) + Sn^{4+}(aq)$$

Tin(II) oxide is rapidly oxidised to tin(IV) oxide in air. On heating in the absence of air, it disproportionates into metallic tin and tin(IV) oxide:

$2SnO \rightarrow SnO_2 + Sn$
$\quad +2 \qquad +4 \quad\ \ 0$

Note that the Fe^{3+} equation has to be doubled for the overall equation, so that the number of electrons cancels. Note, too, that the sum of the charges on each side of the overall equation is +8.

Tin(IV) compounds

Tin(IV) compounds are stable relative to tin(II) compounds. Neither tin(IV) oxide nor tin(IV) chloride decompose on heating to form tin(II) compounds. Tin(IV) compounds are not oxidising agents. Compare this with lead(IV) compounds.

Lead

Lead(II) compounds

Lead forms many lead(II) compounds. Most, for example lead(II) chloride and lead(II) sulphate, are insoluble in water.

The +2 state is not oxidising and lead(II) compounds do not disproportionate into lead(IV) compounds and metallic lead.

Lead(II) hydroxide can be precipitated by adding aqueous sodium hydroxide or ammonia solution to a solution of a lead salt:

$$Pb^{2+}(aq) + 2OH^-(aq) \rightarrow Pb(OH)_2(s)$$

Lead(II) hydroxide is amphoteric and 'dissolves' in excess sodium hydroxide, forming plumbate(II) ions:

$$Pb(OH)_2(s) + 2OH^-(aq) \rightarrow [Pb(OH)_4]^{2-}(aq)$$

It also dissolves in dilute acid to form lead(II) cations:

$$Pb(OH)_2(s) + 2H^+(aq) \rightarrow Pb^{2+}(aq) + 2H_2O(l)$$

Lead(IV) compounds

Lead(IV) is a highly oxidising state. Lead(IV) oxide, PbO_2, oxidises concentrated hydrochloric acid to lead(II) chloride and chlorine gas:

$$PbO_2 + 4HCl \rightarrow PbCl_2 + Cl_2 + 2H_2O$$

Lead(IV) chloride decomposes at room temperature to lead(II) chloride and chlorine:

$$PbCl_4 \rightarrow PbCl_2 + Cl_2$$

Here, the lead(IV) atom oxidises two of the chlorine atoms in the $PbCl_4$ molecule.

Relative stability of the +2 and +4 oxidation states

The stability of the +2 state relative to the +4 state increases down the group. This can be illustrated by comparing the chemistry of tin and lead:

- Tin(II) is a reducing agent; lead(II) is not a reducing agent.
- Tin(IV) is not an oxidising agent; lead(IV) is an oxidising agent.
- Tin(IV) chloride is stable to heat; lead(IV) chloride decomposes.

The reason why the stability of the +2 state increases down the group is because the atomic radius of the elements increases. With the larger lead atom, the bond energy gained by forming two more bonds is not sufficient to overcome the energy required to promote an electron into an empty d-orbital.

Chlorides

All the elements form tetrachlorides in which the group 4 element is in the +4 oxidation state.

Compound	Boiling temperature/°C
CCl_4	77
$SiCl_4$	58
$GeCl_4$	83
$SnCl_4$	114
$PbCl_4$	Decomposes

The low boiling temperatures show that all the chlorides have weak intermolecular forces and, therefore, are simple molecules bonded covalently. The increase in boiling temperature down the group is caused by the increasing number of electrons in the molecule and, therefore, stronger dispersion (van der Waals) forces. CCl_4 is an exception because the smaller spherical molecules pack more efficiently.

Carbon and silicon tetrachlorides

Structure

In the tetrachlorides of both carbon and silicon, the four chlorine atoms are bonded covalently. So the central atom is surrounded by four bonding pairs of

e Carbon monoxide appears to be an exception to increased stability of the +2 state down the group. This is because, in carbon monoxide, carbon has gained four electrons in bonding. Tin has only two electrons involved in tin(II) compounds.

electrons that repel each other to a position of maximum separation. This causes both molecules to be tetrahedral in shape, with a bond angle of 109.5°:

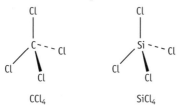

The carbon atom is small relative to the chlorine atoms, which completely surround it. Silicon is a bigger atom than carbon, so the chlorine atoms do not completely surround it. This results in less contact with neighbouring molecules. Therefore, even though $SiCl_4$ has more electrons than CCl_4, the induced dipole–induced dipole forces are weaker.

Hydrolysis

There are three possible mechanisms for hydrolysis of the tetrachlorides.

One possibility is that an empty orbital of the group 4 atom is attacked by a lone pair of electrons on the oxygen atom in a water molecule.

The valence electrons in silicon are in the third orbit, so it has empty $3d$-orbitals that can accept this pair of electrons. The bond energy released is sufficient to cause a Si–Cl bond to break heterolytically, forming a Cl^- ion. One of the H atoms on the oxygen then breaks off as an H^+ ion, which becomes hydrated by the solvent. This process is repeated until all four chlorine atoms have been substituted. This is a very rapid process, because the activation energy for the first step is low as no bonds have to be broken.

The carbon in CCl_4 does not have any $2d$-orbitals or other empty orbitals at a suitable energy level, and so cannot accept the lone pair from a water molecule and form a dative bond.

The second mechanism is the much slower S_N2 mechanism, similar to that between halogenoalkanes and an alkali (p. 265). Here the water molecule approaches, and, as a new bond begins to form between the lone pair on the oxygen and the central atom, the bond to the halogen starts to break. This simultaneous making and breaking of bonds does not happen with carbon tetrachloride because the carbon atom is totally surrounded by chlorine atoms, which sterically hinder the attack by the water molecule.

The third possibility is an S_N1 mechanism in which a Cl^- ion breaks off as the first step. This leaves a Cl_3C^+ ion that would be destabilised by the electron-withdrawing effect of the remaining three chlorine atoms. Therefore, this does not happen either. The last two mechanisms do not happen with silicon tetrachloride because the activation energy is much higher than that involving silicon's $3d$-orbitals.

The result is that carbon tetrachloride is not hydrolysed by water or by aqueous alkali, except very slowly when heated under pressure.

e Do not say that carbon does not have any empty d-orbitals. It has lots of them — $3d$, $4d$, $5d$ and so on — but these are at the wrong energy level to take part in bonding.

1 Explain why iodine can form seven covalent bonds but fluorine never forms more than one covalent bond.

2 Explain the following:
   a The atomic radius of the elements in the third period decreases across the period from sodium to chlorine.
   b The first ionisation energy of magnesium is greater than that of sodium.
   c The first ionisation energy of aluminium is less than that of magnesium.

3 Explain, in terms of structure and bonding, why magnesium is a good conductor of electricity.

4 What is meant by the term 'amphoteric oxide'?

5 Explain, in terms of bonding, why the oxides of the elements in the third period become more acidic across the period from sodium to sulphur.

6 Write equations for the reaction of sodium and phosphorus with:
   a chlorine
   b water
   c oxygen

7 Write ionic equations for the reactions, if any, of magnesium hydroxide and aluminium hydroxide with:
   a dilute acid
   b dilute alkali

8 Carbon dioxide is an acidic oxide. Write the equation for its reaction with potassium hydroxide solution.

9 Explain why solutions of hydrated aluminium chloride are acidic.

10 Write equations for the reaction of water with:
   a anhydrous aluminium chloride
   b silicon tetrachloride
   c phosphorus pentachloride
   d chlorine

11 Write an equation to show lithium chloride dissolving in water.

12 Explain, in terms of the bonding in the chlorides, the reactions of the third-period chlorides with water.

13 Phosphorus trichloride is rapidly hydrolysed by water to phosphoric(III) acid and hydrochloric acid. By considering the electronic structures of phosphorus trichloride and nitrogen trichloride, NCl_3, explain why phosphorus trichloride is rapidly hydrolysed but nitrogen trichloride is hydrolysed only slowly.

14 On warming primary halogenoalkanes with aqueous sodium hydroxide, the C–Cl bond in the primary halogenoalkane is hydrolysed. However, the C–Cl bond in tetrachloromethane (carbon tetrachloride) is resistant to hydrolysis. Explain these facts.

15 The following tests were carried out on a solution of a group 2 compound:
   a A solution of sodium hydroxide was added. A white precipitate was obtained.
   b A concentrated solution of sodium sulphate was added. There was no precipitate.
   What does each of these tests tell you about the identity of the group 2 cation present?

16 Explain why the first ionisation energy of the group 4 elements decreases down the group and how this affects the metallic nature of the elements.

17 By considering the acid–base properties of carbon, tin and lead, give evidence for the change in metallic character down the elements in group 4.

18 a Write the equation for the redox reaction of lead(IV) oxide with concentrated hydrochloric acid.
   b Why does tin(IV) oxide not react in the same way?

19 Use chemical equations to show that tin is more stable in the +4 state than in the +2 state, but lead is more stable in the +2 state than the +4 state.

20 The silicon that is used to manufacture semi-conductors has to be extremely pure. Research the Web to discover how highly pure silicon is obtained.

Equilibrium

Some reactions go to completion, and others do not. The latter type of reaction is called a **reversible** reaction.

Consider the gaseous reaction:

$$H_2(g) + I_2(g) \rightleftharpoons 2HI(g)$$

When hydrogen and iodine are mixed in a sealed container at a temperature, T, and left, **dynamic equilibrium** is eventually reached. At this point, there is no further change in the concentrations of the reactants and products but the reactions have not stopped. The forward and backward reactions are continuing at the same rate.

> Rate of forward reaction = rate of backward reaction

> In a dynamic equilibrium, the rates of the forward and reverse reactions are the same. Therefore, there is no further change in the concentrations of the reactants and products.

Liquid bromine in equilibrium with gaseous bromine

The reaction between hydrogen and iodine was studied by Guldberg and Waage in 1864. They mixed different amounts of hydrogen and iodine and allowed the mixtures to reach equilibrium at 480°C.

They then measured the concentration of the three substances at equilibrium and tried to find a mathematical relationship between these concentrations.

Typical results for this are shown in Table 3.1.

ZAHOOR UL-HAQ

> Square brackets around the symbol of a species mean the concentration, in mol dm^{-3}, of that substance.

Initial $[H_2]$	Initial $[I_2]$	$[H_2]$ at equilibrium	$[I_2]$ at equilibrium	$[HI]$ at equilibrium	$\dfrac{[HI]}{[H_2][I_2]}$	$\dfrac{[HI]^2}{[H_2][I_2]}$
0.040	0.040	0.0089	0.0089	0.062	783	49
0.080	0.040	0.0426	0.0026	0.0748	675	51
0.080	0.080	0.018	0.018	0.124	383	47
0.020	0.080	0.0005	0.0605	0.0389	1286	50

Table 3.1 Reaction between hydrogen and iodine

The values in the final column are constant to within experimental error, so from these results, it appears that:

$$\frac{[HI]_{eq}^2}{[H_2]_{eq}[I_2]_{eq}} = \text{a constant}$$

The equilibrium constant, K_c

Law of mass action and K_c

The results given in Table 3.1, and those of other equilibrium reactions, enabled Guldberg and Waage to formulate the **law of mass action**. This states that when reactions reach equilibrium, the equilibrium concentrations of the products multiplied together and divided by the equilibrium concentrations of the reactants also multiplied together, with the concentration of each substance raised to the power appropriate to the reaction stoichiometry, are a constant at a given temperature.

For example, for the reaction:

$$N_2(g) + 3H_2(g) \rightleftharpoons 2NH_3(g)$$

$$\frac{[NH_3]_{eq}^2}{[N_2]_{eq}[H_2]_{eq}^3} = \text{a constant}$$

where $[NH_3]_{eq}$ is the concentration, in mol dm^{-3}, of ammonia at *equilibrium*.

The constant is called the **equilibrium constant** (measured in terms of concentrations) and has the symbol, K_c.

The value of the equilibrium constant depends on:
- the nature of the reaction
- the temperature at equilibrium

The value of K_c does *not* depend on the pressure or the presence of a catalyst.

In general, for a reaction:

$$x\text{A} + y\text{B} \rightleftharpoons n\text{C} + m\text{D}$$

where x, y, n and m are the stoichiometric amounts in the equation:

$$K_c = \frac{[C]_{eq}^n[D]_{eq}^m}{[A]_{eq}^x[B]_{eq}^y}$$

The right-hand side of this expression is called the 'concentration term' or the 'reaction quotient' and given the symbol Q.

The chemical equation and the expression for K

An equilibrium constant has no meaning unless it is linked to a chemical equation. Consider the equilibrium reaction of sulphur dioxide and oxygen reacting reversibly to form sulphur trioxide. This reaction can be represented by two equations and hence by two expressions for the equilibrium constant, K_c. The values given below are at 727°C.

The equilibrium constant, K_c, equals the concentration term or fraction only when the system has reached equilibrium.

e Remember, that in an equilibrium constant expression, the products are on top and the reactants are on the bottom.

$$2SO_2(g) + O_2(g) \rightleftharpoons 2SO_3(g)$$

$$K_c = \frac{[SO_3]^2_{eq}}{[SO_2]^2_{eq}[O_2]_{eq}}$$

$$= 0.0413 \ mol^{-1} \ dm^3$$

or

$$SO_2(g) + \tfrac{1}{2}O_2(g) \rightleftharpoons SO_3(g)$$

$$K_c' = \frac{[SO_3]_{eq}}{[SO_2]_{eq}[O_2]^{\frac{1}{2}}_{eq}}$$

$$= 0.203 \ mol^{-\frac{1}{2}} \ dm^{\frac{3}{2}}$$

The reaction can also be written in the other direction, giving a third expression for K:

$$2SO_3(g) \rightleftharpoons 2SO_2(g) + O_2(g)$$

$$K_c'' = \frac{[SO_3]^2_{eq}[O_2]_{eq}}{[SO_3]^2_{eq}}$$

$$= 24.2 \ mol \ dm^{-3}$$

The three equilibrium constants are connected by the expression:

$$K_c = (K_c')^2 = \frac{1}{K_c''}$$

Estimating the extent of a reaction

The value of the equilibrium constant gives an estimate of how complete a reaction is at a particular temperature:

- very large values of K_c ($>10^{10}$) — reaction almost complete
- large values of K_c (between 10^4 and 10^{10}) — reaction favours products
- intermediate values of K_c (between 10^{-4} and 10^4) — reactants and products in similar amounts
- small values of K_c (between 10^{-10} and 10^{-4}) — reaction favours reactants
- very small values of K_c ($<10^{-10}$) — reaction not noticeable

The equilibrium constant for the reaction:

$$2H_2(g) + O_2(g) \rightleftharpoons 2H_2O(g)$$

is 1.4×10^{53} at 200°C, so the reaction of hydrogen and oxygen is virtually complete.

The Haber process:

$$N_2(g) + 3H_2(g) \rightleftharpoons 2NH_3(g)$$

is carried out at a temperature of about 400°C and 200 atm pressure. The equilibrium constant, K_c, at this temperature is 0.26 $mol^{-2} \ dm^6$ and there is over 20% ammonia in the equilibrium mixture. As the industrial process does not take place in a closed system, equilibrium is not quite reached in the catalyst chamber and the actual percentage of ammonia leaving the catalyst is only 15%.

e Do not forget that the reaction may be so slow at the temperature of the experiment that equilibrium may not be reached. The system is then said to be thermodynamically unstable but kinetically stable.

Predicting the direction of change

When both reactants and products are present in a vessel at a stated temperature, the system is either at equilibrium or not. Which situation exists can be determined by calculating the value of the concentration term (reaction quotient) and comparing it with the value of the equilibrium constant at that temperature:

- If the two are equal, the system is in equilibrium.
- If the two are not equal, the system is not at equilibrium.

> *Worked example*
>
> Hydrogen and iodine, both at a concentration of 0.0020 mol dm^{-3}, were mixed at 480°C with hydrogen iodide of concentration 0.0040 mol dm^{-3}. $K_c = 49$ at 480°C. Is the system at equilibrium?
>
> **Answer**
> The equation for the equilibrium reaction is:
>
> $$H_2(g) + I_2(g) \rightleftharpoons 2HI(g)$$
>
> $$\frac{[HI]^2}{[H_2][I_2]} = \frac{0.0040^2}{0.0020 \times 0.0020} = 4$$
>
> The value of the concentration term is 4, which is less than the value of K_c (49), and so the system is *not* at equilibrium.

For the system in the worked example to reach equilibrium, the value of the concentration term must increase. This will happen if hydrogen and iodine react to form more hydrogen iodide. Thus, the reaction moves to the right-hand side until the *new* value of the concentration term equals 49. The system is then in equilibrium, and so:

$$\frac{[HI]_{eq}^2}{[H_2]_{eq}[I_2]_{eq}} = 49 = K_c$$

To summarise:

- If K_c equals the concentration term (quotient), the system is at equilibrium. There is no change to the relative amounts of the reactants and products.
- If the concentration term is smaller than K_c, the system is not at equilibrium. The system will react to form more of the products until the concentration term equals K_c. This means that the position of equilibrium moves to the right.
- If the concentration term is greater than K_c, the system is not at equilibrium. The system will react to form more of the reactants until the concentration term equals K_c. This means that the position of equilibrium moves to the left.

e You should use the subscript 'eq' to distinguish between equilibrium concentrations and the initial concentrations, before equilibrium has been reached.

Calculation of K_c from experimental data

A typical question would give the starting amounts of the reactants, the total volume and the percentage that reacted and ask you to calculate the equilibrium constant.

The calculation requires the use of a table, as in the worked example below.

- Write the chemical equation.

- Construct a suitable table and write in the following:
  - the initial amounts (in moles) of the reactants and of the products if their initial amounts were not zero
  - the amounts by which the reactants and the products change in reaching equilibrium — use the stoichiometry of the equation
  - the amount, in moles, of each substance at equilibrium
  - the equilibrium concentration in mol dm^{-3} — divide the equilibrium number of moles by the total volume
- Below the table, write the expression for the equilibrium constant.
- Substitute the equilibrium concentrations into the expression and calculate its value. At the same time, determine the units of K_c and include them in your answer.

Worked example 1

When 0.0200 mol of sulphur trioxide is placed in a flask of volume 1.50 dm^3 and allowed to reach equilibrium at 600°C, 29% of it decomposes into sulphur dioxide and oxygen. Calculate the value of the equilibrium constant, K_c.

Answer

The equation is:

$$2SO_3(g) \rightleftharpoons 2SO_2(g) + O_2(g)$$

	SO_3	SO_2	O_2
Initial moles	0.0200	0	0
Change	$-0.29 \times 0.0200 =$ -0.0058	$+0.0058$	$+\frac{1}{2} \times 0.0058 =$ $+0.0029$
Moles at equilibrium	$0.0200 - 0.0058 =$ 0.0142	$0 + 0.0058 =$ 0.0058	$0 + 0.0029 =$ 0.0029
Concentration at equilibrium/mol dm^{-3}	$0.0142/1.50 =$ 0.00947	$0.0058/1.50 =$ 0.00387	$0.0029/1.50 =$ 0.00193

$$K_c = \frac{[SO_2]^2_{eq}[O_2]_{eq}}{[SO_3]^2_{eq}} = \frac{(0.00387 \text{ mol dm}^{-3})^2 \times (0.00193 \text{ mol dm}^{-3})}{(0.00947 \text{ mol dm}^{-3})^2}$$

$$= 3.2 \times 10^{-4} \text{ mol dm}^{-3}$$

Note that as 0.0058 mol of sulphur trioxide reacts, 0.0058 mol of sulphur dioxide and $\frac{1}{2}$ of 0.0058 = 0.0029 mol of oxygen are produced. This is because the ratio of the three substances in the chemical equation is 2:2:1 or 1:1:$\frac{1}{2}$.

The same method is used when some product, as well as the reactants, is initially present. In this type of question the equilibrium moles of reactants will be less than the initial amounts, but the equilibrium moles of the product will be more than the initial amount.

The units are determined as in worked example 2 on page 58.

Worked example 2

A vessel of volume 2.0 dm^3 was filled with 0.060 mol of methane, CH_4, 0.070 mol of steam and 0.010 mol of hydrogen and allowed to reach equilibrium at a temperature of $T°C$. 80% of the methane reacted. Calculate the value of the equilibrium constant, K_c, at this temperature.

Answer

The equation is

$$CH_4(g) + H_2O(g) \rightleftharpoons CO(g) + 3H_2(g)$$

	CH$_4$	H$_2$O	CO	H$_2$
Initial moles	0.060	0.070	0	0.010
Change	-0.80×0.060 $= -0.048$	-0.048	$+0.048$	$+3 \times 0.048 =$ $+0.144$
Moles at equilibrium	$0.060 - 0.048$ $= 0.012$	$0.070 - 0.048$ $= 0.022$	$0 + 0.048 =$ 0.048	$0.144 + 0.010$ $= 0.154$
Concentration at equilibrium/mol dm^{-3}	$0.012/2.0 =$ 0.0060	$0.022/2.0 =$ 0.011	$0.0029/1.50 =$ 0.00193	$0.154/2 =$ 0.077

$$K_c = \frac{[CO]_{eq}[H_2]_{eq}^3}{[CH_4]_{eq}[H_2O]_{eq}}$$

$$= \frac{0.024 \times (0.077)^3}{0.0060 \times 0.011} = 0.17 \text{ mol}^2 \text{ dm}^{-6}$$

Note that if 0.048 mol of methane reacts, then 0.048 mol of steam also reacts and 0.048 mol of carbon monoxide and 3×0.048 mol of hydrogen are produced. This is because the reaction stoichiometry is 1:1:1:3.

Units of K_c

Care must be taken when evaluating the units of K_c. The simplest way is to look at the equilibrium constant expression and work out the resultant power (dimension) of the concentration, the unit of which is mol dm^{-3}. For example, for the expression:

$$K_c = \frac{[SO_2]_{eq}^2[O_2]_{eq}}{[SO_3]_{eq}^2}$$

the dimension of the top line is (concentration)^3 and that of the bottom line is (concentration)^2. Therefore, the resultant dimension is (concentration)^1 which has units of mol dm^{-3}. Therefore, K_c has units of mol dm^{-3}.

Worked example 1

Calculate the units of the equilibrium constant, K_c, for the following equilibrium reaction:

$$N_2(g) + 3H_2(g) \rightleftharpoons 2NH_3(g)$$

Answer

$$K_c = \frac{[NH_3]_{eq}^2}{[N_2]_{eq}[H_2]_{eq}^3}$$

$$\text{dimensions} = \frac{(\text{concentration})^2}{(\text{concentration})^4} = (\text{concentration})^{-2}$$

units of K_c = (mol dm^{-3})$^{-2}$ or mol^{-2} dm^6

Worked example 2

Calculate the units of the equilibrium constant, K_c, for the following equilibrium reaction:

$$CH_4(g) + H_2O(g) \rightleftharpoons CO(g) + 3H_2(g)$$

Answer

$$K_c = \frac{[CO]_{eq}[H_2]_{eq}^3}{[CH_4]_{eq}[H_2O]_{eq}}$$

$$\text{dimensions} = \frac{(\text{concentration})^4}{(\text{concentration})^2} = (\text{concentration})^2$$

units of $K_c = (\text{mol dm}^{-3})^2$ or $\text{mol}^2\,\text{dm}^{-6}$

ⓔ The marks awarded in questions that ask for the value of K_c to be calculated are for:
- calculating the moles of each substance at equilibrium
- dividing these values by the volume to find the equilibrium concentrations
- correctly stating the expression for the equilibrium constant
- correctly substituting equilibrium concentrations into the expression and calculating the value of K_c
- working out the units (if there are no units, you must state this)

◀ If the volume is not given, divide the moles by V, which will later cancel out when the concentration values are substituted into the expression for K_c.

[H₂O] in equilibrium expressions
- When water is a reactant but not the solvent, the term $[H_2O]$ must always appear in the expression for the equilibrium constant.
- When water is in the gaseous state, $[H_2O]$ or $p(H_2O)$ (p. 63) must appear in equilibrium constant expressions.
- When water is the solvent, even if it is also a reactant or product, $[H_2O]$ does *not* appear in the K_c expression. This is because its concentration remains constant.

In aqueous solution or in pure water, $[H_2O]$ is the number of moles of water divided by the volume. For example:
- 1 dm³ of water has a mass of 1000 g
- It contains $\dfrac{1000 \text{ g}}{18 \text{ g mol}^{-1}} = 55.6 \text{ mol}$
- So, $[H_2O]$ in aqueous solutions and in pure water $= 55.6 \text{ mol dm}^{-3}$

Worked example 1
Write the expression for the equilibrium constant, K_c, for the reaction:
$$CH_3COOH + C_2H_5OH \rightleftharpoons CH_3COOC_2H_5 + H_2O$$

Answer

$$K_c = \frac{[CH_3COOC_2H_5]_{eq}[H_2O]_{eq}}{[CH_3COOH]_{eq}[C_2H_5OH]_{eq}}$$

◀ Water is a product and *not* the solvent, so $[H_2O]$ appears in the equilibrium expression.

Worked example 2
Write the expression for the equilibrium constant, K_c, for the reaction:
$$CH_3COOH(aq) + H_2O(l) \rightleftharpoons H_3O^+(aq) + CH_3COO^-(aq)$$

Answer

$$K_c = \frac{[H_3O^+]_{eq}[CH_3COO^-]_{eq}}{[CH_3COOH]_{eq}}$$

◀ Water is a reactant *and* the solvent, so $[H_2O]$ is omitted from the equilibrium expression.

The equilibrium constant in terms of partial pressure, K_p

The molecules of a gas are in constant and random motion. The pressure of a gas is caused by the frequency and momentum of the collisions of its molecules with the container walls.

In a mixture of gases, every gas molecule contributes to the overall pressure. The sum of the individual contributions equals the total pressure. The contribution of one gas to the total pressure is called the **partial pressure** of that substance.

> The partial pressure of a gas A in a mixture of gases is the pressure that the gas A would exert if it were alone in the container at that particular temperature.

This definition is better expressed as:

> The partial pressure of a gas A, $p(A)$, is equal to the mole fraction of gas A multiplied by the total pressure.

> **e** $\quad$ mole fraction $= \dfrac{\text{number of moles of a gas}}{\text{total number of moles of gas}}$

$$p(A) = \frac{\text{moles of A}}{\text{total number of moles}} \times P$$

The sum of the partial pressures of the gases in a mixture equals the total pressure. For a mixture of three gases A, B and C:

$$p(A) + p(B) + p(C) = P$$

The symbol for partial pressure is a lower case p with the identity of the gas in brackets, i.e. $p(A)$, or as a subscript, i.e. p_A. The total pressure is an upper case P.

Dry air is a mixture of 78% nitrogen, 21% oxygen and 1% argon (plus small amounts of CO_2 and other gases). The partial pressure of nitrogen when the total air pressure is 1.0 atm is:

$$\frac{78}{100} \times 1.0 \text{ atm} = 0.78 \text{ atm}$$

When a diver descends to a depth of 10 m, the pressure doubles. The partial pressure of nitrogen is now:

$$\frac{78}{100} \times 2.0 \text{ atm} = 1.56 \text{ atm}$$

At this higher partial pressure, nitrogen dissolves in the blood. When the diver returns to the surface, the nitrogen comes out of solution. This causes pain and could even result in the death of the diver. This condition is called the 'bends'. To minimise the problem of the bends, experienced sports divers use an air mixture called 'nitrox' that has a lower mole fraction of nitrogen.

The partial pressure of a gas is a measure of its concentration in the mixture. Therefore, partial pressures can be used to calculate equilibrium constants. The units are those of pressure and not mol dm^{-3}, so the values of the equilibrium constant will be different. The equilibrium constant in terms of pressures is given the symbol K_p.

The relation between the equilibrium constant, K_p, and partial pressures is similar to that for K_c and concentrations. For a reaction:

$$xA(g) + yB(g) \rightleftharpoons mR(g) + nS(g)$$

$$K_p = \frac{p(R)^m p(S)^n}{p(A)^x p(B)^y}$$

The units of K_p are $(atm)^{m+n-x-y}$.

In all equilibrium constant calculations, the total pressure, and hence the partial pressures, must be measured in atmospheres (atm). The reason for this is beyond A-level.

The gas law states that:

$$PV = nRT$$

where P is the pressure, V is the volume, n is the number of moles, R is the gas constant and T is the temperature in kelvin.

Thus:

$$P = \frac{n}{V} \times RT$$

where n/V is the concentration. Therefore, the partial pressure of a gas is directly proportional to its molar concentration. This results in the following relationship between K_c and K_p:

$$K_p = K_c(RT)^{\Delta n}$$

where Δn is the change in the number of moles of gas in the reaction. The gas constant has a value of 0.082 dm^3 atm K^{-1} mol^{-1}.

For the reaction:

$$N_2(g) + 3H_2(g) \rightleftharpoons 2NH_3(g) \qquad \Delta n = -2$$

$$K_p = \frac{p(NH_3)^2}{p(N_2)p(H_2)^3}$$

$$K_c = 0.26 \text{ mol}^{-2} \text{ dm}^6 \text{ at } 673 \text{ K}$$

$$K_p = K_c(RT)^{-2} = 0.26 \times (0.082 \times 673)^{-2} = 8.5 \times 10^{-5} \text{ atm}^{-2}$$

The units for K_p can be worked out easily because the dimensions of K_p are obtained from the equilibrium expression. In this example, the dimensions are:

$$\frac{(pressure)^2}{(pressure) \times (pressure)^3}$$

$$= \frac{1}{(pressure)^2}$$

$$= (pressure)^{-2}$$

Hence, the unit is atm^{-2}.

For the reaction:
$$H_2(g) + I_2(g) \rightleftharpoons 2HI(g)$$
$$K_p = \frac{p(HI)^2}{p(H_2)p(I_2)}$$

$\Delta n = 0$

so $K_p = K_c$

Neither constant has units as both atm (for K_p) and mol dm^{-3} (for K_c) cancel.

The partial pressure term equals the value of K_p only when the system is in equilibrium, so equilibrium partial pressures must always be used in K_p calculations. If K_p does not equal the partial pressure term, the system is not at equilibrium — reaction will take place until equilibrium is established.

To summarise:
- If K_p equals the partial pressure term, the system is at equilibrium. There is no change to the relative amounts of the reactants and products.
- If the partial pressure term is smaller than K_p, the system is not at equilibrium. The system will react to form more products until the partial pressure term equals K_p. This means that the position of equilibrium moves to the right.
- If the partial pressure term is greater than K_p, the system is not at equilibrium. The system will react to form more reactants until the concentration term equals K_p. This means that the position of equilibrium moves to the left.

Calculation of K_p from experimental data

The calculation of K_p from experimental data is carried out in a similar way to the calculation of K_c. However, there is an extra step, which is the calculation of the total number of moles at equilibrium.

The calculation requires the use of a table, as in the worked example below.
- Write the chemical equation.
- Construct a suitable table and write in the following:
  - the initial amounts (in moles) of the reactants and of the products if their initial amounts were not zero
  - the amounts by which the reactants and the products change in reaching equilibrium — use the stoichiometry of the equation
  - the amount, in moles, of each substance at equilibrium; then add these values to find the total number of moles
  - the **mole fraction** of each gas — divide the equilibrium number of moles by the total number of moles
  - the partial pressure of each gas — multiply the mole fraction of each substance by the total pressure
- Below the table, write the expression for the equilibrium constant.
- Substitute the equilibrium concentrations into the equilibrium constant expression and calculate its value. At the same time, work out the units of K_p and include them in your answer.

e Never use square brackets in K_p expressions. Square brackets around a formula mean the concentration, in mol dm^{-3}, of that substance and so must be used only in K_c expressions.

e When there is only one reactant, you might not be told its initial amount. You must assume that it is 1 mol. You will be told the percentage that reacts.

Worked example 1

Phosphorus pentachloride decomposes on heating:

$$PCl_5(g) \rightleftharpoons PCl_3(g) + Cl_2(g)$$

When some phosphorus pentachloride was heated to 250°C in a flask, 69% of it dissociated and the total pressure in the flask was 2.0 atm. Calculate the value of the equilibrium constant, K_p.

Answer

	PCl₅	PCl₃	Cl₂
Initial moles	1	0	0
Change	−0.69	+0.69	+0.69
Equilibrium moles	1 − 0.69 = 0.31	0 + 0.69 = 0.69	0 + 0.69 = 0.69

Total number of moles at equilibrium = 0.31 + 0.69 + 0.69 = 1.69

	PCl₅	PCl₃	Cl₂
Mole fraction	0.31/1.69 = 0.18	0.69/1.69 = 0.41	0.69/1.69 = 0.41
Partial pressure/atm	0.18 × 2.0 = 0.36	0.41 × 2.0 = 0.82	0.41 × 2.0 = 0.82

$$K_p = \frac{p(PCl_3)p(Cl_2)}{p(PCl_5)} = \frac{0.82 \times 0.82}{0.36} = 1.9 \text{ atm at } 250°C$$

Worked example 2 is more complicated because the stoichiometry is not 1:1.

Worked example 2

One of the important reactions by which the gaseous fuel methane, CH_4, is produced from coal is:

$$3H_2(g) + CO(g) \rightleftharpoons CH_4(g) + H_2O(g)$$

Hydrogen and carbon monoxide were mixed in a 3:1 ratio and allowed to reach equilibrium at a temperature of 1000 K. 65% of the hydrogen reacted and the total pressure was 1.2 atm. Calculate the value of the equilibrium constant, K_p.

Answer

	3H₂	CO	CH₄	H₂O
Initial moles	3	1	0	0
Change	−0.65 × 3 = −1.95	−1.95/3 = −0.65	+0.65	+0.65
Equilibrium moles	3 − 1.95 = 1.05	1 − 0.65 = 0.35	0 + 0.65 = 0.65	0 + 0.65 = 0.65

Total number of moles at equilibrium = 1.05 + 0.35 + 0.65 + 0.65 = 2.7

	3H₂	CO	CH₄	H₂O
Mole fraction	1.05/2.7 = 0.39	0.35/2.7 = 0.13	0.65/2.7 = 0.24	0.65/2.7 = 0.24
Partial pressure/atm	0.39 × 1.2 = 0.47	0.13 × 1.2 = 0.16	0.24 × 1.2 = 0.29	0.24 × 1.2 = 0.29

$$K_p = \frac{p(CH_4)p(H_2O)}{p(H_2)^3 p(CO)} = \frac{0.29 \times 0.29}{(0.47)^3 \times 0.16} = 5.1 \text{ atm}^{-2}$$

$$\text{dimensions} = \frac{(\text{pressure})^2}{(\text{pressure})^4} = (\text{pressure})^{-2}$$

units of K_p = atm^{-2}

Calculations using K_c and K_p

Calculating the percentage of reactant converted from an equilibrium constant is difficult and can involve solving quadratic and cubic equations. Only the two simplest types of calculation are required at A-level.

The first type is when two reactant molecules react reversibly to form two product molecules. This calculation involves letting the fraction of one substance that reacts equal an unknown, z. A table is used as in the calculation of an equilibrium constant. The value of z is found by taking the square root of the equilibrium expression.

Worked example

The esterification of ethanol with ethanoic acid is represented by the equation:

$$C_2H_5OH + CH_3COOH \rightleftharpoons CH_3COOC_2H_5 + H_2O$$

The equilibrium constant K_c at 25°C is 4.0.

Calculate the percentage of ethanol that is converted to ester when 1.0 mol of ethanol is mixed with 1.0 mol of ethanoic acid in a solvent of volume 1.0 dm³ and allowed to reach equilibrium.

Answer

	C_2H_5OH	CH_3COOH	$CH_3COOC_2H_5$	H_2O
Initial moles	1.0	1.0	0	0
Change	$-z$	$-z$	$+z$	$+z$
Equilibrium moles	$(1-z)$	$(1-z)$	z	z
Equilibrium concentration/mol dm⁻³	$\frac{(1-z)}{1.0} = 1-z$	$\frac{(1-z)}{1.0} = 1-z$	$\frac{z}{1.0} = z$	$\frac{z}{1.0} = z$

$$K_c = \frac{[CH_3COOC_2H_5][H_2O]}{[C_2H_5OH][CH_3COOH]}$$

$$= \frac{z \times z}{(1-z)(1-z)}$$

$$= \frac{z^2}{(1-z)^2} = 4.0$$

Taking the square root of both sides:

$$\frac{z}{(1-z)} = \sqrt{4} = 2.0$$

$$z = 2.0 - 2z$$

$$3z = 2.0$$

$$z = 0.67, \text{ so } 67\% \text{ of the ethanol reacted}$$

The second type of calculation is when one substance decomposes into two substances or two molecules of one substance. This is a much more difficult calculation and involves knowing that $(1-x)(1+x) = (1-x^2)$.

Worked example

Consider the reaction:

$$A(g) \rightleftharpoons B(g) + C(g)$$

$$K_p = \frac{p(B)p(C)}{p(A)}$$

Calculate the percentage of A that dissociates in this reaction in which the value of K_p is 10 atm and the total pressure, P, is 3.0 atm.

Answer

Assume that there is 1 mol at the start and let the fraction of A that reacts equal α at a pressure P atm.

	A	B	C
Initial moles	1	0	0
Change	$-\alpha$	$+\alpha$	$+\alpha$
Equilibrium moles	$(1-\alpha)$	α	α

Total number of moles at equilibrium $= 1 - \alpha + 2\alpha = 1 + \alpha$

Mole fraction	$(1-\alpha)/(1+\alpha)$	$\alpha/(1+\alpha)$	$\alpha/(1+\alpha)$
Partial pressure/atm	$\dfrac{(1-\alpha)}{(1+\alpha)} \times P$	$\dfrac{\alpha}{(1+\alpha)} \times P$	$\dfrac{\alpha}{(1+\alpha)} \times P$

$$K_p = \frac{p(B)p(C)}{p(A)} = 10 \text{ atm}$$

$$= \frac{\alpha^2}{(1+\alpha)^2} \times 3.0^2 \text{ divided by } \frac{(1-\alpha)}{(1+\alpha)} \times 3.0$$

$$= \frac{\alpha^2 \times 9.0 \times (1+\alpha)}{(1+\alpha)^2 \times (1-\alpha) \times 3.0}$$

$$= \frac{3.0\alpha^2}{(1+\alpha) \times (1-\alpha)} = \frac{3.0\alpha^2}{(1-\alpha^2)} = 10$$

This simplifies to:

$$10 - 10\alpha^2 = 3.0\alpha^2$$

$$(3.0 + 10)\alpha^2 = 10$$

$$\alpha^2 = \frac{10}{13} = 0.77$$

$$\alpha = \sqrt{0.77} = 0.88$$

Substance A is 88% dissociated under these conditions.

Heterogeneous equilibria

In all the examples so far, the reactants and products have been in the same phase. Some reversible reactions involve reactants and products in different phases.

There are three physical states — solid, liquid and gas.

- All gases mix completely. Therefore, a mixture of gases always forms a single phase in which any one part is identical with any other part.

The term 'phase' is used to distinguish between different physical states and the alternative forms of a given physical state.

- Two liquids mix to form either a single phase or, if they are immiscible, two layers — two liquid phases.
- Solids that dissolve in a solvent form a single liquid phase.
- A mixture of a solid and a gas forms two distinct phases.
- Mixtures of solids are usually in two different solid phases.

In a heterogeneous equilibrium reaction at least one substance is in a different phase from the others. An example of this is the reaction between carbon and steam to form carbon monoxide and hydrogen:

$$C(s) + H_2O(g) \rightleftharpoons CO(g) + H_2(g)$$

The three gases are in the same phase but carbon is in a different phase. It is solid and so does not have a 'concentration', whatever its mass. It is, therefore, not included in the concentration term or quotient.

For the reaction above, the equilibrium constant, K_c, is given by the expression:

$$K_c = \frac{[CO]_{eq}[H_2]_{eq}}{[H_2O]_{eq}}$$

Involatile solids have no vapour pressure and so they do not appear in the expression for the equilibrium constant, K_p. For the reaction:

$$3Fe(s) + 4H_2O(g) \rightleftharpoons Fe_3O_4(s) + 4H_2(g)$$

$$K_p = \frac{p(H_2)^4}{p(H_2O)^4}$$

where all partial pressures are equilibrium values.

> **Worked example 1**
> Ammonium hydrogen sulphide, NH_4HS, decomposes when heated, according to the equation:
>
> $$NH_4HS(s) \rightleftharpoons NH_3(g) + H_2S(g) \quad K_p = 0.142 \text{ at } 50°C$$
>
> **a** State the expression for K_p.
> **b** Calculate the partial pressure of both gases at 50°C and hence the total pressure.
>
> **Answer**
> **a** $K_p = p(NH_3)p(H_2S) = 0.142$
> **b** As the reaction produces NH_3 and H_2S in a 1:1 ratio, $p(H_2S) = p(NH_3)$
> $$K_p = p(NH_3)^2 = 0.142$$
> $$p(NH_3) = \sqrt{0.142} = 0.377 \text{ atm}$$
> $$p(H_2S) = 0.377 \text{ atm}$$
> total pressure = sum of partial pressures = $0.377 + 0.377 = 0.754$ atm

Another heterogeneous equilibrium is that between solid calcium hydroxide and aqueous calcium and hydroxide ions:

$$Ca(OH)_2(s) + aq \rightleftharpoons Ca^{2+}(aq) + 2OH^-(aq)$$

The solid calcium hydroxide is in one phase and the dissolved ions and the solvent are in another. The expression for the equilibrium constant is:

$$K_c = [Ca^{2+}][OH^-]^2$$

Worked example 2
The value of K_c for dissolving calcium hydroxide is $5.5 \times 10^{-6}\,\text{mol}^3\,\text{dm}^{-9}$ at 25°C. Calculate the concentration of OH^- ions in a saturated solution.

Answer
$$K_c = [Ca^{2+}][OH^-]^2 = 5.5 \times 10^{-5}$$
$$\text{let } [Ca^{2+}] = z$$
ratio of OH^- to Ca^{2+} to 2:1, so $[OH^-] = 2z$
$$K_c = z \times (2z)^2 = 5.5 \times 10^{-5}$$
$$4z^3 = 5.5 \times 10^{-5}$$
$$z = 0.024$$
$$[OH^-] = 2z = 0.048\,\text{mol dm}^{-3}$$

e Note that the system is in equilibrium when the solution is saturated in the presence of excess solid.

Altering equilibrium conditions

Le Chatelier's principle can be used to predict the direction of change of equilibrium position when conditions such as temperature, pressure or concentration are altered. However, the principle does not *explain* the direction of change. It also gives no information about whether the value of the equilibrium constant changes.

A proper understanding is based on the fact that the equilibrium constant equals the concentration (or partial pressure) term only when the system is at equilibrium:

- If K_c is equal to the concentration term, then the system is at equilibrium — there will be no change in the equilibrium position.
- If K_c is *not* equal to the concentration term, then the system is *not* at equilibrium — the position of equilibrium will change until the concentration term equals K_c.

e The position of equilibrium is defined by the ratio of the amounts of products to the amounts of reactants. If the position moves to the right, this ratio increases.

Effect of change in temperature

The only factor that alters the value of the equilibrium constant of a particular reaction is temperature.

For exothermic reactions, an increase in temperature results in lower K_c and K_p values. For endothermic reactions, an increase in temperature results in higher K_c and K_p values.

This is illustrated in Table 3.2.

Exothermic reactions
- An increase in temperature causes the value of K_c to become *smaller*. Therefore, the concentration term is bigger than the new value of K_c.
- The system reacts to make the concentration term smaller — which it does by forming more of the reactants — until the value of the concentration term equals the new value of K_c.
- Thus, the position of equilibrium shifts to the *left*.

A decrease in temperature has the opposite effect.

Reaction	ΔH/kJ mol^{-1}	T/°C	K_p
$N_2(g) + 3H_2(g) \rightleftharpoons 2NH_3(g)$ Exothermic	-92	25	6.8×10^5 atm^{-2}
		125	43 atm^{-2}
		225	3.7×10^{-2} atm^{-2}
		325	1.7×10^{-3} atm^{-2}
		425	7.8×10^{-5} atm^{-2}
$N_2O_4(g) \rightleftharpoons 2NO_2(g)$ Endothermic	$+58$	25	0.24 atm
		80	4.0 atm
		100	46 atm
		200	350 atm

Table 3.2 *Effect of temperature on K_p*

(e) The explanation for the effect of temperature on equilibrium constant is beyond the scope of the Edexcel A-level specification. It depends on the relationship:

$$\ln K_p = -\frac{\Delta H}{RT} + \frac{\Delta S_{system}}{R}$$

where ΔS_{system} is the change in entropy of the system and R is the gas constant.

As can be seen from this equation, if ΔH is negative, the first term is positive and will become smaller as the temperature, T, rises. This makes $\ln K_p$, and hence K_p, smaller.

Endothermic reactions

- An increase in temperature causes the value of K_c to become *larger*. Therefore, the concentration term is smaller than the new value of K_c.
- The system reacts to make the concentration term larger — which it does by forming more of the products — until the value of the concentration term equals the new value of K_c.
- Thus, the position of equilibrium shifts to the *right*.

A decrease in temperature has the opposite effect.

The logic of the effect of temperature on the equilibrium is:

change in temperature → change in the value of K → alteration in the value of the concentration term to regain equality → movement of position of equilibrium

Worked example

The chloride complex of cobalt(II) ions, $CoCl_4^{2-}$, is blue and is in equilibrium with pink hydrated cobalt(II) ions, $Co(H_2O)_6^{2+}$ according to the equation:

$$CoCl_4^{2-} + 6H_2O \rightleftharpoons Co(H_2O)_6^{2+} + 4Cl^-$$

When a blue solution of mainly $CoCl_4^{2-}$ ions is cooled, the colour changes to pink (see p. 69). Deduce whether the reaction as written is exothermic or endothermic.

Answer

On cooling, the equilibrium shifts to the right. This means that the value of K_c is higher at the lower temperature. Therefore, the reaction must be exothermic.

Effect of temperature on the position of equilibrium

Effect of change of pressure or volume of the container

Altering the pressure of a gaseous system or the volume of the container has no effect on the value of either K_p or K_c.

Increase in pressure by decreasing the volume (at constant temperature)

In all the examples below assume that the pressure has been doubled by halving the volume of the container. This will cause the concentrations of all species to double.

The equilibrium involving hydrogen, iodine and hydrogen iodide is an example of a reaction in which the number of gas moles on the left equals the number on the right:

$$H_2(g) + I_2(g) \rightleftharpoons 2HI(g)$$

$$K_c = \frac{[HI]_{eq}^2}{[H_2]_{eq}[I_2]_{eq}}$$

- An increase in pressure (caused by a decrease in the volume of the container) has *no* effect on the value of K_c.
- The concentration of HI rises by a factor of 2, and so $[HI]^2$ increases by a factor of 4.
- The concentrations of both H_2 and I_2 rise by a factor of 2. Therefore, $[H_2]$ multiplied by $[I_2]$ increases by a factor of 4.
- Both the top and the bottom lines of the concentration term rise by the same factor. Therefore, its value does not change.
- Neither K_c nor the concentration term has altered, so there is no change to the position of equilibrium.

The equilibrium between nitrogen, hydrogen and ammonia is an example of a reaction in which the number of gas moles on the left is more than the number on the right:

$$N_2(g) + 3H_2(g) \rightleftharpoons 2NH_3(g)$$

$$K_c = \frac{[NH_3]_{eq}^2}{[N_2]_{eq}[H_2]_{eq}^3}$$

- An increase in pressure (caused by a decrease in the volume of the container) has *no* effect on the value of K_c.
- The concentration of ammonia doubles, so $[NH_3]^2$ rises by a factor of 4.
- $[N_2]$ multiplied by $[H_2]^3$ rises by a factor of 2×2^3. This is a greater increase than that of the top line of the concentration term.
- The concentration term becomes smaller. Therefore, it no longer equals K_c.
- The system reacts to make the concentration term bigger until it once again equals the unaltered value of K_c. It does this by hydrogen reacting with nitrogen to make more ammonia, so the position of equilibrium shifts to the right.

An increase in pressure does not alter K_c, but the concentration term is lowered as there are fewer gas moles on the right. Therefore, the system reacts to make more ammonia, until the concentration term equals K_c once more.

The equilibrium between dinitrogen tetroxide and nitrogen dioxide is an example of a reaction in which the number of gas moles on the left is less than the number on the right:

$$N_2O_4(g) \rightleftharpoons 2NO_2(g)$$

$$K_c = \frac{[NO_2]^2_{eq}}{[N_2O_4]_{eq}}$$

- An increase in pressure (caused by a decrease in the volume of the container) has *no* effect on the value of K_c.
- The concentration of NO_2 doubles, so $[NO_2]^2$ increases by a factor of 4.
- The concentration of N_2O_4 only doubles, so the top line of the concentration term increases more than the bottom line.
- The concentration term becomes bigger and no longer equals K_c.
- The system reacts to make the concentration term smaller until it once again equals the unaltered value of K_c. It does this by converting NO_2 into N_2O_4, so the position of equilibrium shifts to the left.

An increase in pressure does not alter K_c, but the concentration term is increased as there are fewer gas moles on the left. Therefore, the system reacts to make more N_2O_4, until the concentration term equals K_c once more.

> (e) N_2O_4 is a colourless gas and NO_2 is brown. When the pressure is increased on this system at equilibrium, the colour fades as NO_2 is converted into N_2O_4. However, as it is an endothermic reaction from left to right, an increase in temperature causes a darkening of the colour, as the equilibrium position is pushed to the right.

Addition of an inert gas
When pressure is altered by the addition of an inert gas at constant volume, there is no effect on the concentrations of the reactants or products. This is because the number of moles of the reacting species has not been altered and neither has their volumes. Concentration is the number of moles divided by the volume. As neither has altered, the concentration remains the same.

Since the value of the concentration term does not change, neither does the value of K_c. The system is still in equilibrium. The position of equilibrium does not change, even though the pressure has been increased.

Effect of change of concentration of one species

The equilibrium involving sulphur dioxide, oxygen and sulphur trioxide is represented by the equation:

$$2SO_2(g) + O_2(g) \rightleftharpoons 2SO_3(g)$$

$$K_c = \frac{[SO_3]^2_{eq}}{[SO_2]^2_{eq}[O_2]_{eq}}$$

The percentage conversion of sulphur dioxide to sulphur trioxide can be increased by adding more oxygen. Addition of extra oxygen to the system in equilibrium causes the concentration term to become smaller. Therefore, it no longer equals K_c. The system reacts, making more SO_3, until equality is regained. This means that a greater proportion of sulphur dioxide has been converted to sulphur trioxide.

> **Worked example**
>
> State and explain the colour change that occurs when alkali is added to a solution containing dichromate(VI) ions.
>
> **Answer**
>
> $$\underset{\text{orange}}{Cr_2O_7^{2-}(aq)} + H_2O(l) \rightleftharpoons \underset{\text{yellow}}{2CrO_4^{2-}(aq)} + 2H^+(aq)$$
>
> The addition of alkali removes H^+ ions. This reduces the value of the concentration term. Therefore, dichromate(VI) ions react with water to form chromate ions until the concentration term once again equals K_c. The equilibrium position shifts to the right, so the solution turns yellow.

(a) *(b)*

ZAHOOR UL-HAQ

Acidified potassium dichromate (a) before and (b) after the addition of alkali

Effect of adding a catalyst

■ A catalyst has no effect on either the value of the equilibrium constant or the concentration term and so has no effect on the position of equilibrium.
■ A catalyst speeds up both the forward and the back reactions equally. Therefore, equilibrium is reached more quickly.

Catalysts are used in exothermic industrial processes so that a faster rate can be obtained at a lower temperature. This results in an increased yield, compared with the same reaction carried out at a higher temperature in the absence of a catalyst.

Industrial processes

The aim in an industrial process is to:
■ maximise the percentage conversion of reactants to products (increase the equilibrium yield)
■ make this amount of product as quickly as possible (fast rate of reaction)
■ keep the costs as low as possible

The Haber process

The reaction is:

$$N_2(g) + 3H_2(g) \rightleftharpoons 2NH_3(g) \quad \Delta H = -92 \text{ kJ mol}^{-1}$$

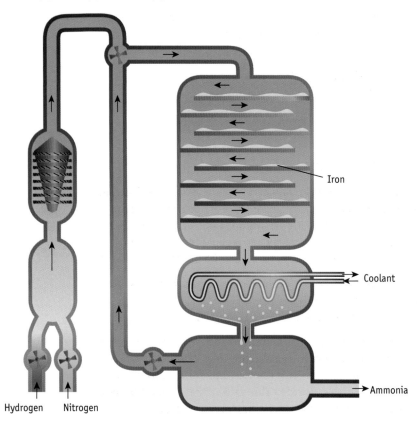

Hydrogen   Nitrogen

Iron

Coolant

Ammonia

> The cost of heating to a high temperature can always be partially recovered by the use of heat exchangers. High pressure is expensive, not only in the energy costs of compression, but also in the extra cost of a plant that will withstand the high pressure.

> The hydrogen is obtained from methane by reacting it with steam at a high temperature. The overall reaction is:
>
> $CH_4(g) + 2H_2O(g) \rightleftharpoons CO_2(g) + 4H_2(g)$
> $\Delta H = +165 \text{ kJ mol}^{-1}$
>
> The nitrogen is obtained from the air.

Schematic diagram of the Haber process. Hydrogen and nitrogen are mixed and compressed. The mixture cycles through the reaction tower over trays of iron.

The conditions are:

- temperature of 400°C
- pressure of 200 atm
- catalyst — iron promoted by traces of aluminium and potassium oxides

The rate is extremely slow and so an iron catalyst is used to speed up the reaction. This catalyst allows the reaction to take place at a reasonable rate at a temperature of 400°C. A higher temperature would result in a lower yield; a lower temperature would mean that the rate would be uneconomically slow. So, a compromise temperature of 400°C is used, together with an efficient catalyst.

At 400°C, the equilibrium constant, K_p, is 3.9×10^{-4} atm^{-2}, so the yield at 1 atm pressure is low. Fritz Haber understood the principles of equilibrium and realised that high pressure would increase the yield. His co-worker, Carl Bosch, designed apparatus that could work at 200 atm pressure.

Even under these extreme conditions only about 15% of the hydrogen is converted to ammonia. To obtain an economic overall yield, the ammonia is removed from the equilibrium system by cooling the gases until the ammonia liquefies. Unreacted nitrogen and hydrogen are then recycled through the catalyst chamber. In this way almost all the hydrogen is eventually converted to ammonia.

Both Haber and Bosch were awarded the Nobel prize for their work, which enables nitrogenous fertilisers to be manufactured cheaply.

The Contact process

The crucial step in the manufacture of sulphuric acid is:

$$2SO_2(g) + O_2(g) \rightleftharpoons 2SO_3(g) \quad \Delta H = -196 \text{ kJ mol}^{-1}$$

The conditions are:

- temperature of 425°C
- pressure of 2 atm
- catalyst — vanadium(V) oxide, V_2O_5

The rate is slow at room temperature, so a catalyst is used to speed up the reaction. This catalyst allows the reaction to take place at a reasonable rate at a temperature of 425°C. A higher temperature would result in a lower yield; a lower temperature would mean that the rate would be uneconomically slow. So, a compromise temperature of 425°C is used, together with an efficient catalyst.

The yield under these conditions is over 95%. It would not make economic sense to increase it further by using high pressure. However, a pressure above atmospheric pressure is needed to push the gases through the industrial plant.

Sulphur trioxide is removed from the equilibrium mixture by absorbing it in concentrated sulphuric acid. The unreacted sulphur dioxide and air are then passed through another bed of catalyst. This results in almost total conversion of the sulphur dioxide into sulphur trioxide. This makes the Contact process efficient and also prevents pollution from acidic sulphur dioxide gas.

Questions

1 Write the expressions for the equilibrium constant, K_c, for the following reactions:
   a $CO(g) + 2H_2(g) \rightleftharpoons CH_3OH(g)$
   b $NO(g) + \frac{1}{2}O_2(g) \rightleftharpoons NO_2(g)$
   c $4NH_3(g) + 5O_2(g) \rightleftharpoons 4NO(g) + 6H_2O(g)$

2 $K_c = 40 \ mol^{-1} \ dm^3$ at 250°C for the reaction:
   $$PCl_3(g) + Cl_2(g) \rightleftharpoons PCl_5(g)$$
   Calculate the value of K_c, at 250°C, for the reaction:
   $$PCl_5(g) \rightleftharpoons PCl_3(g) + Cl_2(g)$$

3 $K_c = 1.0$ at 1100 K for the reaction:
   $$CO(g) + H_2O(g) \rightleftharpoons CO_2(g) + H_2(g)$$
   a 1.5 mol of carbon monoxide and 1.5 mol of steam at 1100 K are mixed with 3.0 mol of carbon dioxide and 1.0 mol of hydrogen in a container of volume 100 dm^3. Calculate whether the system is in equilibrium. If it is not, explain in which direction the system will move in order to reach equilibrium.
   b A mixture of the four gases at equilibrium at 500°C contained 0.010 mol dm^{-3} carbon dioxide, 0.0040 mol dm^{-3} steam and 0.035 mol dm^{-3} carbon monoxide. Given that the value of K_c at 500°C = 0.20, calculate the concentration of hydrogen at equilibrium.

4 Sulphur trioxide was heated to 700°C in a vessel of volume 10 dm^3 and allowed to reach equilibrium:
   $$2SO_3(g) \rightleftharpoons 2SO_2(g) + O_2(g)$$
   The equilibrium mixture was found to contain 0.035 mol sulphur trioxide, 0.044 mol sulphur dioxide and 0.022 mol oxygen. Calculate the value of the equilibrium constant, K_c, at 700°C.

5 0.20 mol of sulphur dioxide and 0.10 mol of oxygen were mixed with 2.0 mol of sulphur trioxide in a vessel of volume 20 dm^3 and heated to 425°C.
   $$2SO_2(g) + O_2(g) \rightleftharpoons 2SO_3(g)$$
   The equilibrium constant $K_c = 1.7 \times 10^6 \ mol^{-1} \ dm^3$ at 425°C.

   Is the system in equilibrium? If not, in which direction will the system move when a catalyst of vanadium(V) oxide is added?

6 1.00 mol of methane, CH_4, and 2.00 mol of steam were mixed in a vessel of volume 10 dm^3 and allowed to reach equilibrium at 1200 K:

$$CH_4(g) + H_2O(g) \rightleftharpoons CO(g) + 3H_2(g)$$
   Analysis of the equilibrium mixture showed that 0.25 mol of methane was present.
   a Write the expression for the equilibrium constant, K_c.
   b Calculate the value of the equilibrium constant, K_c, at a temperature of 1200 K.

7 Methanol, CH_3OH, can be made by passing carbon monoxide and hydrogen over a heated zinc oxide and chromium(III) oxide catalyst:
   $$CO(g) + 2H_2(g) \rightleftharpoons CH_3OH(g)$$
   When 0.100 mol of carbon monoxide and 0.300 mol of hydrogen were heated to 400°C in a vessel of volume 10 dm^3, equilibrium was reached after 30% of the carbon monoxide had reacted. Calculate the value of the equilibrium constant, K_c.

8 The ester, dimethyl ethanedioate, is hydrolysed by water:
   $$CH_3OOCCOOCH_3 + 2H_2O \rightleftharpoons HOOCCOOH + 2CH_3OH$$
   11.8 g of dimethyl ethanedioate were mixed with 5.40 g of water and allowed to reach equilibrium. 75% of the ester reacted and the total volume was 15.0 cm^3. Calculate the value of the equilibrium constant, K_c, at the temperature of the experiment.

9 Write the expression for K_p for the following reactions:
   a $SO_2Cl_2(g) \rightleftharpoons SO_2(g) + Cl_2(g)$
   b $2NO(g) + O_2(g) \rightleftharpoons 2NO_2(g)$
   c $2SO_2(g) + O_2(g) \rightleftharpoons 2SO_3(g)$

10 At 35°C, dinitrogen tetroxide, N_2O_4, is 15% dissociated in a flask at a pressure of 1.2 atm:
   $$N_2O_4(g) \rightleftharpoons 2NO_2(g)$$
   Calculate the value of the equilibrium constant, K_p.

11 Nitrogen and hydrogen were mixed in a 1:3 ratio and heated to 400°C over an iron catalyst at a pressure of 30 atm until equilibrium was reached. 15% of the nitrogen was converted to ammonia:
   $$N_2(g) + 3H_2(g) \rightleftharpoons 2NH_3(g)$$
   a Write the expression for K_p.
   b Calculate its value under these conditions.

12 Hydrogen and iodine react reversibly to form hydrogen iodide:
   $$H_2(g) + I_2(g) \rightleftharpoons 2HI(g)$$

The value of the equilibrium constant, K_c, at $420\,°C = 49$.

Calculate the percentage of hydrogen that reacts when 1.0 mol of hydrogen and 1.0 mol of iodine reach equilibrium at $420\,°C$ in a vessel of volume $50\ dm^3$.

13 Write the expression for K_p for the following reactions:
   a $CaCO_3(s) \rightleftharpoons CaO(s) + CO_2(g)$
   b $H_2O(g) + C(s) \rightleftharpoons CO(g) + H_2(g)$

14 Write the expression for K_c for the reactions:
   a $Cr_2O_7^{2-}(aq) + H_2O(l) \rightleftharpoons 2CrO_4^{2-}(aq) + 2H^+(aq)$
   b $2CH_3COOH + HOCH_2CH_2OH \rightleftharpoons$
      $CH_3COOCH_2CH_2OOCCH_3 + 2H_2O$

15 Silver carbonate decomposes according to the equation:
   $Ag_2CO_3(s) \rightleftharpoons Ag_2O(s) + CO_2(g)$
   $K_p = 1.48$ atm at $500\,°C$

   Calculate the partial pressure of carbon dioxide at $500\,°C$.

16 Methane is trapped deep under the arctic sea in the form of solid methane hydrate $[CH_4(H_2O)_6]$. The equilibrium reaction for release of methane is:
   $[CH_4(H_2O)_6](s) \rightleftharpoons CH_4(g) + 6H_2O(s)$
   ΔH is endothermic.
   a State and explain the effect of a decrease in pressure on this equilibrium at $-40\,°C$.
   b State and explain the effect of increasing the temperature of methane hydrate from $-40\,°C$ to $-5\,°C$.
   c If the partial pressure of methane at $-40\,°C$ is 0.86 atm, calculate the value of the equilibrium constant, K_p.

17 Consider the reaction in which ammonia is oxidised by air at $900\,°C$ over a platinum catalyst at a pressure of 2 atm:
   $4NH_3(g) + 5O_2(g) \rightleftharpoons 4NO(g) + 6H_2O(g)$
   $\Delta H = -906\ kJ\ mol^{-1}$

   Explain the effect on the equilibrium constant and on the position of equilibrium of:
   a decreasing the temperature
   b increasing the pressure
   c adding excess air
   d removing the catalyst from the equilibrium mixture

18 Consider the following:
   ■ Soils become infertile if crops are continually grown and removed and no fertilisers are added.
   ■ Organic fertilisers such as manure and compost have to be broken down by bacteria to form inorganic nitrates before they can be absorbed by plants.
   ■ Seasonal flooding, such as used to happen in the Nile Delta, brought nitrates and other inorganic nutrients to the fields.

   Comment on the effect of Haber's work on feeding the increasing global population.

Acid–base equilibria

Acids were first defined in terms of their sour taste. When indicators such as litmus were discovered, an acid was thought of as any substance that turned litmus red. Later, the understanding of acidity led Arrhenius to define an acid as a substance that produces H^+ ions in aqueous solution. This definition is limited to aqueous solutions and it was extended by Lowry and Brønsted to include non-aqueous solvents. Their definitions of acids and bases are given below.

An acid is a substance that gives a proton (H^+ ion) to a base.

A base is a substance that accepts a proton (H^+ ion) from an acid.

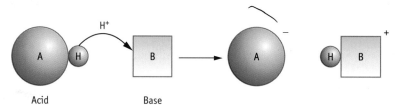

Lewis extended this idea further — for a base to be able to accept a proton, it must have a lone pair of electrons.

A base is a species that has a lone pair of electrons, which it uses to form a covalent bond. An acid is a substance that can accept the pair of electrons and form a bond.

For example, an aluminium ion, Al^{3+}, is a Lewis acid as it accepts lone pairs of electrons from water molecules when the hydrated ion is formed.

Acid–base conjugate pairs

The reaction of an acid with a base can be written as the chemical equation:

$$HA + B \rightarrow BH^+ + A^-$$

For many acids this is a reversible reaction:

$$HA + B \rightleftharpoons BH^+ + A^-$$

- For the left-to-right reaction, HA is the acid and B is the base.
- For the right-to-left reaction, the acid is BH^+ and A^- is the base.

The acid, HA, and the base, A^-, derived from it by loss of a proton, are called an acid–conjugate base pair. The base, B, and the acid, BH^+, derived from it by acceptance of a proton, are a base–conjugate acid pair.

The acid HCl reacts with the base H_2O:

Cl^- is the conjugate base of the acid HCl; the conjugate acid of the base H_2O is H_3O^+.

Ammonia is a base and reacts with water, which acts as an acid giving a proton to the ammonia molecule:

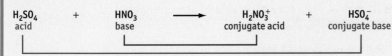

The relationship between conjugate pairs is:

- acid $-$ H^+ $\rightarrow$ conjugate base
- base $+$ H^+ $\rightarrow$ conjugate acid

> **Conjugate** means joined together, here by the loss or gain of a proton.

Worked example

Concentrated sulphuric acid reacts with concentrated nitric acid:

$$H_2SO_4 + HNO_3 \rightarrow H_2NO_3{}^+ + HSO_4{}^-$$

Mark in the acid–base conjugate pairs.

Answer

$$
\begin{array}{ccccccc}
H_2SO_4 & + & HNO_3 & \longrightarrow & H_2NO_3^+ & + & HSO_4^- \\
\text{acid} & & \text{base} & & \text{conjugate acid} & & \text{conjugate base}
\end{array}
$$

> In this reaction, nitric acid is acting as a base, as it is protonated by the sulphuric acid, which is a stronger acid.

Some acid–base conjugate pairs are listed in Table 4.1 in order of decreasing acid strength and increasing base strength.

| | Acid | | | Base |
---	Name	Formula	Formula	Name
	Sulphuric acid	H_2SO_4	HSO_4^-	Hydrogensulphate ion
	Hydroiodic acid	HI	I^-	Iodide ion
Strong acids	Hydrobromic acid	HBr	Br^-	Bromide ion
	Hydrochloric acid	HCl	Cl^-	Chloride ion
	Nitric acid	HNO_3	NO_3^-	Nitrate ion
	Hydronium ion	H_3O^+	H_2O	Water
	Hydrogensulphate ion	HSO_4^-	SO_4^{2-}	Sulphate ion
	Hydrofluoric acid	HF	F^-	Fluoride ion
	Ethanoic acid	CH_3COOH	CH_3COO^-	Ethanoate ion
Weak acids	Carbonic acid	H_2CO_3	HCO_3^-	Hydrogencarbonate ion
	Ammonium ion	NH_4^+	NH_3	Ammonia
	Hydrogencarbonate ion	HCO_3^-	CO_3^{2-}	Carbonate ion
	Water	H_2O	OH^-	Hydroxide ion

> *Table 4.1*
> *Acid–conjugate base pairs*

Strong and weak acids and bases

A strong acid is an acid that is *totally* ionised in aqueous solution.

For example, hydrochloric acid, HCl(aq), is a strong acid:
$$HCl(aq) + H_2O(l) \rightarrow H_3O^+(aq) + Cl^-(aq)$$

A weak acid is an acid that is only *very slightly* ionised in aqueous solution.

For example, ethanoic acid is a weak acid:
$$CH_3COOH(aq) + H_2O(l) \rightleftharpoons H_3O^+(aq) + CH_3COO^-(aq)$$

A 0.1 mol dm^{-3} solution of ethanoic acid is only 1.3% ionised.

A strong base is *totally* ionised in aqueous solution.

For example, sodium hydroxide is a strong base:
$$NaOH(aq) \rightarrow Na^+(aq) + OH^-(aq)$$

A weak base is protonated to only a small degree in solution.

For example, ammonia is a weak base:
$$NH_3(aq) + H_2O(l) \rightleftharpoons NH_4^+(aq) + OH^-(aq)$$

e Do not say that a weak acid is only partially ionised because this could mean that the ionisation is considerable but less than complete. Even HF, which is one of the strongest 'weak' acids, is only 5.7% ionised in a 0.1 mol dm^{-3} solution.

Acid and base equilibrium constants

Acid dissociation constant, K_a

A weak acid is in equilibrium with its conjugate base in aqueous solution. Consider a weak acid, HA:
$$HA + H_2O \rightleftharpoons H_3O^+ + A^-$$

The expression for the equilibrium constant (known in this context as the **acid dissociation constant, K_a**) is:

$$K_a = \frac{[H_3O^+][A^-]}{[HA]}$$

[H$_2$O] is not included in this expression as the concentration of water, in aqueous solutions, is constant (p. 59).

The true expression of the equilibrium constant includes [H$_2$O].

$$K_{true} = \frac{[H_3O^+][A^-]}{[HA][H_2O]}$$

1 dm^3 of water has a mass of 1000 g

It contains $\dfrac{1000 \text{ g}}{18 \text{ g mol}^{-1}} = 55.6$ mol

Thus, the concentration of water in an aqueous solution is 55.6 mol dm^{-3}.

e State symbols need not be written in equations in this topic, as all the substances are in solution.

◀ Never include [H$_2$O] in the expression for K_a.

This is a constant for all aqueous equilibria involving weak acids. Therefore, its value can be incorporated into the equilibrium expression:

$$K_{true} \times 55.6 = \frac{[H_3O^+][A^-]}{[HA]}$$

$$K_a = K_{true} \times 55.6$$

Base dissociation constant, K_b

An aqueous solution of a weak base is in equilibrium with its conjugate acid, for example:

$$NH_3 + H_2O \rightleftharpoons NH_4^+ + OH^-$$

The expression for the **base dissociation constant, K_b**, is:

$$K_b = \frac{[NH_4^+][OH^-]}{[NH_3]}$$

As with weak acids, $[H_2O]$ is omitted from the expression because its value is constant in aqueous equilibria involving weak bases.

Auto-ionisation of water and the pH scale

Water is amphoteric. It can act as both a base, as in its reaction with hydrogen chloride, or as an acid, as in its reaction with ammonia.

The amphoteric nature of water is even evident in the absence of another acid or base. One molecule of water can protonate another molecule of water:

$$H_2O \quad + \quad H_2O \quad \rightleftharpoons \quad H_3O^+ \quad + \quad OH^-$$
acid   base   conjugate acid   conjugate base

The equilibrium constant for this reaction is given the symbol K_w. The equilibrium expression does not include the term $[H_2O]$ because its value is constant.

$$K_w = [H_3O^+][OH^-]$$

This is often written as $K_w = [H^+][OH^-]$.

K_w is also called the **ionic product** of water. Its value, at 25°C, is $1.0 \times 10^{-14} \text{ mol}^2 \text{ dm}^{-6}$.

> **e** The reaction, as written, is the reverse of neutralisation of a strong acid with a strong base and so is endothermic. This means that at a higher temperature, the value of K_w is greater. At 37°C (normal blood temperature), the value of K_w is $2.4 \times 10^{-14} \text{ mol}^2 \text{ dm}^{-6}$ and at 100°C it is $5.13 \times 10^{-13} \text{ mol}^2 \text{ dm}^{-6}$. Therefore, at 37°C neutral pH is 6.8 and at 100°C it is 6.1.

e The equation for a weak acid is sometimes written as $HA \rightleftharpoons H^+ + A^-$. So the expression for K_a is:

$$K_a = \frac{[H^+][A^-]}{[HA]}$$

$[H^+]$ can be regarded as being shorthand for $[H_3O^+]$.

pH scale

Hydrogen ion concentration varies over a huge range of values (by a factor of about a trillion), so a logarithmic scale of measurement was devised. To avoid negative numbers in most cases, the scale was defined as:

$$pH = -\log_{10}[H^+] \quad \text{(this is often written as } -\log[H^+])$$

pH equals the negative logarithm to the base 10 of the hydrogen ion (hydronium ion) concentration.

◀ $[H^+] = 10^{-pH}$

In practice, the pH scale runs from about -1 to just over 14.

> **Worked example**
> Calculate the pH of a solution in which $[H^+]$ is equal to:
> a 10 mol dm^{-3}
> b 0.10 mol dm^{-3}
> c $1.23 \times 10^{-4} \text{ mol dm}^{-3}$
> d $4.56 \times 10^{-9} \text{ mol dm}^{-3}$
> e $7.89 \times 10^{-15} \text{ mol dm}^{-3}$
>
> **Answer**
> a $pH = -\log 10 = -1.00$
> b $pH = -\log 0.10 = 1.00$
> c $pH = -\log 1.23 \times 10^{-4} = 3.91$
> d $pH = -\log 4.56 \times 10^{-9} = 8.34$
> e $pH = -\log 7.89 \times 10^{-15} = 14.10$

ⓔ If an answer to a question is a pH value, you should report it to two decimal places.

Neutrality

A neutral solution is one in which the concentrations of H^+ and OH^- ions are the same:

$$K_w = [H^+][OH^-] = 1.0 \times 10^{-14} \text{ mol}^2 \text{ dm}^{-6} \text{ at } 25°C$$
$$[H^+] = [OH^-]$$
$$[H^+]^2 = 1.0 \times 10^{-14} \quad or \quad [H^+] = \sqrt{(1.0 \times 10^{-14})} = 1.0 \times 10^{-7} \text{ mol dm}^{-3}$$
$$pH = -\log 1.0 \times 10^{-7} = 7.00$$

In all aqueous solutions at 25°C, $[H^+] \times [OH^-] = 1.0 \times 10^{-14}$.

An acidic solution has $[H^+] > [OH^-]$. Therefore $[H^+] > 1.0 \times 10^{-7}$ and the solution has pH < 7.

An alkaline solution has $[H^+] < [OH^-]$. Therefore $[H^+] < 1.0 \times 10^{-7}$ and the solution has pH > 7.

◀ At 25°C, neutral pH = 7; acidic pH < 7; alkaline pH > 7.

pK_w, pOH and pK_a

The prefix 'p', in this context, means 'the negative log of'.

$$pK_w = -\log K_w \qquad pOH = -\log[OH^-] \qquad pK_a = -\log K_a$$

$$pK_w = -\log 1.0 \times 10^{-14} = 14 \text{ (at } 25°C)$$
$$K_w = [H^+][OH^-]$$

Since $\log (a \times b) = \log a + \log b$:

$$\log K_w = \log[H^+] + \log[OH^-]$$
$$pK_w = pH + pOH \quad or \quad pH + pOH = 14$$

The pH of strong acids and bases

The pH of strong acids

A strong acid, such as nitric acid, HNO_3, is totally ionised in aqueous solution. Thus, for example, a nitric acid solution of concentration 0.123 mol dm^{-3} has a hydrogen ion concentration of 0.123 mol dm^{-3}.

$$pH = -\log 0.123 = 0.91$$

Worked example 1

Calculate the pH of a solution of HCl made by dissolving 4.56 g of hydrogen chloride, HCl (or 3.00 dm^3 of HCl gas) in water and making the solution up to a volume of 250 cm^3.

Answer

amount of HCl $= \dfrac{4.56 \text{ g}}{36.5 \text{ g mol}^{-1}} = 0.125 \text{ mol}$ $\left(or \; \dfrac{3.00 \text{ dm}^3}{24.0 \text{ dm}^3 \text{ mol}^{-1}} = 0.125 \text{ mol} \right)$

$[HCl] = \dfrac{\text{mol}}{\text{volume}} = \dfrac{0.125 \text{ mol}}{0.250 \text{ dm}^3} = 0.500 \text{ mol dm}^{-3}$

$pH = -\log 0.500 = 0.30$

Worked example 2

Calculate the pH of a 2.0 mol dm^{-3} solution of hydrochloric acid.

Answer

$[H^+] = 2.0 \text{ mol dm}^{-3}$

$pH = -\log 2.0 = -0.30$

Sulphuric acid, H_2SO_4, is only a strong acid in its first ionisation:

$$H_2SO_4 \rightarrow H^+ + HSO_4^-$$

The second ionisation is weak:

$$HSO_4^- \rightleftharpoons H^+ + SO_4^{2-}$$

and is suppressed by the H^+ ions from the first ionisation. So, a solution of sulphuric acid of concentration 0.10 mol dm^{-3} has $[H^+]$ of just above 0.10 mol dm^{-3}, *not* 0.20 mol dm^{-3}.

The pH of strong bases

A strong base is totally ionised in aqueous solution. For example, a solution of a soluble base MOH of concentration 0.123 mol dm^{-3} has a hydroxide ion concentration of 0.123 mol dm^{-3}.

The pH can be worked out in one of two ways.

e Note that if a strong acid has a concentration greater than 1 mol dm^{-3}, it will have a negative pH.

Method 1

- Using the expression pH + pOH = 14, calculate $[OH^-]$ and hence pOH.

If $[OH^-] = 0.123$ mol dm^{-3}

$\quad$ pOH = $-\log[OH^-]$ = $-\log 0.123 = 0.91$

$\quad$ pH = $14 - $ pOH = $14 - 0.91 = 13.09$

Method 2

- Using the expression $[H^+] \times [OH^-] = 1.0 \times 10^{-14}$ mol^2 dm^{-6}, calculate $[OH^-]$ and hence $[H^+]$.

In the example above

$\quad [OH^-] = 0.123$ mol dm^{-3}

$\quad [H^+] = \dfrac{1.0 \times 10^{-14}}{[OH^-]} = \dfrac{1.0 \times 10^{-14}}{0.123} = 8.13 \times 10^{-14}$ mol dm^{-3}

$\quad$ pH = $-\log[H^+]$ = $-\log 8.13 \times 10^{-14} = 13.09$

Worked example

Calculate the pH of a 0.0444 mol dm^{-3} solution of barium hydroxide, $Ba(OH)_2$.

Answer using method 1
1 mol of $Ba(OH)_2$ produces 2 mol of OH^- ions.
$\quad [OH^-] = 2 \times 0.0444 = 0.0888$ mol dm^{-3}
$\quad$ pOH = $-\log 0.0888 = 1.05$
$\quad$ pH = $14 -$ pOH = $14 - 1.05 = 12.95$

Answer using method 2
1 mol of $Ba(OH)_2$ produces 2 mol of OH^- ions.
$\quad [OH^-] = 2 \times 0.0444 = 0.0888$ mol dm^{-3}
$\quad [H^+] = \dfrac{1.0 \times 10^{-14}}{0.0888} = 1.13 \times 10^{-13}$
$\quad$ pH = $-\log[H^+]$ = $-\log 1.13 \times 10^{-13} = 12.95$

ⓔ You should always check your calculation of pH to ensure it makes sense. An acid solution at 298 K cannot have a pH > 7; an alkaline solution cannot have a pH < 7. If you have obtained an impossible answer as a result of a calculation, then you should do the calculation again.

Titration of a strong acid with a strong base

In an experiment, 20.0 cm^3 of hydrochloric acid (a strong acid) of concentration 0.100 mol dm^{-3} was titrated with a solution of sodium hydroxide (a strong base) of concentration 0.100 mol dm^{-3}.

The variation of pH with the volume of sodium hydroxide added can be estimated by calculating the pH at certain points:

pH at the start
The acid concentration is 0.100 mol dm^{-3}, so pH = $-\log 0.100 = 1.00$.

pH after the addition of 10.0 cm^3 sodium hydroxide
$0.0200 \times 0.100 = 0.00200$ mol of acid were present originally. Half the acid has reacted, so $\frac{1}{2} \times 0.00200 = 0.00100$ mol are present in 30.0 cm^3 of solution.

ⓔ You must convert the volume in cm^3 to dm^3 by dividing by 1000.

Therefore,

$$[H^+] = \frac{0.00100}{0.0300} = 0.0333 \text{ mol dm}^{-3}.$$

$$pH = -\log 0.0333 = 1.48$$

pH at equivalence point (after 20.0 cm³ added)

All the acid has reacted and the solution contains sodium chloride which is neutral at pH = 7.

pH after the addition of 30.0 cm³ of sodium hydroxide

Two-thirds of the sodium hydroxide has reacted, so 10.0 cm³ did not react. Therefore, $0.100 \times 0.0100 = 0.00100$ mol of NaOH are present in 50.0 cm³ of solution.

$$pOH = \frac{-\log 0.00100}{0.0500} = 1.70$$

$$pH = 14 - 1.70 = 12.30$$

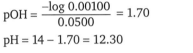

Performing a titration

The pH values at different points during this titration are given in Table 4.2.

Volume of NaOH added/cm³	pH	Volume of NaOH added/cm³	pH
0	1.00	20.0	7.00
10	1.48	20.1	10.40
15	1.85	21.0	11.39
19	2.59	30.0	12.30
19.9	3.60	40.0	12.52

Table 4.2 pH during the titration of 20 cm³ 0.100 mol dm⁻³ HCl with 0.100 mol dm⁻³ NaOH

These data can be presented as a graph (Figure 4.1).

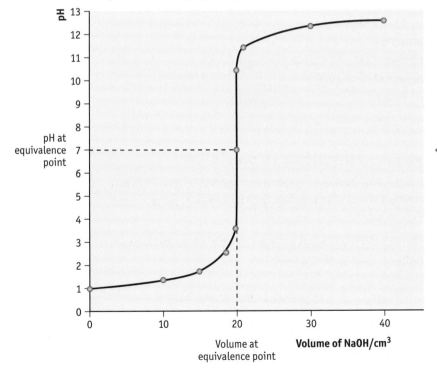

Figure 4.1 Titration of a strong acid with a strong base

◀ Notice that the graph rises slowly to start with, then vertically at the equivalence point, before flattening off just below pH 13.

If the acid were added to 20 cm³ of the alkali, the graph would have a similar shape but would be a mirror image. It would start at pH 13, fall slowly, then just before the equivalence volume of 20.0 cm³ of acid, it would plunge vertically from about pH 10 to pH 3. Finally, it would flatten off just above pH 1.

The pH of weak acids and bases

The pH of weak acids

A weak acid is in equilibrium with its conjugate base:

$$HA + H_2O \rightleftharpoons H_3O^+ + A^-$$

The rates of the forward and back reactions are so rapid, that the system is always in equilibrium. The equilibrium constant (the acid dissociation constant, K_a) is given by:

$$K_a = \frac{[H_3O^+][A^-]}{[HA]}$$

The reaction is sometimes simplified to:

$$HA \rightleftharpoons H^+ + A^-$$
$$\text{then } K_a = \frac{[H^+][A^-]}{[HA]}$$

[H₂O] is omitted from these expressions, as its concentration is effectively constant.

The pH of a solution of a weak acid can be calculated using the same method as for K_c calculations.

Consider a 0.10 mol dm⁻³ solution of a weak acid with $K_a = 1.0 \times 10^{-5}$ mol dm⁻³. Let x mol of HA ionise per dm³:

	HA	H₃O⁺	A⁻
Initial concentration	0.10	0	0
Equilibrium concentration	(0.10 – x)	x	x

$$K_a = \frac{[H_3O^+][A^-]}{[HA]} = \frac{x^2}{(0.10 - x)} = 1.0 \times 10^{-5} \text{ mol dm}^{-3}$$

This can be solved only by using the formula for a quadratic equation, which is outside the A-level specification. However, if the value of x is much less than the initial concentration of the weak acid, the term $(0.10 - x)$ can be approximated to 0.10. The value of x can now be solved easily:

$$\frac{x^2}{0.10} = 1.0 \times 10^{-5}$$

$$x = \sqrt{(1.0 \times 10^{-5} \times 0.10)} = 1.0 \times 10^{-3} \text{ mol dm}^{-3}$$

Thus,

$$[H_3O^+] = 1.0 \times 10^{-3} \text{ mol dm}^{-3}$$

$$pH = -\log 1.0 \times 10^{-3} = 3.0$$

e In A-level answers either expression for K_a is acceptable, unless the equation in the question has H_3O^+ on the right-hand side, in which case $[H_3O^+]$ must be used.

e You should check that the approximation is fair. Look at the value of x that you have calculated and check that it is small compared with the initial value of [HA]. In this example, the value of x is 0.0010. This is small compared with 0.10, as x is only 1% of [HA].

In calculations involving weak acids, the following assumptions are made:

- The tiny amount of H_3O^+ ions from the auto-ionisation of water is ignored. (This is because the degree of ionisation of water is very small and is suppressed by the H_3O^+ ions formed from the ionisation of the weak acid, HA.)
- $[H_3O^+] = [A^-]$. (There is no other source of A^- ions and the tiny amount of H_3O^+ ions from the auto-ionisation of water has been ignored.)
- [HA] at equilibrium is equal to the initial concentration of the acid HA. (Only about 1% of the weak acid molecules are ionised, so this is a fair assumption.)

These assumptions allow the expression for K_a to be simplified:

$$K_a = \frac{[H_3O^+][A^-]}{[HA]} = \frac{[H_3O^+]^2}{[HA]_{initial}}$$

This simplified expression can be used to calculate the pH of a solution of a weak acid, given its concentration and the value of K_a.

> ### Worked example
> Calculate the pH of a 0.135 mol dm^{-3} solution of ethanoic acid. (K_a for ethanoic acid = 1.8×10^{-5} mol dm^{-3} at 25°C)
>
> #### Answer
> Ethanoic acid ionises in water:
> $$CH_3COOH + H_2O \rightleftharpoons H_3O^+ + CH_3COO^-$$
> $$K_a = \frac{[H_3O^+][CH_3COO^-]}{[CH_3COOH]} = \frac{[H_3O^+]^2}{0.135}$$
> $$= 1.8 \times 10^{-5} \text{ mol dm}^{-3}$$
> $$[H_3O^+]^2 = 0.135 \times 1.8 \times 10^{-5}$$
> $$= 2.43 \times 10^{-6} \text{ mol}^2 \text{ dm}^{-6}$$
> $$[H_3O^+] = \sqrt{(2.43 \times 10^{-6})}$$
> $$= 0.00156 \text{ mol dm}^{-3}$$
> $$pH = -\log[H_3O^+] = -\log 0.00156 = 2.81$$

e Always use the equilibrium constant expression in these and buffer solution calculations. It is safer than trying to remember a formula such as $pH = \frac{1}{2}pK_a - \frac{1}{2}\log c$ (where c = the concentration of the acid).

Some questions give the pK_a value of the weak acid. In this case, pK_a must be converted to K_a.

$$K_a = 10^{pK_a}$$

For example, pK_a for methanoic acid = 3.75
$$K_a = 10^{-3.75} = 1.78 \times 10^{-4} \text{ mol dm}^{-3}$$

The pH of a solution can be measured using a pH meter (p. 165). If the pH and the concentration of a weak acid are known, the value of its acid dissociation constant, K_a, can be calculated.

> ### Worked example
> The pH of a 0.200 mol dm^{-3} solution of propanoic acid was found to be 2.78. Calculate the value of its acid dissociation constant, K_a.

Answer

Propanoic acid ionises according to the equilibrium:

$$C_2H_5COOH \rightleftharpoons H^+ + C_2H_5COO^-$$

pH = 2.78, so $[H^+] = 10^{-2.78} = 0.00166$ mol dm^{-3}

$$K_a = \frac{[H^+][C_2H_5COO^-]}{[C_2H_5COOH]_{initial}}$$

$$= \frac{[H^+]^2}{[C_2H_5COOH]_{initial}}$$

$$= \frac{0.00166^2}{0.200} = 1.38 \times 10^{-5} \text{ mol dm}^{-3}$$

$[C_2H_5COOH]_{initial}$ = the original concentration of the acid

In the worked example above, the approximation:

$$[C_2H_5COOH]_{eq} = [C_2H_5COOH]_{initial}$$

need not have been made. The question gives the solution pH of 2.78, which equals a hydrogen ion concentration of 0.00166 mol dm^{-3}. Therefore, 0.00166 mol dm^{-3} of acid must have dissociated, leaving $[C_2H_5COOH]$ = 0.200 − 0.00166 = 0.19834 mol dm^{-3}. This difference is so small that the true value of K_a obtained without using the approximation is 1.39×10^{-5} mol dm^{-3}, which is hardly any different from that calculated using the approximation.

However, with weak acids such as HF and HNO$_2$, which are stronger than propanoic acid, the approximation should not be made.

e Note that in this worked example a simplified equilibrium expression was written, with H^+ being used instead of H_3O^+. Both are acceptable.

Worked example

The pH of a 0.100 mol dm^{-3} solution of hydrofluoric acid, HF, was found to be 2.14. Calculate the value of the acid dissociation constant, K_a, of hydrofluoric acid.

Answer

$[H^+] = 10^{-pH} = 10^{-2.14} = 0.00724$ mol dm^{-3}

$[H^+] = [F^-]$

0.00724 mol dm^{-3} of H^+ ions were produced, so 0.00724 mol of HF must have dissociated.

$[HF] = [original] - [amount\ dissociated] = (0.100 - 0.00724) = 0.0928$ mol dm^{-3}

$$K_a = \frac{[H^+][F^-]}{[HF]} = \frac{0.00724^2}{0.0928} = 5.65 \times 10^{-4} \text{ mol dm}^{-3}$$

In the worked example above, if the approximation:

$$[HF] = [original\ acid] = 0.100 \text{ mol dm}^{-3}$$

had been made, the value of K_a would have been 5.24×10^{-4} mol dm^{-3}.

Diprotic acids

These are acids that can produce two H^+ ions per molecule. Sulphuric acid, H_2SO_4, is an example. It is a strong acid from its first ionisation:

$$H_2SO_4 \rightarrow H^+ + HSO_4^-$$

A 0.10 mol dm^{-3} solution of sulphuric acid produces 0.10 mol dm^{-3} of H^+ ions in its *first* ionisation.

The HSO_4^- ion is only a weak acid and so the second H^+ is only partially ionised:

$$HSO_4^- \rightleftharpoons H^+ + SO_4^{2-}$$

$$K_2 = \frac{[H^+][SO_4^{2-}]}{[HSO_4^-]} = 1.0 \times 10^{-2} \text{ mol dm}^{-3}$$

The H^+ ions produced by the first ionisation suppress the second ionisation. The amount of H^+ produced by the second ionisation is only 0.0080 mol dm^{-3}.

pH of 0.10 mol dm^{-3} sulphuric acid = $-\log (0.10 + 0.008) = 0.97$

It would be quite wrong to assume that in a 0.10 mol dm^{-3} solution of H_2SO_4, $[H^+] = 2 \times 0.10 = 0.20$ mol dm^{-3} and hence that the pH = $-\log 0.20 = 0.70$.

The pH of weak bases

A weak base is partially protonated in water. Ammonia is an example of a weak base:

$$NH_3 + H_2O \rightleftharpoons NH_4^+ + OH^-$$

$$K_b = \frac{[NH_4^+][OH^-]}{[NH_3]}$$

As with weak acids, the term $[H_2O]$ is omitted, as its value is constant.

The same type of assumptions can be made as with weak acids:

$[NH_4^+] = [OH^-]$ and $[NH_3]_{eq} = [NH_3]_{initial}$

Thus:

$$K_b = \frac{[OH^-]^2}{[NH_3]}$$

$$[OH^-]^2 = K_b \times [NH_3]$$

The value of K_b for ammonia at 25°C = 1.78×10^{-5} mol dm^{-3}, so the pH of a 0.100 mol dm^{-3} ammonia solution can be calculated:

$[OH^-] = \sqrt{(1.78 \times 10^{-5} \times 0.100)} = 0.00133$ mol dm^{-3}

pOH = $-\log [OH^-] = -\log 0.00133 = 2.88$

pH = $14 - $ pOH $= 14 - 2.88 = 11.12$

Buffer solutions

A buffer solution is one in which the pH remains *almost* constant, even if a *small* amount of acid or base is added.

- An **acid buffer solution** consists of a mixture of a weak acid and its conjugate base of *similar* concentration — for example, the weak acid ethanoic acid, CH_3COOH, and its salt sodium ethanoate, CH_3COONa.
- An **alkaline buffer solution** consists of a weak base and its conjugate acid of *similar* concentration — for example, the weak base ammonia, NH_3, and its salt ammonium chloride, NH_4Cl.

The crucial points are that the members of the acid–base conjugate pair must be at a similar concentration, which should be not less than 0.05 mol dm^{-3}.

e Although this calculation, which involves solving a quadratic equation, is beyond the A-level specification, candidates are expected to be able to explain why the $[H^+]$ in a solution of sulphuric acid is only slightly more than that caused by its first ionisation.

e Do not state that a buffer has constant pH. A buffer solution resists the change in pH, but it does not completely remove all the added H^+ or OH^- ions. Therefore, the pH does change, but only very slightly.

Blood plasma has a pH of 7.4 and acts as a buffer solution. The pH is maintained mainly by the mixture of carbonic acid and hydrogencarbonate ions. Inside the red blood cells, the pH is 7.25. Here, the buffer is also carbonic acid–hydrogencarbonate ions, but haemoglobin molecules are acidic and lower the pH.

Calculation of the pH of a buffer solution

Consider a buffer solution made up of a weak acid, HA, and its sodium salt, NaA. The salt is totally ionised:

$$NaA \rightarrow Na^+ + A^-$$

The weak acid is only slightly ionised:

$$HA \rightleftharpoons H^+ + A^-$$

$$K_a = \frac{[H^+][A^-]}{[HA]}$$

Ionisation of the weak acid is *suppressed* by the A^- ions from the totally ionised salt. This means that both [HA] and $[A^-]$ are fairly large and both are much larger than $[H^+]$. The following assumptions can be made:

- The number of H^+ ions from the auto-ionisation of water is so small in comparison with the H^+ ions from the ionisation of the weak acid that it can be ignored.
- The number of A^- ions from the totally ionised salt is much greater than the few A^- ions from the weak acid, so it can be assumed that $[A^-]$ = [salt] (the concentration of salt originally present).
- The ionisation of the weak acid is so suppressed that [HA] = [weak acid] (the concentration of weak acid originally present).

The equilibrium expression can, therefore, be simplified:

$$K_a = \frac{[H^+][A^-]}{[HA]} = \frac{[H^+][salt]}{[weak\ acid]}$$

The pH of a buffer solution can be calculated given K_a for the weak acid and the concentrations or amounts of the weak acid and its salt.

> **e** In the calculation of the pH of a weak acid, the assumption was made that $[H^+]$ = $[A^-]$. This is true only when the sole source of A^- ions is the weak acid. In a buffer solution this is not true because A^- ions are formed from the ionisation of the salt.

> **Worked example 1**
>
> Calculate the pH of a buffer solution made by adding 50 cm³ of 0.100 mol dm⁻³ ethanoic acid to 50 cm³ of 0.200 mol dm⁻³ sodium ethanoate. (K_a for ethanoic acid = 1.80×10^{-5} mol dm⁻³)
>
> **Answer**
>
> $$CH_3COONa \rightarrow CH_3COO^- + Na^+$$
> $$CH_3COOH \rightleftharpoons H^+ + CH_3COO^-$$
> $$K_a = \frac{[H^+][CH_3COO^-]}{[CH_3COOH]} = \frac{[H^+][salt]}{[weak\ acid]}$$
> $$= 1.80 \times 10^{-5}\ mol\ dm^{-3}$$
> $$[H^+] = K_a \times \frac{[weak\ acid]}{[salt]} = 1.80 \times 10^{-5} \times \frac{0.0500}{0.100}$$
> $$= 9.00 \times 10^{-6}\ mol\ dm^{-3}$$
> $$pH = -\log[H^+] = -\log 9.00 \times 10^{-6} = 5.05$$

Note that mixing the two solutions doubles the total volume. Therefore, the concentration of the weak acid was halved from 0.100 to 0.0500 mol dm⁻³ and that of the salt was halved from 0.200 to 0.100 mol dm⁻³.

Worked example 2

Calculate the pH of a buffer solution made by adding 1.42 g of potassium methanoate, HCOOK, to 50.0 cm^3 of a 0.111 mol dm^{-3} solution of methanoic acid, HCOOH. (K_a for methanoic acid = 1.78×10^{-4} mol dm^{-3})

Answer

molar mass of potassium methanoate = $1 + 12 + (2 \times 16) + 39 = 84$ g mol^{-1}

amount of potassium methanoate = $\dfrac{1.42\,g}{84\,g\,mol^{-1}} = 0.0169$ mol

$[HCOOK] = \dfrac{0.0169\,mol}{0.0500\,dm^3} = 0.338$ mol dm^{-3}

$HCOOK \rightarrow HCOO^- + K^+$

$HCOOH \rightleftharpoons H^+ + HCOO^-$

$K_a = \dfrac{[H^+][HCOO^-]}{[HCOOH]} = \dfrac{[H^+][salt]}{[weak\,acid]} = 1.78 \times 10^{-4}$ mol dm^{-3}

$[H^+] = K_a \times \dfrac{[weak\,acid]}{[salt]} = 1.78 \times 10^{-4} \times \dfrac{0.111}{0.338} = 5.85 \times 10^{-5}$ mol dm^{-3}

$pH = -\log [H^+] = -\log 5.85 \times 10^{-5} = 4.23$

A more complicated calculation involving buffers arises when an *excess* of weak acid is mixed with a strong alkali. All the alkali reacts with some of the acid, forming a salt of the weak acid and, therefore, creating a buffer solution. The amount of salt formed is equal to the amount of alkali. The total volume of the solution is the sum of the volumes of the two solutions that were mixed.

Worked example

Calculate the pH of a buffer solution made by mixing 60 cm^3 of 0.20 mol dm^{-3} ethanoic acid solution with 40 cm^3 of sodium hydroxide solution of concentration 0.10 mol dm^{-3}.
(K_a for ethanoic acid = 1.80×10^{-5} mol dm^{-3})

Answer

amount of alkali taken = $0.10 \times 0.040 = 0.0040$ mol = amount of salt formed

amount of acid taken = $0.20 \times 0.060 = 0.012$ mol

amount of acid left = $0.012 - 0.004 = 0.0080$ mol in a total volume of 100 cm^3

$[salt] = \dfrac{0.0040}{0.10} = 0.040$ mol dm^{-3}

$[weak\,acid] = \dfrac{0.0080}{0.10} = 0.080$ mol dm^{-3}

$CH_3COONa \rightarrow CH_3COO^- + Na^+$

$CH_3COOH \rightleftharpoons H^+ + CH_3COO^-$

$K_a = \dfrac{[H^+][CH_3COO^-]}{[CH_3COOH]} = \dfrac{[H^+][salt]}{[weak\,acid]}$

$= 1.80 \times 10^{-5}$ mol dm^{-3}

$[H^+] = K_a \times \dfrac{[weak\,acid]}{[salt]} = 1.8 \times 10^{-5} \times \dfrac{0.080}{0.040}$

$= 3.6 \times 10^{-5}$ mol dm^{-3}

$pH = -\log [H^+] = -\log 3.6 \times 10^{-5} = 4.44$

Calculation of the composition of a buffer solution

Calculation of the composition of a buffer solution requires the use of the expression for K_a. There are two types of calculation. In the first, the amount of solid salt has to be calculated.

Worked example

Calculate the mass of sodium ethanoate, CH_3COONa, that has to be added to 100 cm^3 of a 1.00 mol dm^{-3} solution of ethanoic acid to make a buffer solution of pH = 4.38. (K_a for ethanoic acid = 1.80×10^{-5} mol dm^{-3})

Answer

$[H^+] = 10^{-pH} = 10^{-4.38} = 4.17 \times 10^{-5}$ mol dm^{-3}

$$K_a = \frac{[H^+][CH_3COO^-]}{[CH_3COOH]} = \frac{[H^+][\text{salt}]}{[\text{weak acid}]} = 1.80 \times 10^{-5} \text{ mol dm}^{-3}$$

$$[\text{salt}] = K_a \times \frac{[\text{weak acid}]}{[H^+]} = \frac{1.80 \times 10^{-5} \times 1.00}{4.17 \times 10^{-5}} = 0.432 \text{ mol}$$

molar mass of $CH_3COONa = 12 + 3 + 12 + (2 \times 16) + 23 = 82$ g mol^{-1}

mass of sodium ethanoate required for 1 dm^3 = 0.432 mol × 82 g mol^{-1} = 35 g

mass for 100 cm^3 of solution = 3.5 g

In the second type of calculation, the volumes of the solutions of the weak acid and the salt have to be calculated. In this type of calculation there is no unique answer. It is the ratio of the volumes of the two solutions that is found.

Worked example

Calculate the relative volumes of a 1.0 mol dm^{-3} solution of ethanoic acid and a 1.0 mol dm^{-3} solution of sodium ethanoate that have to be mixed to give a solution of pH = 4.00. (K_a for ethanoic acid = 1.80×10^{-5} mol dm^{-3})

Answer

$[H^+] = 10^{-pH} = 1.00 \times 10^{-4}$ mol dm^{-3}

$$K_a = \frac{[H^+][CH_3COO^-]}{[CH_3COOH]} = \frac{[H^+][\text{salt}]}{[\text{weak acid}]} = 1.80 \times 10^{-5} \text{ mol dm}^{-3}$$

$$\frac{[\text{weak acid}]}{[\text{salt}]} = \frac{[H^+]}{K_a} = \frac{1.00 \times 10^{-4}}{1.80 \times 10^{-5}} = 5.6$$

ratio of the volumes of solutions of ethanoic acid to sodium ethanoate = 5.6 : 1

Mode of action of a buffer solution

Consider a buffer solution made of a weak acid, HA, and its sodium salt, NaA. The salt is totally ionised:

$$NaA \rightarrow Na^+ + A^-$$

The weak acid is only slightly ionised and its ionisation is *suppressed* by the A^- ions from the totally ionised salt:

$$HA \rightleftharpoons H^+ + A^-$$
$$K_a = \frac{[H^+][A^-]}{[HA]} = \frac{[H^+][salt]}{[weak\ acid]}$$

This means that both [HA] and $[A^-]$ are large and both are much greater than $[H^+]$.

When a *small* amount of H^+ ions is added, the ions react with the reservoir of A^- ions from the salt:

$$H^+ + A^- \rightarrow HA$$

The value of $[A^-]$ decreases slightly and that of [HA] increases slightly, but these changes are insignificant in relation to the original values of $[A^-]$ (from the totally ionised salt) and [HA] (from the almost unionised weak acid), which remain virtually unchanged. As nothing has changed significantly in the expression for K_a, the hydrogen ion concentration and hence the pH will not change greatly.

When a *small* amount of OH^- ions is added, the ions react with the HA molecules of the weak acid:

$$OH^- + HA \rightarrow H_2O + A^-$$

The value of $[A^-]$ increases slightly and that of [HA] decreases slightly, but these changes are insignificant in relation to the original values of $[A^-]$ and [HA], which remain virtually unchanged. As nothing has changed significantly in the expression for K_a, the hydrogen ion concentration and hence the pH will not change greatly.

> **e** The addition of OH^- ions can also be explained by stating that they drive the equilibrium $HA \rightleftharpoons H^+ + A^-$ to the right, by removal of the H^+ ions. This causes an increase in $[A^-]$. However, the increase is not significant because of the relatively large value of $[A^-]$ from the salt. [HA] also decreases slightly, but also by an insignificant amount. Therefore, the pH hardly changes.

A weak acid on its own is not a buffer as $[A^-]$ is very small. Where H^+ or OH^- are added, the change in $[A^-]$ is significant.

The pH of solutions of salts

Salts of weak bases

The cations in the salts of weak bases are their conjugate acids. For example, the ammonium ion, NH_4^+, is the conjugate acid of the weak base ammonia, NH_3.

A solution of ammonium chloride is totally ionised:

$$NH_4Cl \rightarrow NH_4^+ + Cl^-$$

The ammonium ions act as an acid, reacting reversibly with water to produce H_3O^+ ions, which make the solution acidic.

$$NH_4^+ + H_2O \rightleftharpoons H_3O^+ + NH_3$$

$$K_a = \frac{[H_3O^+][NH_3]}{[NH_4^+]}$$

K_a for $NH_4^+ = 5.62 \times 10^{-10}$ mol dm^{-3}

Using the usual assumptions for a weak acid:

$$[H_3O^+]^2 = K_a \times [NH_4^+]$$

For a 0.10 mol dm^{-3} solution of ammonium chloride:

$$[H_3O^+] = \sqrt{5.62 \times 10^{-10} \times 0.100} = 7.50 \times 10^{-6} \text{ mol dm}^{-3}$$

$$pH = -\log[H_3O^+] = -\log 7.50 \times 10^{-6} = 5.13$$

The pH is less than 7, so the solution is acidic.

Salts of weak acids

The anions in the salts of weak acids are their conjugate bases. For example, the ethanoate ion in sodium ethanoate is the conjugate base of ethanoic acid, which is a weak acid.

Sodium ethanoate is totally ionised:

$$CH_3COONa \rightarrow CH_3COO^- + Na^+$$

The CH_3COO^- ions react reversibly with water:

$$CH_3COO^- + H_2O \rightleftharpoons CH_3COOH + OH^-$$

The formation of OH^- ions makes the solution alkaline.

$$K_b = \frac{[CH_3COOH][OH^-]}{[CH_3COO^-]}$$

The value of K_b of a conjugate base can be found by using the formula:

$$K_a \times K_b = K_w$$

K_a for ethanoic acid $= 1.80 \times 10^{-5}$ mol dm^{-3}

So

$$K_b \text{ for the ethanoate ion} = \frac{1.0 \times 10^{-14}}{1.80 \times 10^{-5}} = 5.56 \times 10^{-10} \text{ mol dm}^{-3}$$

The pH of a 0.10 mol dm^{-3} solution of sodium ethanoate can be calculated:

$$[OH^-]^2 = K_b[CH_3COO^-]$$

$$[OH^-] = \sqrt{5.56 \times 10^{-10} \times 0.10} = 7.46 \times 10^{-6} \text{ mol dm}^{-3}$$

$$pOH = -\log[OH^-] = -\log 7.46 \times 10^{-6} = 5.13$$

$$pH = 14 - pOH = 14 - 5.13 = 8.87$$

The pH is greater than 7, so the solution is alkaline.

The weaker the acid, the stronger is its anion as a conjugate base, and the more

e Remember that a solution is acidic if $[H^+]$ or $[H_3O^+] >$ $[OH^-]$. A neutral solution becomes acidic if H^+ ions are produced. NH_4^+ ions produce H^+ ions and so the solution has a pH < 7.

alkaline is the solution of its salt. For example, carbonic acid, H_2CO_3, is a weaker acid than ethanoic acid, so a solution of sodium carbonate has a higher pH than a solution of sodium ethanoate.

Salts of strong acids and strong bases

The conjugate base of a strong acid, such as HCl, is too weak to react with water:

$$Cl^- + H_2O \rightarrow \text{no reaction}$$

Similarly, the conjugate acid of a strong base does not react, so the salts of strong acids and strong bases dissolve in water without any reaction taking place. Their solutions are neutral, pH 7.

The reaction $NaCl + H_2O \rightarrow HCl + NaOH$ does *not* occur. In fact, the reverse reaction goes to completion.

Universal indicator in various salt solutions (left to right: ammonium chloride, sodium chloride, sodium ethanoate and sodium carbonate)

The rule of two

- The pH of a 0.1 mol dm^{-3} solution of a strong acid is 1 and that of a 0.1 mol dm^{-3} solution of a strong base is 13.
- The pH of a solution of a salt of a strong acid or a strong base is 7.

The 'rule of two' gives an approximate pH of weak acids, weak bases and their salts:

- pH of weak acid ≈ pH of strong acid + 2 = 1 + 2 = 3
- pH of weak base ≈ pH of strong base − 2 = 13 − 2 = 11
- pH of salt of weak acid and strong base ≈ 7 + 2 = 9
- pH of salt of weak base and strong acid ≈ 7 − 2 = 5

ℯ The rule for going from strong to weak is to add 2 pH units for a weak acid; subtract 2 pH units for a weak base.

Acid–base indicators

In acid–base titrations, the **equivalence point** is the point at which enough alkali has been added from the burette to react with all the acid in the conical flask or when enough acid has been added from the burette to react with all the alkali in the conical flask. For a reaction with a 1:1 stoichiometry, this means an equal number of moles of acid and alkali. If the stoichiometry is 2:1, then the ratio of moles required for the equivalence point is also 2:1.

The pH at the equivalence point is not necessarily 7. This is because at this point the solution consists of the salt of the acid and the alkali. If both the acid and alkali are strong, the solution will be pH 7, but if either is weak, then it will not.

The purpose of an indicator is to show when the equivalence point has been reached. Indicators are weak acids with the colour of the conjugate base being different from that of the weak acid molecule. Shorthand for an indicator molecule is HInd. It dissociates in water according to the equation:

$$HInd \rightleftharpoons H^+ + Ind^-$$
$$\text{colour 1} \qquad\qquad \text{colour 2}$$

$$K_{ind} = \frac{[H^+][Ind^-]}{[HInd]}$$

- When acid is added, the equilibrium is driven to the left and the indicator appears as colour 1.
- When alkali is added, the OH^- ions react with the H^+ ions from the indicator and the equilibrium is driven to the right. The indicator turns colour 2.
- The colour at the equivalence point appears when $[HInd] = [Ind^-]$. At this point:

$$K_{ind} = [H^+] \text{ or pH} = pK_{ind}$$

With most indicators, the eye can see either colour 1 or colour 2 only if at least 10% of that species is present in the mixture. Thus, the range over which the colour is seen to change is from a ratio of $[HInd]:[Ind^-]$ of just less than 10 to just over 0.1. This is a range of pH of approximately ± 1 from the pK_{ind} value.

Indicator	pK_{ind}	pH range	Acid colour	Alkaline colour	Neutral colour
Methyl orange	3.7	3.1–4.4	Red	Yellow	Orange
Bromophenol blue	4.0	3.0–4.6	Yellow	Blue	Green
Bromocresol green	4.7	3.8–5.4	Yellow	Blue	Green
Methyl red	5.1	4.2–6.3	Red	Yellow	Orange
Bromothymol blue	7.0	6.0–7.6	Yellow	Blue	Green
Thymol blue*	8.9	8.0–9.6	Yellow	Blue	Green
Phenolphthalein	9.3	8.3–10.0	Colourless	Red	Pale pink
* Thymol blue also changes from red to yellow around a pH of 2					

Table 4.3 Some common acid–base indicators

The correct choice of indicator depends on the strengths of the acid and base in the titration.

Methyl orange in acid (left) and alkaline (right) solutions

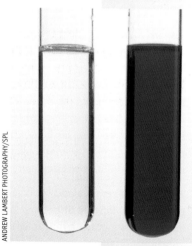

Phenolphthalein in acid (left) and alkaline (right) solutions

Red cabbage extract at (from left) pH 1, 3, 5, 7, 9, 11 and 13

ZAHOOR UL-HAQ

Titration curves

A titration curve shows how the pH of a solution varies as the reagent in the burette is added. The shape of a titration curve depends upon the strength/weakness of the acid and base.

In order to draw a titration curve, the following have to be estimated:

■ the pH at the start
■ the pH at the equivalence point
■ the volume of liquid from the burette required to reach the equivalence point
■ the pH range of the near vertical part of the graph
■ the pH after excess reagent has been added from the burette (final pH)

The pH values at different points during a typical titration are shown in Table 4.4. The figures are only approximate, because they vary depending on the concentrations and on how weak the acids and bases are.

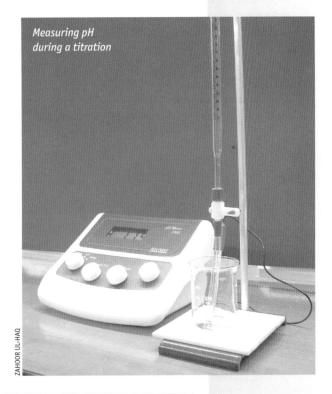

Measuring pH during a titration

ZAHOOR UL-HAQ

Reagent in conical flask	Reagent in burette	Initial pH	Equivalence point pH	Vertical range pH	Final pH
Strong acid	Strong base	1	7	3–11	Just < 13
Strong base	Strong acid	13	7	11–3	Just > 1
Weak acid	Strong base	3	9	7–11	Just < 13
Strong base	Weak acid	13	9	11–7	Just > 3
Strong acid	Weak base	1	5	3–7	Just < 11
Weak base	Strong acid	11	5	7–3	Just > 1

Table 4.4 *Variation of pH during different types of titration*

The volume at the equivalence point has to be worked out by the usual titration method. In most questions the acids and bases react in a 1:1 ratio. For example, if a 0.10 mol dm^{-3} solution of a base is added to 20 cm^3 of 0.10 mol dm^{-3} acid, the equivalence point is at 20 cm^3 of added base. Note that if the acid had a concentration of 0.20 mol dm^{-3}, the equivalence point would be at 40 cm^3 of added base.

In the titration curves below:
- the starting volume in the flask is 20 cm^3
- the equivalence point is at 20 cm^3 of added reagent
- The left-hand graph of each pair shows the change in pH as base is added to acid; the right-hand graphs show the pH change as acid is added to base.

Strong acid–strong base titration

The variation of pH as sodium hydroxide solution is added to a strong acid, such as HCl, is given in Table 4.2 on page 83. The values are plotted in Figure 4.2. The graphs show the reaction between hydrochloric acid of concentration 0.10 mol dm^{-3} and sodium hydroxide of the same concentration.

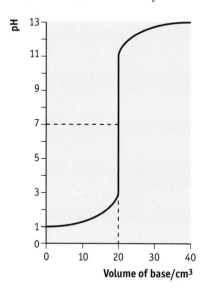
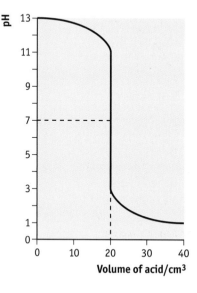

Figure 4.2 Strong acid/strong base

Weak acid–strong base titration

The graphs in Figure 4.3 show the variation of pH during the reaction between solutions of a weak acid, such as ethanoic acid, and a strong base, such as sodium hydroxide. The concentration of both reagents is 0.10 mol dm^{-3}.

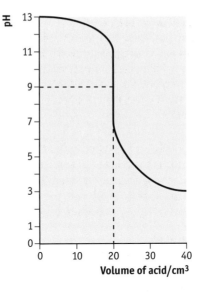

Figure 4.3 Weak acid/strong base

Strong acid–weak base titrations

The graphs in Figure 4.4 show the variation of pH during the reaction between solutions of a strong acid, such as hydrochloric acid, and a weak base such as ammonia. The concentration of both reagents is 0.10 mol dm^{-3}.

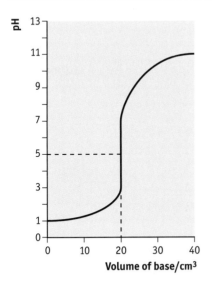

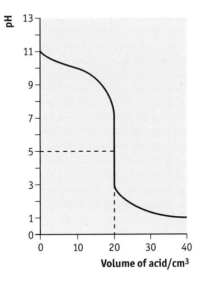

Figure 4.4 Strong acid/weak base

Evaluation of K_a and K_b from titration curves

When a strong base is added to a solution of a weak acid, the point halfway to the equivalence point is when half the acid has been neutralised. For a weak acid, HA:

$$K_a = \frac{[H^+][A^-]}{[HA]}$$

At the half-neutralisation point [HA] = [A⁻]. Therefore, at this point, K_a = [H⁺], so pK_a = pH. The pH at the half-neutralisation point can be read off the graph.

At the half-neutralisation point, the mixture is a buffer solution because both the weak acid and its conjugate base are present in equal and, therefore, significant, quantities.

The evaluation is similar for a weak base. If a strong acid is added to a weak base, the pH at the half-neutralisation point is equal to pK_b of the weak base, B.

$$B + H_2O \rightleftharpoons BH^+ + OH^-$$

$$K_b = \frac{[BH^+][OH^-]}{[B]}$$

At the half-neutralisation point, [B] = [BH⁺]. Therefore, at this point K_b = [OH⁻], so pK_b = pOH. The pH at the half-neutralisation point can be read off the graph and K_b equals 14 in pH.

Choice of indicator

For an indicator to work, the entire range during which it changes colour must lie completely within the vertical section of the titration curve.

For a strong acid–strong base titration, the pH range of the indicator must lie completely within the range of pH 3–11. Therefore, all the indicators listed in Table 4.3 will give an accurate result. The indicators most usually chosen are methyl orange and phenolphthalein.

> ⓔ People who are red–green colour blind have great difficulty seeing the end point of a titration using methyl orange. They should use screened methyl orange instead. This contains a blue dye, so the acid colour is purple (red plus blue), the alkaline colour is green (yellow plus blue) and the neutral colour is grey (red plus blue plus yellow).

For a weak acid–strong base titration, the range must be completely within pH 7–11. Of the indicators in Table 4.3, only thymol blue and phenolphthalein will give the correct result.

For a weak base–strong acid titration, the colour change of the indicator must be completely within the range of pH 3–7. Methyl orange, bromophenol blue, bromocresol green and methyl red are all suitable indicators.

Enthalpy of neutralisation of acids

The standard enthalpy of neutralisation, $\Delta H^{\ominus}_{neut}$, is defined as the enthalpy change when an acid and a base react to form 1 mol of water under standard conditions of 1.0 mol dm⁻³ solutions, 1 atm pressure and a stated temperature, usually 298 K (25 °C).

For example, it is the molar enthalpy change for:

$$HCl(aq) + NaOH(aq) \rightarrow NaCl(aq) + H_2O(l)$$
$$\tfrac{1}{2}H_2SO_4(aq) + KOH(aq) \rightarrow \tfrac{1}{2}K_2SO_4(aq) + H_2O(l)$$
$$CH_3COOH(aq) + NaOH(aq) \rightarrow CH_3COONa(aq) + H_2O(l)$$

Strong acids neutralised by strong bases

Strong acids and strong bases are both totally ionised, so the equation for the reaction between them can be written ionically. For example, for the neutralisation of hydrochloric acid by sodium hydroxide the full ionic equation is:

$$H^+(aq) + \cancel{Cl^-}(aq) + \cancel{Na^+}(aq) + OH^-(aq) \rightarrow \cancel{Na^+}(aq) + \cancel{Cl^-}(aq) + H_2O(l)$$

The spectator ions can be crossed out, leaving the net ionic equation:

$$H^+(aq) + OH^-(aq) \rightarrow H_2O(l)$$

This equation represents the neutralisation of all strong acids by strong bases. Therefore, ΔH for all these reactions is approximately the same.

For a strong acid neutralised by a strong base, $\Delta H_{neut} = -57.2$ kJ mol^{-1}.

Weak acids neutralised by strong bases

The ionic equation given above does not apply to the neutralisation of a weak acid by a strong base because the acid is not totally ionised. The neutralisation can be regarded as the sum of two reactions:

$$
\begin{array}{ll}
HA(aq) \rightleftharpoons H^+(aq) + A^-(aq) & \Delta H_1 \\
H^+(aq) + OH^-(aq) \rightarrow H_2O(l) & \Delta H_2 \\
\hline
HA(aq) + OH^-(aq) \rightarrow A^-(aq) + H_2O(l) & \Delta H_{neut}
\end{array}
$$

$$\Delta H_{neut} = \Delta H_1 + \Delta H_2$$
where $\Delta H_2 = -57.2$ kJ mol^{-1}

- If ΔH_1 is endothermic, the value of ΔH_{neut} is *less* exothermic than ΔH_{neut} of a strong acid.
- If ΔH_1 is exothermic, the value of ΔH_{neut} is *more* exothermic than ΔH_{neut} of a strong acid.

Hydrofluoric acid, HF, is a weak acid. It ionises exothermically because of the small size of the F$^-$ ion (the smallest anion that can exist in solution), which forms strong hydrogen bonds with water molecules.

Other weak acids ionise endothermically. The weaker the acid, the more endothermic is its ionisation. Some examples are given in Table 4.5.

> Even though the acid is only about 1% ionised, the removal of H$^+$ ions by the base drives the equilibrium to the right until all the acid has been neutralised.

Acid	K_a/mol dm^{-3}	Base	ΔH_{neut}/kJ mol^{-1}
HF	5.6×10^{-4}	NaOH	−68.6
CH$_3$COOH	1.8×10^{-5}	NaOH	−55.2
H$_2$S	8.9×10^{-7}	NaOH	−32.2
HCN	4.9×10^{-10}	NaOH	−11.7

Table 4.5 Enthalpy of neutralisation of some weak acids

The enthalpy of ionisation of ethanoic acid is only +2 kJ mol^{-1}. This is why its enthalpy of neutralisation is so close to that of a strong acid.

The structure of acids

Acids can be classified according to three types. In the first type of acid, a hydrogen atom is joined to an oxygen atom in a molecule. The oxo-acids (e.g. sulphuric, nitric, carbonic) and all the organic acids fall into this category.

> **e** In oxo-acids containing an element that can have more than one oxidation state, the lower the oxidation state the weaker the acid is. For example, sulphuric acid (oxidation state of sulphur $= +6$) is a stronger acid than sulphurous acid (oxidation state of sulphur $= +4$)

In addition to the oxygen attached to the hydrogen, an oxo-acid also contains one or more X=O groups. For example, the structure of sulphuric acid is:

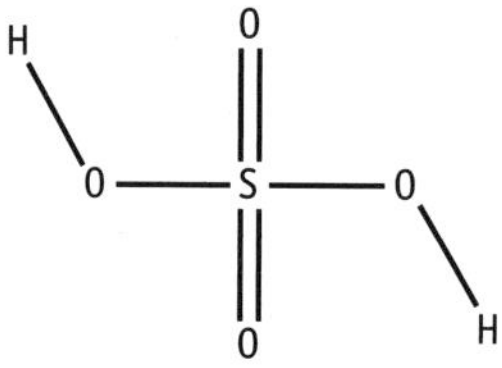

The structure of nitric acid is:

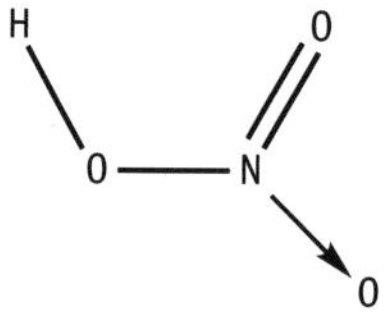

The structure of carbonic acid is:

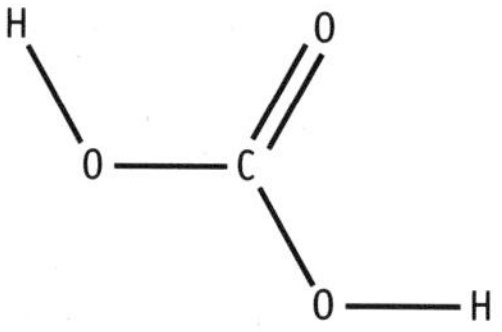

e Note that in the nitric acid molecule, one of the bonds is a dative bond between the lone pair of electrons on the nitrogen atom and one of the oxygen atoms.

In the second type of acid, a hydrogen atom is joined to an electronegative atom other than oxygen. Well-known examples of this type of acid are HF, HCl, HBr and HI. The strength of these acids depends mainly on the strength of the H–X bond: the stronger the bond, the weaker the acid. This is why HF is the weakest acid of the hydrogen halide acids and HI is the strongest. The bond enthalpies are:

H–F: $+562$ kJ mol^{-1}

H–I: $+299$ kJ mol^{-1}

H_2S and HCN are other examples of this type of acid.

The third type of acid is a hydrated metal ion. The polarising power of the cation, especially small 3+ ions such as Al^{3+} or Fe^{3+}, draws electrons away from the H–O bond in the surrounding water molecules. This means that a water molecule can be deprotonated easily:

$$[Al(H_2O)_6]^{3+} + H_2O \rightleftharpoons [Al(H_2O)_5OH]^{2+} + H_3O^+$$

H_3O^+ ions are produced and so the solution becomes acidic.

Questions

1 Hydrogen chloride gas reacts with water. Write the equation for the reaction and use it to explain why HCl can be classified as a Brønsted–Lowry acid and why the solution is acidic.

2 When ethanoic acid reacts with ethanol in the presence of concentrated sulphuric acid, the first step is the reaction between sulphuric acid and ethanoic acid:

$$CH_3COOH + H_2SO_4 \rightarrow CH_3COOH_2^+ + HSO_4^-$$

Identify the acid–base conjugate pairs.

3 State the conjugate bases of the following acids:
   a HCN
   b NH_3
   c $HClO_3$
   d OH^-
   e $[Fe(H_2O)_6]^{3+}$

4 Write the formulae for the conjugate acids of the following bases:
   a NH_3
   b CH_3NH_2
   c OH^-
   d HNO_3

5 Explain why the pH of pure water is not always 7.

6 At 25 °C, $pK_w = 14$. Calculate the $[OH^-]$ of the following solutions and state whether the solutions are acidic or alkaline:
   a $[H^+] = 1.0 \times 10^{-2}$ mol dm^{-3}
   b $[H^+] = 2.2 \times 10^{-7}$ mol dm^{-3}
   c $[H^+] = 3.3 \times 10^{-10}$ mol dm^{-3}

7 At 25 °C, $K_w = 1.0 \times 10^{-14}$ mol^2 dm^{-6}. Calculate the pH of the following solutions in which:
   a $[H^+] = 4.4 \times 10^{-5}$ mol dm^{-3}
   b $[H^+] = 5.5 \times 10^{-9}$ mol dm^{-3}
   c $[OH^-] = 6.6 \times 10^{-2}$ mol dm^{-3}
   d $[OH^-] = 7.7 \times 10^{-11}$ mol dm^{-3}

8 Calculate the ratio of $[H^+]$ to $[OH^-]$ ions in solutions of pH:
   a 7
   b 10
   c 3

9 Calculate the pH of the following solutions:
   a 0.200 mol dm^{-3} hydrobromic acid, HBr, which is a strong acid

   b 0.200 mol dm^{-3} lithium hydroxide, LiOH, which is a strong base
   c 0.0500 mol dm^{-3} strontium hydroxide, Sr(OH)$_2$, which is a strong base

10 Chloric(I) acid, HOCl, is a weak acid with $K_a = 3.02 \times 10^{-11}$ mol dm^{-3}.
   a Write the equation for its ionisation in water and hence the expression for the acid dissociation constant, K_a.
   b Calculate the pH of a 0.213 mol dm^{-3} solution of chloric(I) acid.

11 Nitrous acid, HNO$_2$, is also called nitric(III) acid. It is a weak acid. A 0.200 mol dm^{-3} solution of HNO$_2$ has a pH of 2.02. Calculate the value of its acid dissociation constant, K_a.

12 Propanoic acid is a weak acid with $K_a = 1.35 \times 10^{-5}$ mol dm^{-3}. A solution of the acid has a pH = 3.09. Calculate the concentration of the solution.

13 Hydroxyethanoic acid, CH$_2$(OH)COOH, has a $pK_a = 3.83$. Calculate the pH of a 1.05 mol dm^{-3} solution of this weak acid.

14 Methylamine is a weak base, with $K_b = 4.36 \times 10^{-4}$ mol dm^{-3}:

$$CH_3NH_2 + H_2O \rightleftharpoons CH_3NH_3^+ + OH^-$$

   a Give the expression for K_b.
   b Calculate the pH of 0.200 mol dm^{-3} methylamine solution.

15 a Define 'buffer solution'.
   b Calculate the pH of a buffer solution made by mixing 100 cm^3 of 1.00 mol dm^{-3} ethanoic acid solution with 5.65 g of sodium ethanoate, CH$_3$COONa. (K_a for ethanoic acid = 1.80×10^{-5} mol dm^{-3})

16 Calculate the pH of a buffer solution made by adding 50 cm^3 of 2.00 mol dm^{-3} sodium hydroxide solution to 150 cm^3 of 1.00 mol dm^{-3} ethanoic acid solution. (K_a for ethanoic acid = 1.80×10^{-5} mol dm^{-3})

17 What volume of 1.00 mol dm^{-3} propanoic acid, $pK_a = 4.87$, is needed to make a buffer solution

of pH 4.50 with 50 cm³ of 1.00 mol dm⁻³ sodium propanoate solution?

18 What mass of calcium ethanoate, $Ca(CH_3COO)_2$, must be added to 100 cm³ of 1.25 mol dm⁻³ ethanoic acid solution to make a buffer solution of pH = 5.00? (K_a for ethanoic acid = 1.80×10^{-5} mol dm⁻³)

19 What volume of 1.00 mol dm⁻³ sodium hydroxide must be added to 100 cm³ of 1.00 mol dm⁻³ ethanoic acid solution to make a buffer solution of pH = 4.44? (K_a for ethanoic acid = 1.80×10^{-5} mol dm⁻³)

20 Write the equation for the reaction, if any, of the following ions with water and state whether their solutions would be neutral, acidic or alkaline:
   a $CH_3NH_3^+$
   b CN^-
   c CO_3^{2-}
   d I^-

21 Sketch the titration curve obtained when 40 cm³ of 0.20 mol dm⁻³ hydrochloric acid is added to 40 cm³ of 0.10 mol dm⁻³ ammonia solution. Use Table 4.3 (p. 94) to select a suitable indicator. Justify your choice.

22 20 cm³ of a 0.100 mol dm⁻³ solution of a weak acid, HA, was placed in a conical flask. Sodium hydroxide solution of concentration 0.100 mol dm⁻³ was added in portions and the pH of the stirred solution read after each addition. The readings obtained are given in the table below.

Volume of NaOH/cm³	pH	Volume of NaOH/cm³	pH
0	2.9	19.9	7.0
2.5	3.9	20.1	10.4
5.0	4.3	20.5	11.1
15.0	5.2	21.0	11.4
17.5	5.6	25.0	12.0
19.0	6.0	30.0	12.3
19.5	6.3	35.0	12.4

   a Plot a graph of pH (y-axis) against the volume of sodium hydroxide (x-axis).
   b Use the graph to find a value for the acid dissociation constant, K_a, of the weak acid, HA.
   c Estimate the pH of a 0.050 mol dm⁻³ solution of the salt, NaA.
   d Use the data in Table 4.3 (p. 94) to select a suitable indicator for this titration. Justify your choice.

23 Thymol blue can be regarded as a weak acid of formula HThy. Use the data in Table 4.3 (p. 94) to explain the colour changes that take place when dilute hydrochloric acid, followed by an excess of sodium hydroxide solution, is added to a solution of thymol blue.

24 a Explain why the standard enthalpies of neutralisation of hydrobromic acid and hydrochloric acid by aqueous sodium hydroxide are both −57 kJ mol⁻¹.
   b Ethanoic acid is only about 1% ionised in solution, yet its enthalpy of neutralisation is −55 kJ mol⁻¹. Explain why its value is so similar to that of hydrobromic and hydrochloric acids.
   c Explain why the very weak acid, hydrocyanic acid, HCN, has a much lower exothermic enthalpy of neutralisation than that for a strong acid.

25 Draw the structural formula, showing all the bonds, of each of the following:
   a chloric(v) acid, $HClO_3$
   b hydrocyanic acid (hydrogen cyanide), HCN
   c sulphurous acid (sulphuric(IV) acid), H_2SO_3

26 Explain why a solution of the weak acid HOCl, in the absence of its salt (e.g. NaOCl), is not a buffer solution, when small amounts of either H^+ ions or OH^- ions are added.

Isomerism

Chapter 5

Isomers are different compounds that have the same molecular formula.

Structural isomerism

Structural isomers are compounds with the same molecular formula but different structural formulae. Structural isomers can be divided into three categories: carbon-chain, positional and functional group.

Carbon-chain isomerism

In carbon-chain isomerism, the difference between the isomers is the length of the carbon chain. For example, if the compound contains four carbon atoms, they can be arranged with two different chain lengths:

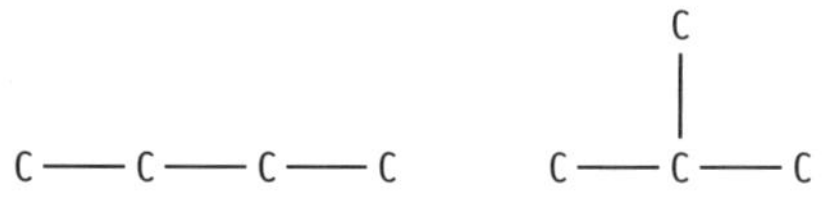

Skeleton A   Skeleton B

Note that the carbon skeleton below is the same as that of A above, because they both contain a chain of four carbon atoms:

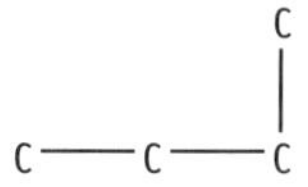

Positional isomerism

Positional isomers have the same functional group in different locations on the carbon skeleton. For example, there are two isomers of molecular formula C_3H_8O. In one isomer (propan-1-ol) the –OH group is bonded to an end carbon atom; in the other (propan-2-ol) it is bonded to the middle carbon atom:

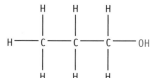

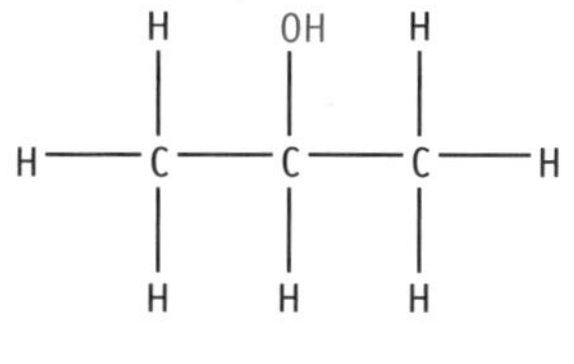

Functional-group isomerism

In functional-group isomerism, the isomers are members of different homologous series and, therefore, have different functional groups. For example,

ⓔ Structural and geometric isomerism are covered in the AS course.

there are two isomers of molecular formula C_2H_6O. One isomer is the alcohol, ethanol, CH_3CH_2OH; the other is the ether, methoxymethane, CH_3OCH_3.

Worked example
Draw and name the structural isomers of C_4H_9Cl.

Answer
There are two ways of arranging the four carbon atoms:

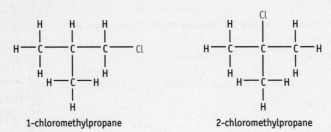

Skeleton A 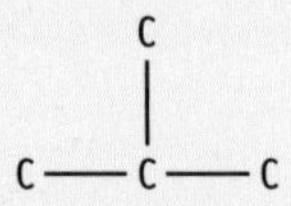   Skeleton B

There are two positions on the four-carbon chain skeleton for the chlorine atom:

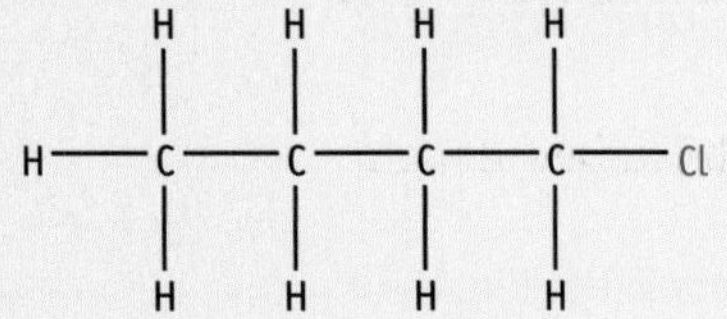

1-chlorobutane 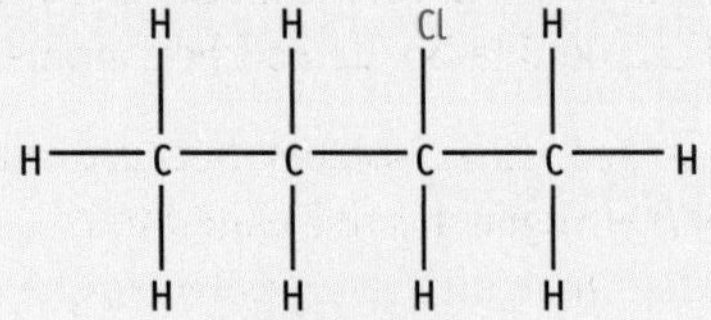   2-chlorobutane

There are also two positions on the three-carbon skeleton for the chlorine atom:

1-chloromethylpropane   2-chloromethylpropane

Stereoisomerism

Stereoisomers are compounds with the same structural formula but which have the atoms arranged differently in space.

There are two types of stereoisomerism — geometric and optical.

Geometric isomerism

Geometric isomerism is also called *cis–trans* isomerism. In organic chemistry, it is caused by the presence of a functional group that restricts rotation. For example, a C=C group consists of a σ-bond, which lies along the axis between the two carbon atoms and a π-bond which is above and below that axis:

For rotation round the σ-bond to occur, the π-bond would have to break and then reform. The energy required to do this is far too great for this to occur at room temperature.

Alkenes exhibit geometric isomerism if there are different groups on each carbon atom of the C=C bond. The simplest example is but-2-ene, which has two geometric isomers:

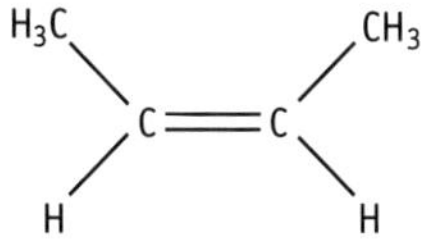

cis-but-2-ene 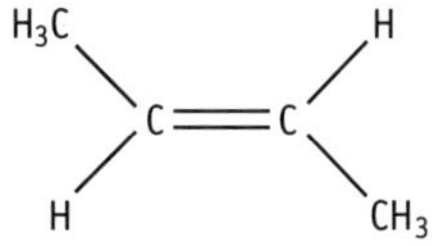   trans-but-2-ene

In cis-but-2-ene, the two –CH_3 groups are on the same side of the double bond; in trans-but-2-ene they are on opposite sides. These two compounds are isomers because the double bond restricts rotation and there are different groups (–H and –CH_3) on each of the double-bonded carbon atoms.

But-1-ene does not have geometric isomers, because one of the carbon atoms in the C=C group has two hydrogen atoms bonded to it:

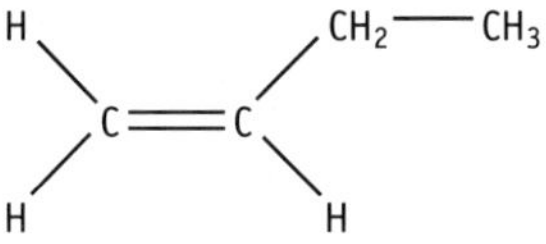

More complex compounds with a C=C group can also show geometric isomerism, for example, but-2-enoic acid:

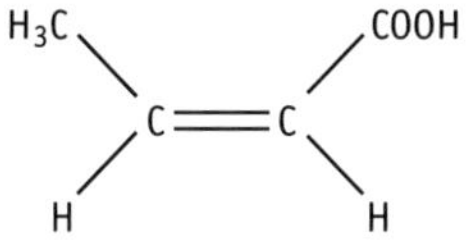

cis-but-2-enoic acid 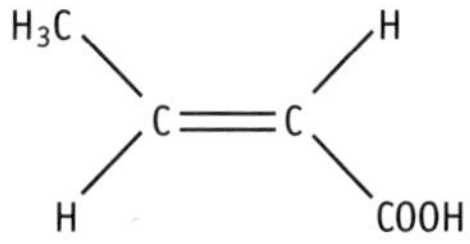   trans-but-2-enoic acid

Geometric isomers have the same chemical properties, but their biological properties may differ. Cis-retinal occurs in receptor cells in the retina of the human eye. When it absorbs a photon of visible light, the π-bond breaks. The molecule reforms as the trans-isomer. This change in shape causes a nerve impulse to be sent to the brain.

Geometric isomerism can occur in cyclic compounds in which rotation is not possible. When chlorine adds to cyclohexene, one of two possible geometric isomers is formed (see p. 104):

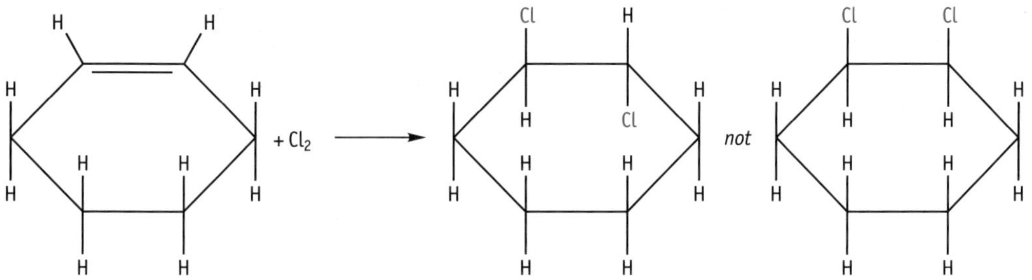

e It is advisable to draw correct bond angles around the C=C bond.

Geometric isomerism also occurs in some transition metal complexes. For example, platinum(II) forms planar complexes with four ligands. The complex [PtCl$_2$(NH$_3$)$_2$] exists as two geometric isomers:

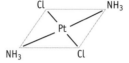 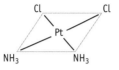

cis-diamminedichloroplatinum(II)   trans-diamminedichloroplatinum(II)

The *cis*-isomer (known as cisplatin) and similar *cis*-platinum complexes are used in the treatment of cancer. The complexes inhibit cell division and cancer cells are particularly susceptible. The treatment, known as chemotherapy, also causes hair loss because cisplatin stops the regrowth of hair. The *trans*-isomer has no biological activity.

Optical isomerism

Compounds that show optical isomerism do not have a plane (or axis or centre) of symmetry. They are said to be **chiral.** Such compounds have two isomers, which are mirror images. The isomers are called **enantiomers**.

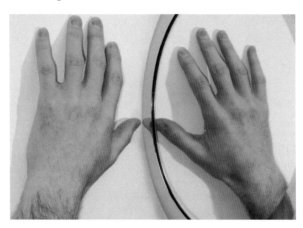

A chiral centre in a molecule or ion causes it to have two optical isomers, which are called enantiomers.

An enantiomer is an isomer that has a non-superimposable mirror image.

The most common cause of chirality in organic chemistry is when a carbon atom has four different groups or atoms attached to it. For example, the compound CHFClBr is chiral:

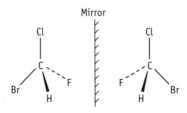

Cisplatin blocks DNA replication because it is the correct shape to bond to the base guanine in DNA. The *trans*-form cannot do this.

A left hand and its reflection

A left hand is different from a right hand, yet looks like a right hand when reflected in a mirror.

Non-superimposable means that it is impossible to put one beside the other in such a way that their shapes are the same.

Note that the two isomers are drawn as mirror images. The wedges and dashes are meant to give an idea of the three-dimensional shapes of the molecules.

Lactic acid is produced when milk goes sour and in muscles as a result of anaerobic respiration. Its formula is $CH_3CH(OH)COOH$ and its systematic name is 2-hydroxypropanoic acid. It contains a chiral carbon atom which has a –H, –OH, –CH_3 and –COOH attached. The presence of these four different groups means that the substance exists as two optical isomers:

> ℯ Always make sure that the bonds are drawn from the central carbon atom to the correct atom in the group, for example, to the oxygen atom of the –OH group and to the carbon atom of the –CH_3 group.

Enantiomers have identical chemical properties and the same boiling temperatures and solubilities. They differ in two ways:

- Uniquely among chemical compounds, they rotate the plane of polarisation of plane-polarised light.
- Optical isomers often have different biochemical reactions.

> This property is optical and provides the origin of the name 'optical isomerism'.

Glucose, $CHO(CHOH)_4CH_2OH$ is one of 16 optical isomers. Glucose is the only one of the 16 that can be metabolised by humans.

Plane-polarised light

Light waves have peaks and troughs in all planes. When ordinary light is passed through a piece of Polaroid, the light that comes out only has peaks and troughs in a single plane. This light is said to be polarised.

A solution of one enantiomer rotates the plane of polarisation of plane-polarised light in a clockwise direction (+); the other enantiomer rotates it in an anticlockwise direction (–).

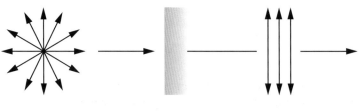

Figure 5.1 Unpolarised and polarised light

Unpolarised light
vibrating in all planes

Polariser

Polarised light
vibrating in one plane

Lactic acid produced in muscles is a crystalline solid that melts at 26°C and rotates the plane of polarisation clockwise. Lactic acid obtained from the action of microorganisms on milk sugar (lactose) is a crystalline solid that also melts at 26°C, but rotates the plane of polarisation of plane-polarised light in an anti-clockwise direction.

> A solution containing equimolar amounts of the two enantiomers is called a racemic mixture. It does not rotate the plane of polarisation of plane-polarised light.

The extent by which an enantiomer rotates the plane of polarisation can be measured using a **polarimeter**.

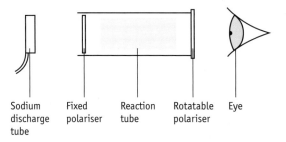

*Figure 5.2
A polarimeter*

Sodium   Fixed   Reaction   Rotatable Eye
discharge polariser tube   polariser
tube

The angle through which the plane of polarisation is rotated depends on:
- the nature of the enantiomer
- the concentration of the enantiomer in the solution

The second factor is useful in determining the change in concentration during a reaction. For example, the rate of the hydrolysis of sucrose can be followed using a polarimeter:

$$C_{12}H_{22}O_{11} + H_2O \rightarrow C_6H_{12}O_6 + C_6H_{12}O_6$$
sucrose   glucose   fructose

Sucrose rotates the plane of polarisation in one direction and the mixture of glucose and fructose rotate it in the other direction.

The rate of hydrolysis of one enantiomer of a halogenoalkane can also be followed using a polarimeter:

$$CH_3CHClC_2H_5 + OH^- \rightarrow CH_3CH(OH)C_2H_5 + Cl^-$$
one enantiomer   a racemic mixture

The intermediate of this reaction is planar:

$$H_3C \diagdown \overset{+}{\underset{H}{\diagup}} C - C_2H_5$$

Therefore, it can be attacked by the hydroxide ion from above or below, and so a racemic mixture of products is obtained. The rotation of the plane of polarisation of plane-polarised light drops from the original value to zero as the reaction progresses.

Two chiral centres

If a molecule has two different chiral centres, there are four possible optical isomers. Let one chiral centre be called A. It has two mirror image structures, one of which will rotate the plane of polarisation of plane-polarised light clockwise, +A; the other will rotate it anticlockwise, −A. Let the second chiral centre be called B. The B centre also has two mirror image structures, +B and −B.

The four optical isomers are: +A with +B, −A with −B and +A with −B, −A with +B.

The first isomer rotates the plane of polarisation of plane-polarised light clockwise, the fourth rotates it anticlockwise by the same amount and the second and third each rotate it slightly, depending on the extent to which the A and B chiral centres each rotate the plane.

To summarise:

■ Optical activity occurs in organic compounds when four different groups are attached to the same carbon atom. This carbon atom is the chiral centre of the molecule.

■ A chiral centre results in two optical isomers (enantiomers) that are non-superimposable mirror images of each other.

■ Enantiomers rotate the plane of polarisation of plane-polarised light in opposite directions.

■ An equimolar mixture of enantiomers is called a racemic mixture. It has no effect on plane-polarised light.

> ⓔ If a molecule has two identical chiral centres, the isomer with a plane of symmetry will not be optically active because one chiral centre will rotate the plane of polarisation of plane-polarised light clockwise and the other chiral centre will rotate it equally anticlockwise.

Questions

1 a Draw and name the four structural isomers of $C_3H_6Cl_2$.
  b One of these exists as optical isomers. Identify which and draw the structural formulae of these two isomers, clearly showing how they differ.

2 Explain why 1-chloropropene, $CH_3CH=CHCl$, exists as two geometric isomers whereas 3-chloropropene, $CH_2=CHCH_2Cl$, does not.

3 The complex ion $[Cr(NH_3)_4(Cl)_2]^+$ has four ammonia molecules and two chloride ions attached to the central chromium ion by dative

covalent bonds. Its shape is octahedral and similar to that of the hydrated magnesium ion $[Mg(H_2O)_6]^{2+}$. Draw the two geometric isomers of the chromium complex ion. Mark in the bond angles on your diagram.

4 Geraniol is a perfume found in rose petals. Its formula is:

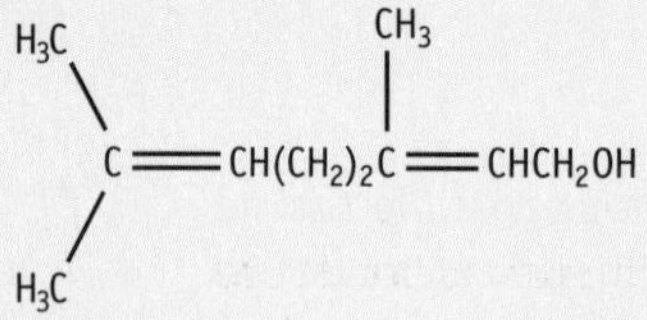

Explain why geraniol exists as two geometric isomers.

5 Draw the two optical isomers of $CH_3CH(OH)C_2H_5$ to show clearly the way in which they differ.

6 Limonene is a chiral molecule found in the oil of citrus fruits. Its structure is:

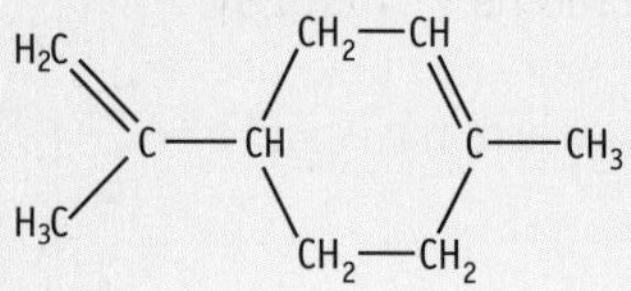

Redraw the structure, marking the chiral centre with an asterisk, *.

7 Alanine, 2-aminopropanoic acid, is an amino acid found in many proteins. It is chiral.
  a Explain the meaning of the term 'chiral'.
  b Draw the structures of the two optical isomers of alanine.
  c Describe how optical activity is detected experimentally.

8 Tartaric acid, 2,3-dihydroxybutanedioic acid, has the formula $HOOCCH(OH)CH(OH)COOH$.
  a Draw the full structural formula of this molecule, marking each chiral centre with an asterisk, *.
  b Explain why there are only three optical isomers of this compound.

9 Search the web for information on cisplatin and write approximately 100 words about its discovery, uses and problems.

Carbonyl compounds and Grignard reagents

Chapter 6

Carbonyl compounds

Introduction

Carbonyl compounds contain the $>C=O$ group. The carbon atom is bonded to the oxygen by a σ-bond and a π-bond. Oxygen is more electronegative than carbon, so the bonding electrons are pulled towards the oxygen atom making it δ^- and the carbon δ^+:

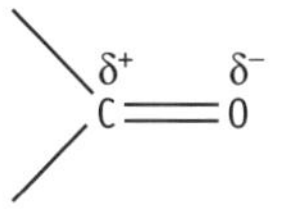

The polar nature of the bond makes the carbon atom susceptible to attack by nucleophiles.

> A nucleophile is a species with a lone pair of electrons that is used to form a bond with a δ^+ atom.

There are two types of carbonyl compounds: aldehydes and ketones.

Aldehydes

- Aldehydes have a hydrogen atom bonded to the carbon of the $>C=O$ group.
- The formulae of aldehydes can be represented by RCHO, where R is a hydrogen atom, an alkyl group or benzene ring, for example $-CH_3$, $-C_2H_5$ or $-C_6H_5$.
- Aldehydes have the general formula $C_nH_{2n+1}CHO$, where n is 0, 1, 2, 3 etc.

n	Formula	Name	Boiling temperature/°C
0	HCHO	Methanal	−21
1	CH_3CHO	Ethanal	20
2	CH_3CH_2CHO	Propanal	49
3	$CH_3CH_2CH_2CHO$	Butanal	76
3	$(CH_3)_2CHCHO$	Methylpropanal	62

If you are asked for the structural formula in an exam, you must show the bonding in the –CHO group. For example, the structural formula of ethanal is:

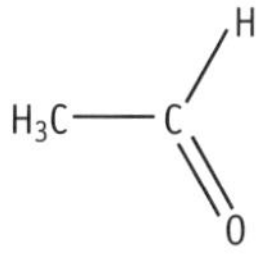

Never write the formula of an aldehyde as RCOH.

Ketones

- Ketones do *not* have a hydrogen atom bonded to the carbon of the $>C=O$ group.

- The formulae of ketones can be represented as RCOR', where R and R' are alkyl or benzene ring groups such as $-CH_3$, $-C_2H_5$ or $-C_6H_5$. The simplest ketone is propanone, which contains three carbon atoms.

Formula	Name	Boiling temperature/°C
CH_3COCH_3	Propanone	56
$CH_3CH_2COCH_3$	Butanone	80
$CH_3CH_2COCH_2CH_3$	Pentan-3-one	102
$CH_3COCH_2CH_2CH_3$	Pentan-2-one	102
$CH_3COCH(CH_3)_2$	Methylbutanone	94

Propanone used to be called acetone.

If you are asked for the structural formula in an exam, you must show the bonding in the carbonyl group. For example, the structural formula of propanone is:

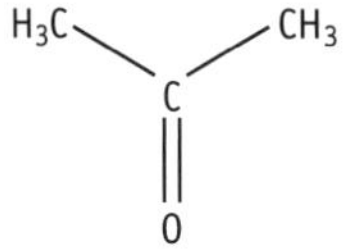

General structural formulae

The general structural formulae of aldehydes and ketones can be represented by:

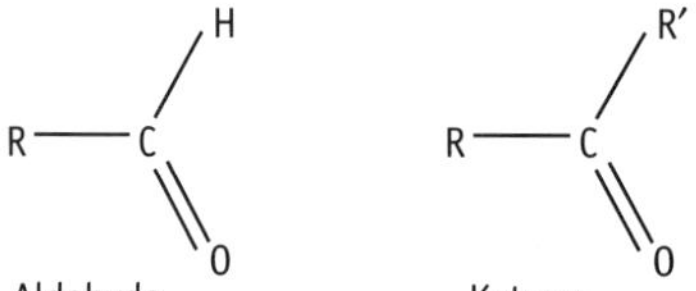

Aldehyde   Ketone

Geometry around the C=O group

The carbon atom has two single bonds, one double bond and no lone pairs, so the electrons in the three bonds repel each other and the bonds take up the position of maximum separation. This is a planar triangular shape with bond angles of 120°:

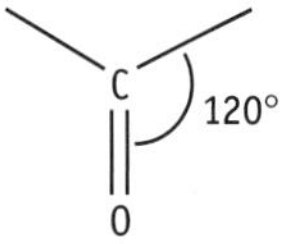

This planar shape makes it easy for nucleophiles to attack the carbon atom from either above or below, and so a single optical isomer is never obtained by addition to carbonyl compounds.

The polarity of the $\overset{\delta^+}{>}C=\overset{\delta^-}{O}$ group is not cancelled out by the other two groups attached to the carbon atom. Therefore aldehyde and ketone molecules are polar.

Physical properties

Boiling point

Methanal is a gas. The other carbonyl compounds are liquid at room temperature.

The molecules are polar, so dipole–dipole forces as well as instantaneous induced dipole–induced dipole (dispersion) forces exist between them. Alkanes and alkenes are not polar, so their intermolecular forces are weaker and their boiling points lower than those of aldehydes and ketones with the same number of electrons in the molecule. Intermolecular hydrogen bonding is not possible in carbonyl compounds because neither aldehydes nor ketones have a hydrogen atom that is sufficiently δ^+. Therefore, they have boiling points that are lower than those of alcohols, which do form intermolecular hydrogen bonds.

Solubility

The lower members of both series are soluble in water. This solubility is due to hydrogen bonding between the δ^- oxygen in the carbonyl compound and the δ^+ hydrogen in a water molecule.

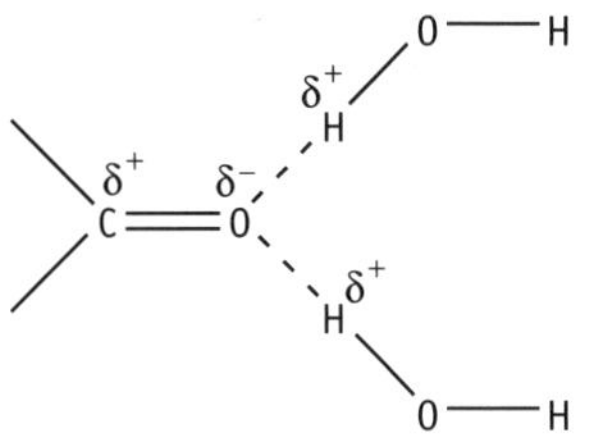

Propanone is an excellent solvent for organic substances.

Smell

- The lower members of the homologous series of aldehydes have pungent odours.
- Ketones have much sweeter smells than aldehydes.
- Complex aldehydes and ketones are often used as perfumes. Citral, an ingredient of lemon grass oil, is an aldehyde; β-ionone is a ketone that smells of violets and is used in perfume:

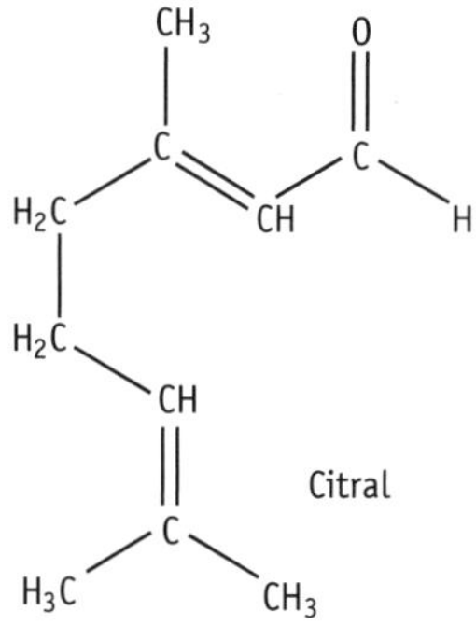

Citral

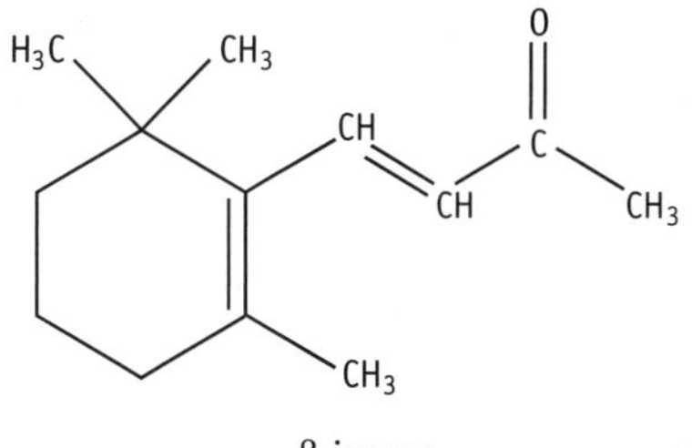

β-ionone

Laboratory preparation

Aldehydes

Aldehydes are prepared by the partial oxidation of a *primary* alcohol. The usual oxidising agent is a solution of potassium (or sodium) dichromate(VI) in dilute sulphuric acid. The temperature must be below the boiling point of the alcohol and above that of the aldehyde. In this way the aldehyde is boiled off as it is formed and, therefore, cannot be oxidised further. If the mixture were to be heated under reflux, the aldehyde would be further oxidised to a carboxylic acid.

Ethanal can be prepared as follows:

- Heat ethanol in a flask to about 60°C, using an electric heater.
- Add a solution of potassium dichromate(VI) in dilute sulphuric acid slowly from a tap funnel.
- As it distils off, collect the ethanal in a flask surrounded by iced water.

The reaction is exothermic and so heat is generated. This maintains the temperature above the boiling point of ethanal, so it boils off before it can be oxidised further.

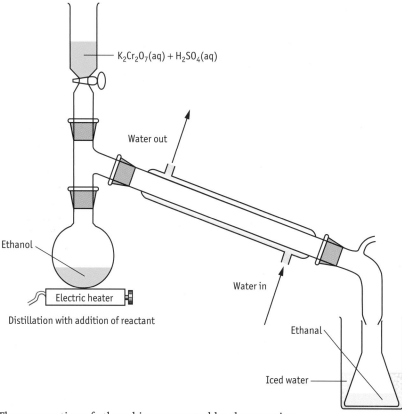

Figure 6.1 *Laboratory preparation of ethanal*

The preparation of ethanal is represented by the equation:

$$CH_3CH_2OH + [O] \rightarrow CH_3CHO + H_2O$$

> *e* [O] can be used in equations for oxidation reactions in organic chemistry, apart from those involving oxygen gas. [H] can be used for all reduction reactions in organic chemistry, apart from when hydrogen gas is the reducing agent. Equations containing [O] or [H] must still balance.

Reagents: ethanol and potassium dichromate(VI) dissolved in dilute sulphuric acid

Conditions: a temperature of 60°C; collect the ethanal as it distils off

Observation: the orange colour of potassium dichromate(VI) changes to green because chromium(III) ions are formed.

e A Bunsen flame must *not* be used as both ethanol and ethanal are highly flammable.

e The iced water keeps the collecting flask cool and so prevents evaporation of the ethanal.

Ethanal can be purified by re-distilling it, using a water bath as a source of heat and collecting the fraction that boils in the range 20–23°C.

Ketones

Ketones are prepared by the oxidation of *secondary* alcohols. If acidified potassium dichromate(VI) is used as the oxidising agent, the ketone is not further oxidised.

Propanone can be prepared as follows:
- Place propan-2-ol and a solution of potassium dichromate(VI) in dilute sulphuric acid in a round-bottomed flask.
- Fit a reflux condenser.
- Heat, using an electric heater, so that the mixture boils for about 15 minutes.
- Remove the reflux condenser and set up the apparatus for distillation. Distil off the propanone (boiling point 56°C) from any unreacted propan-2-ol (boiling point 82°C).

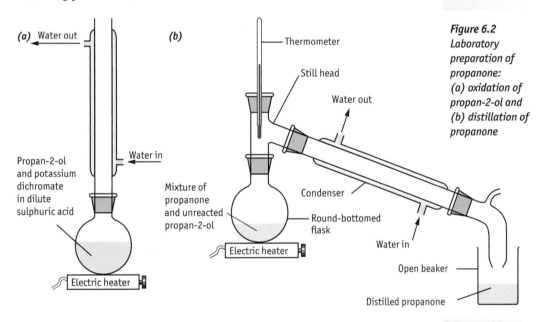

Figure 6.2
Laboratory preparation of propanone:
(a) oxidation of propan-2-ol and
(b) distillation of propanone

The preparation of propanone is represented by the equation:
$$CH_3CH(OH)CH_3 + [O] \rightarrow CH_3COCH_3 + H_2O$$

Reagents: propan-2-ol and potassium dichromate(VI) dissolved in dilute sulphuric acid

Conditions: heat under reflux for about 15 minutes, then distil off the propanone

Observation: the orange colour of potassium dichromate(VI) changes to green because chromium(III) ions are formed

Aromatic ketones

Ketones that have a benzene ring attached to the carbonyl group, such as phenylethanone, $C_6H_5COCH_3$, can be prepared using the **Friedel–Crafts reaction** (p. 238).

Reactions of aldehydes and ketones

- Both aldehydes and ketones undergo **nucleophilic addition** reactions because of the polar nature of the C=O bond.
- Aldehydes and ketones both undergo **addition/elimination** reactions.
- Aldehydes can be oxidised to carboxylic acids. Therefore, aldehydes are reducing agents.
- Ethanal and methylketones react with iodine in alkali to form a precipitate of iodoform, CHI_3. This is called the **iodoform reaction**.

Nucleophilic addition

Alkenes and carbonyl compounds contain π-bonds. However, C=C is non-polar whereas C=O is polar. The electron cloud above and below the σ-bond in the C=C group is an area of negative charge that is attacked by electrophiles. The electron cloud in the C=O group is distorted, with the carbon atom being δ^+. This δ^+ carbon can be attacked by nucleophiles. The δ^- oxygen is not attacked by electrophiles, such as Br_2 or HBr, because the oxygen atom is itself strongly electronegative.

The $-CH_3$ group is electron-releasing, so the carbon in methanal, HCHO (which has no $-CH_3$ group), is more δ^+ than the carbon of the C=O group in ethanal. The carbonyl carbon in propanone is even less δ^+ than that in ethanal. The reactivity in nucleophilic addition is: $HCHO > CH_3CHO > CH_3COCH_3$.

Reaction with hydrogen cyanide

The reaction between ethanal and hydrogen cyanide takes place only at about pH 8:

$$CH_3CHO + HCN \rightarrow CH_3CH(OH)CN$$

The required pH is usually created by adding a trace of alkali to hydrogen cyanide or adding some acid to potassium cyanide.

The product is 2-hydroxypropanenitrile.

Hydrogen cyanide, HCN, is a very weak acid and produces few CN^- ions in solution. Some base is added to produce the nucleophilic CN^- ions that attack the δ^+ carbon atom:

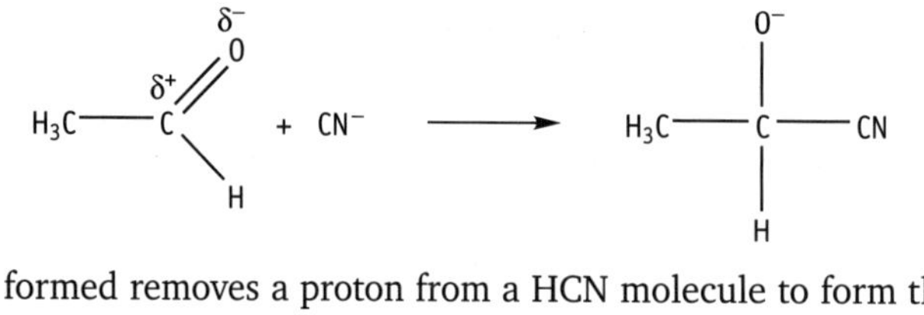

The anion formed removes a proton from a HCN molecule to form the organic product and another CN^- ion:

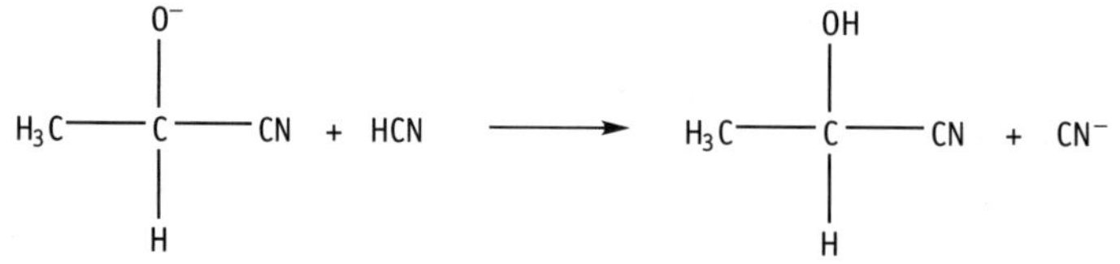

If the pH is too low, there are not enough CN^- ions for the first step to take place; if the pH is too high there are not enough HCN molecules for the second step.

The same type of reaction occurs with ketones, but at a slower rate — for example, with propanone:

The product is 2-hydroxy-2-methylpropanenitrile.

Hydroxynitriles produced in this way can be hydrolysed to hydroxycarboxylic acids, for example:

$$CH_3CH(OH)CN + 2H_2O + H^+ \rightarrow CH_3CH(OH)COOH + NH_4^+$$

The reaction mixture is heated under reflux. This product is 2-hydroxypropanoic acid, which is also called lactic acid. Since the CN^- ion can attack the C=O group from above or below the plane of the molecule, a racemic mixture of two optical isomers is produced.

Hydroxynitriles can also be reduced to hydroxyamines, for example:

$$CH_3CH(OH)CN + 4[H] \rightarrow CH_3CH(OH)CH_2NH_2$$

Suitable reducing agents for this reaction are lithium tetrahydridoaluminate(III) (lithium aluminium hydride), $LiAlH_4$, in dry ether solution or hydrogen gas with a platinum catalyst or sodium in ethanol.

The common name for lithium tetrahydrido-aluminate(III), $LiAlH_4$, is lithium aluminium hydride.

Reduction

Aldehydes and ketones can be reduced by lithium tetrahydridoaluminate(III), $LiAlH_4$.

This compound acts as a source of H^- ions. The reaction takes place in two distinct steps:

■ The first step is the addition of H^- to the δ^+ carbon atom. In this step the reagents must be kept dry. It is carried out in ether solution.
■ The second step is the addition of an aqueous solution of an acid, which protonates the O^- formed in the first step.

The result is that the carbonyl compound is *reduced* to an alcohol. For example, ethanal is reduced to ethanol:

$$CH_3CHO + 2[H] \rightarrow CH_3CH_2OH$$
ethanal   ethanol

When aldehydes are reduced, *primary* alcohols are formed.

Reduction of ketones takes place by a similar two-step reaction. The equation for the reduction of propanone is:

$$CH_3COCH_3 + 2[H] \rightarrow CH_3CH(OH)CH_3$$
propanone   propan-2-ol

When ketones are reduced, *secondary* alcohols are formed.

LiAlH$_4$ is a reducing agent that reacts specifically with polar π-bonds. Thus, it reduces C=O in aldehydes, ketones, acids and acid derivatives, and C=N in nitriles, but does *not* reduce the π-bond in C=C groups, which are non-polar.

The C=O group can also be reduced by sodium tetrahydridoborate(III) (sodium borohydride), NaBH$_4$, in aqueous solution. This reagent, too, does not reduce the C=C group.

Both C=C and C=O groups can be reduced by hydrogen and a platinum catalyst.

To summarise:
- Aldehydes and ketones are reduced to alcohols ($>$C=O to $>$CH(OH)) by:
  - LiAlH$_4$ in dry ether
  - NaBH$_4$(aq)
  - H$_2$/Pt
- Alkenes are reduced ($>$C=C$<$ to $>$CH–CH$<$) by H$_2$/Pt only.

Addition of Grignard reagents
Grignard reagents are compounds that contain an alkyl group bonded to a magnesium atom. The carbon that is bonded to the magnesium is δ$^-$ and so acts as a nucleophile. Details of Grignard reagents and reactions between them and carbonyl compounds are given later in this chapter (p. 122).

Addition–elimination reactions
Both aldehydes and ketones react with compounds containing an H$_2$N– group. The lone pair of electrons on the nitrogen atom acts as a nucleophile and forms a bond with the δ$^+$ carbon atom in the C=O group. However, instead of an H$^+$ ion adding on to the O$^-$ formed, the substance loses a water molecule and a C=N bond is formed.

The general equation is:
$$>\!C=O + H_2N\!-\!X \rightarrow \,>\!C=N\!-\!X + H_2O$$

Since, the nitrogen atom has a lone pair of electrons, the bond angles around the nitrogen in the product are 120°. This means that in this type of reaction aldehydes (other than methanal) and asymmetrical ketones produce a mixture of two geometric isomers:

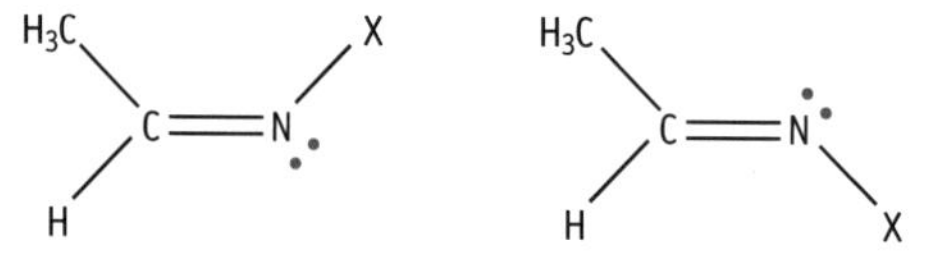

One compound that reacts in this way is 2,4-dinitrophenylhydrazine, in which the 'X' group is:

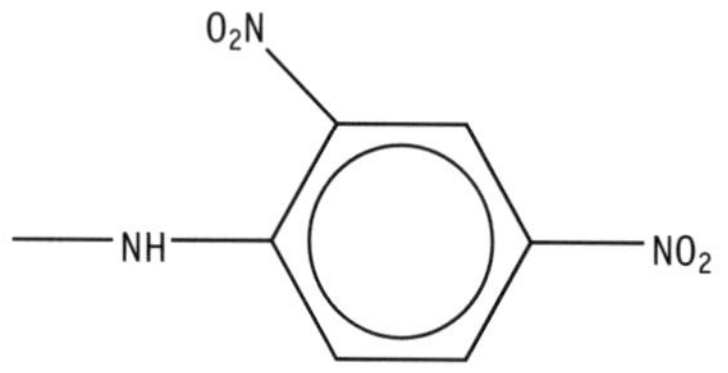

The full formula for 2,4-dinitrophenylhydrazine is:

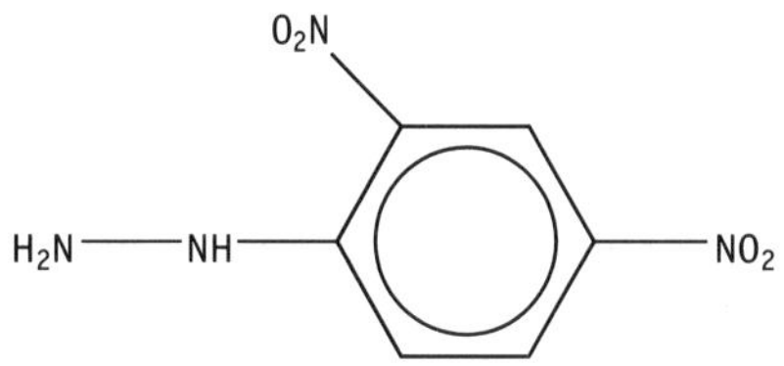

The equation for the reaction between ethanal and 2,4-dinitrophenylhydrazine is:

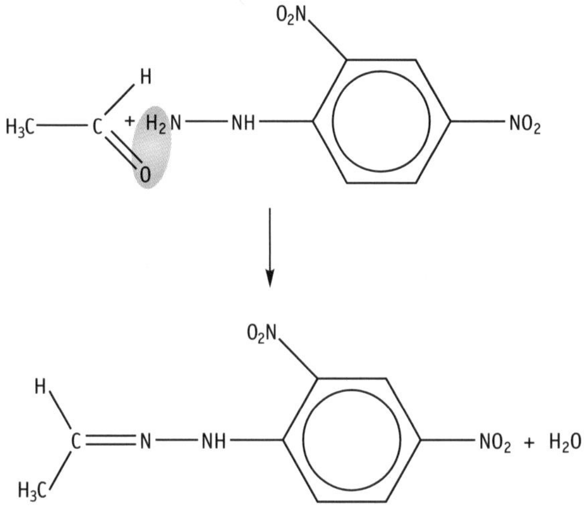

The equation for the reaction between propanone and 2,4-dinitrophenyl-hydrazine is:

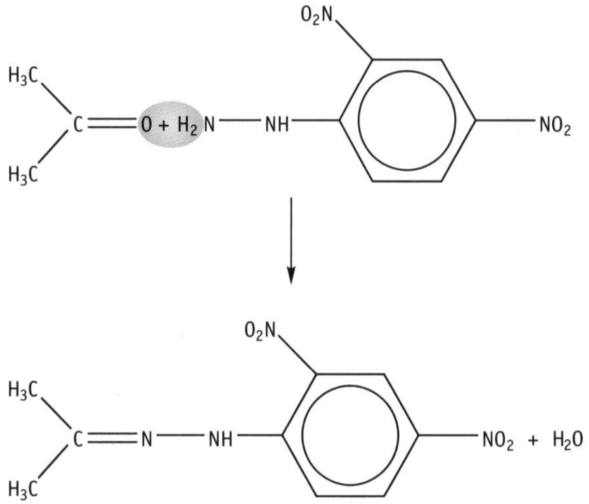

The importance of the reaction of carbonyl compounds with 2,4-dinitrophenyl-hydrazine is that the product is insoluble. Therefore, this reaction can be used as a test for the presence of a carbonyl group.

A solution of 2,4-di nitrophenylhydrazine is called Brady's reagent.

Test for a carbonyl group in a compound

Add a solution of 2,4-dinitrophenylhydrazine (Brady's reagent) to the suspected carbonyl compound:

- Simple aldehydes and ketones give yellow precipitates.
- Aromatic aldehydes (e.g. benzaldehyde, C_6H_5CHO) and ketones (e.g. phenylethanone, $C_6H_5COCH_3$) give orange precipitates.

Oxidation

Aldehydes (but *not* ketones) are readily oxidised. If the reaction is carried out in acid or neutral solution the product is a carboxylic acid:

$$RCHO + [O] \rightarrow RCOOH$$

There are a number of suitable oxidising agents:

- Potassium manganate(VII) oxidises aldehydes in acidic, neutral or alkaline solution. In acidic solution, the purple manganate(VII) is reduced to give colourless Mn^{2+}. In neutral or alkaline solution, it is reduced to a brown precipitate of MnO_2.
- Orange potassium dichromate(VI) in acidic solution is reduced to green Cr(III) on heating with an aldehyde.
- Bromine water turns from brown to colourless when added to an aldehyde.
- Fehling's solution (a mixture of copper(II) sulphate and sodium potassium tartrate in alkali) is reduced from a deep blue solution to a red precipitate of copper(I) oxide, Cu_2O, when warmed with an aldehyde. (Benedict's solution is a similar mixture and also produces a red precipitate of copper(I) oxide when warmed with an aldehyde.)
- A solution of silver nitrate in dilute ammonia is reduced to give a silver mirror on warming with an aldehyde. (Tollens' reagent is a similar mixture and also produces a silver mirror with aldehydes.)

The reaction with Fehling's solution does not work with aldehydes of large molecular mass because they are too insoluble in water.

Test to distinguish an aldehyde from a ketone

An aldehyde can be distinguished from a ketone by the production of:

- a red precipitate on warming with Fehling's solution
- a silver mirror on warming with ammoniacal silver nitrate solution

In both reactions, the aldehyde is oxidised to the salt of a carboxylic acid, for example, with ethanal:

$$CH_3CHO + [O] + OH^- \rightarrow CH_3COO^- + H_2O$$
ethanal   ethanoate ion

Ketones do not undergo these reactions. Therefore, if these tests are carried out on a ketone, Fehling's solution remains blue and Tollens' reagent remains colourless.

Iodoform reaction

Ethanal and methyl ketones undergo the iodoform reaction with iodine in alkali, a complicated process in which the hydrogen atoms of the $CH_3C=O$ group are replaced by iodine atoms. The alkali present in the reaction mixture then causes the C–C bond to break and a pale yellow precipitate of **iodoform** (triiodomethane), CHI_3, is formed.

Sodium hydroxide solution is added to iodine solution to form iodate(I) ions (IO⁻):

$$I_2 + OH^- \rightarrow IO^- + I^-$$

These substitute into the –CH$_3$ group next to the C=O group, forming a CI$_3$C=O group. The electron-withdrawing effect of the three halogen atoms and the oxygen atom weaken the σ-bond between the two carbon atoms and this breaks forming iodoform:

$$CH_3COR \xrightarrow{\substack{OI^-(aq) \\ }} CI_3COR \xrightarrow{\substack{OH^-(aq) \\ }} CHI_3 + RCOO^-$$

The overall equation is:

$$CH_3COR + 3I_2 + 4NaOH \rightarrow CHI_3 + RCOONa + 3NaI + 3H_2O$$

where R is a hydrogen atom (ethanal) or an organic group such as –CH$_3$, –C$_2$H$_5$ or –C$_6$H$_5$.

To carry out the iodoform reaction, the organic substance is warmed with either a mixture of iodine and sodium hydroxide solution or with a solution of potassium iodide in sodium chlorate(I).

The iodoform reaction also works with ethanol and methyl secondary alcohols. These compounds have a CH$_3$CH(OH) group and are oxidised by the iodate(I) ions to CH$_3$CO, which then reacts as described above.

(e) The iodoform reaction is a test for compounds containing CH$_3$C=O or CH$_3$CH(OH) groups.

Summary

Test for a carbonyl group
Add a few drops of the organic compound to a solution of 2,4-dinitrophenylhydrazine. A yellow or orange precipitate indicates the presence of a carbonyl group.

Reactions of aldehydes

RCHO

+ HCN (pH = 8)	→ RCH(OH)CN
+ [H]	→ RCH$_2$OH
+ C$_2$H$_5$MgBr*	→ RCH(OH)C$_2$H$_5$
+ 2,4-dinitrophenyl-hydrazine	→ yellow/orange precipitate
+ K$_2$Cr$_2$O$_7$/H$^+$	→ RCOOH
+ Fehling's or Ag$^+$/NH$_3$	→ RCOO$^-$
+ I$_2$/NaOH	→ CHI$_3$ + HCOO$^-$ (with ethanol only)

* C$_2$H$_5$MgBr is a Grignard reagent (p. 122)

Reactions of ketones

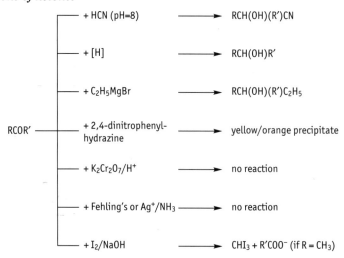

Tests to distinguish between an aldehyde and a ketone

Warm the substance with:

- Fehling's solution — aldehydes give a red precipitate; ketones do not alter the blue colour of the Fehling's solution
- ammoniacal silver nitrate solution — aldehydes give a silver mirror; ketones do not

Iodoform test

If a pale yellow precipitate is obtained when a substance is gently warmed with a solution of iodine and sodium hydroxide, the substance contains either a $CH_3CH(OH)$ or CH_3CO group.

- If the substance is an aldehyde, it can only be ethanal.
- If the substance is a primary alcohol is can only be ethanol.

Grignard reagents

In most organic compounds, the carbon atoms are bonded to non-metals, such as hydrogen, oxygen, nitrogen and the halogens. With the exception of the C–H bond, the bonds are polar, with the carbon atom being δ^+. There are a few compounds in which the carbon atom is bonded to a metal, for example, tetraethyllead, $Pb(C_2H_5)_4$. This compound used to be added to petrol as an anti-knock agent, but its use has been abandoned because of the dangers of lead poisoning. When a carbon atom is bonded to a metal, the carbon becomes δ^- because carbon is more electronegative than metals.

A Grignard reagent consists of an alkyl group bonded to a magnesium atom that is also bonded to a halogen. Such reagents are prepared by mixing a halogenoalkane with magnesium in a solvent of dry ether (ethoxyethane, $C_2H_5OC_2H_5$). These compounds were named after Victor Grignard who discovered them in 1900. The magnesium–carbon bond is polar covalent with the carbon atom being δ^-. The magnesium–halogen bond is mainly ionic. The formula of a typical Grignard reagent is:

$$CH_3 \overset{\delta^-}{\underset{}{-\!\!-}} CH_2 \overset{\delta^+}{\underset{}{-\!\!-}} Mg^+ Br^-$$

The δ^- carbon atom is a powerful nucleophile. It attacks the δ^+ hydrogen atoms in water or alcohols. Therefore, Grignard reagents must be kept dry and in ether solution.

Grignard reagents are named by writing the name of the organic radical, followed by magnesium, followed by the halide ion:
- C_2H_5MgBr is called ethylmagnesium bromide.
- CH_3MgI is called methylmagnesium iodide.

Preparation

- A halogenoalkane mixed with dry ether (ethoxyethane) is placed in a round-bottomed flask.
- Small pieces of magnesium metal are added.
- A reflux condenser is fitted.
- If the reaction does not start at once, a small crystal of iodine is added as a catalyst.
- The reaction is exothermic and produces enough heat to cause the ether solution to boil.
- A warm water bath or electric heater is placed under the flask to allow the reaction to go to completion.

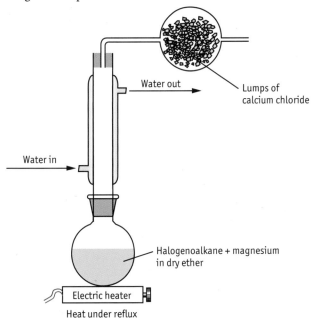

Water out

Lumps of calcium chloride

Water in

Halogenoalkane + magnesium in dry ether

Electric heater

Heat under reflux

Figure 6.3 *Preparation of a Grignard reagent*

e A naked flame must not be used, as ether is highly flammable.

A guard tube containing anhydrous calcium chloride is placed at the top of the condenser. This is to prevent any water vapour getting into the reaction mixture.

The equation for the preparation of ethylmagnesium bromide is:

$$C_2H_5Br + Mg \rightarrow C_2H_5MgBr$$

Reactions

The δ^- carbon atom bonded to the magnesium atom is a powerful nucleophile and attacks δ^+ hydrogen atoms in water, acids and alcohols and δ^+ carbon atoms in aldehydes, ketones and carbon dioxide.

Reaction with water

Grignard reagents are rapidly attacked by water or acids. An alkane is produced, for example:

$$C_2H_5MgBr + H_2O \rightarrow C_2H_6 + Mg(OH)Br$$
$$CH_3CH_2CH_2MgCl + HCl \rightarrow CH_3CH_2CH_3 + MgCl_2$$

This is why water has to be completely excluded when making and using Grignard reagents.

Reaction with aldehydes

Grignard reagents react with aldehydes to form *secondary* alcohols. The first step is the addition of the alkyl group to the δ^+ carbon in the aldehyde. Since the intermediate is attached to the magnesium atom, it has to be hydrolysed by adding a solution of an acid, such as hydrochloric acid. For example, for the reaction of ethylmagnesium bromide with ethanal the overall equation is:

$$C_2H_5MgBr + CH_3CHO + HCl \rightarrow CH_3CH(OH)C_2H_5 + MgBrCl$$

The organic product is butan-2-ol.

> ◀ A *primary* alcohol is made by adding methanal, HCHO, to ethylmagnesium bromide. The organic product is propan-1-ol, $CH_3CH_2CH_2OH$.

The route of the reaction is that the δ^- carbon of the ethyl $-CH_2$ group adds on to the δ^+ carbon of the aldehyde:

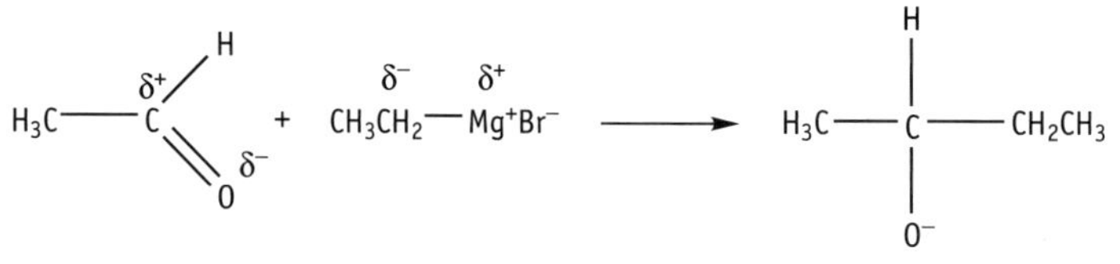

In the second step, the product of this reaction picks up an H^+ from the acid:

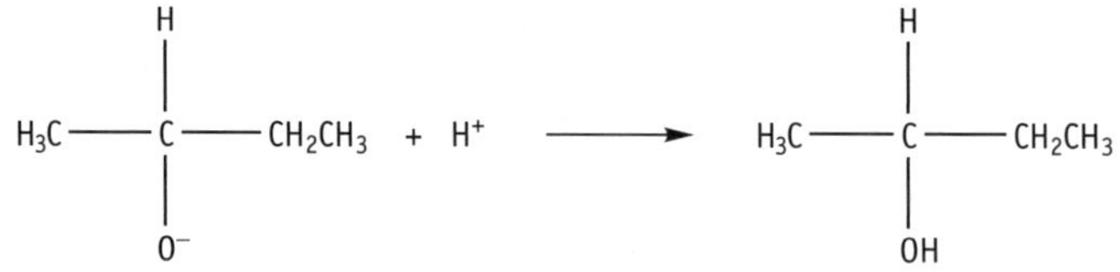

Reaction with ketones

The reaction of Grignard reagents with ketones is similar to that with aldehydes, but the organic product is a *tertiary* alcohol. For example, for the reaction between ethylmagnesium bromide and propanone, CH_3COCH_3, the organic product is the tertiary alcohol $(CH_3)_2C(OH)C_2H_5$.

As before, the δ^- carbon atom in the CH_2 group in the Grignard reagent attacks the δ^+ carbon in the ketone:

$$H_3C-\overset{\underset{|}{CH_3}}{\underset{O^-}{C}}-CH_2CH_3 \xrightarrow{H^+} H_3C-\overset{\underset{|}{CH_3}}{\underset{OH}{C}}-CH_2CH_3$$

Reaction with carbon dioxide

When solid carbon dioxide (dry ice) is added to a solution of a Grignard reagent in ether (ethoxyethane) and the product is acidified, a carboxylic acid is obtained that has one more carbon atom than the Grignard reagent. For example, *ethyl-magnesium* bromide forms *propan*oic acid. The overall equation is:

$$C_2H_5MgBr + CO_2(s) + HCl(aq) \rightarrow C_2H_5COOH + MgBrCl$$

Summary

Reactions of the Grignard reagent, RMgBr, where R is an alkyl group:

RMgBr	+ water	→	alkane
	+ methanal	→	primary alcohol
	+ aldehyde	→	secondary alcohol
	+ ketone	→	tertiary alcohol
	+ solid CO_2	→	carboxylic acid

In all reactions, except that with water, the product has a longer carbon chain than the original Grignard reagent.

> **e** When working out the structure of the alcohol produced from the reaction of a Grignard reagent with a carbonyl compound, it is important to realise that the alkyl group of the Grignard reagent adds on to the carbonyl carbon atom, forming a new C–C bond.

Questions

1 What is the difference in structure between an aldehyde and a ketone?

2 When propanal is prepared from propan-1-ol, the mixture is kept at a temperature between the boiling temperatures of propanal and propan-1-ol. Explain why this is necessary.

3 Explain why ethanal is soluble in water but pentanal is almost insoluble.

4 Explain, in terms of the relative strengths of all the intermolecular forces present, why butanone has a boiling temperature between those of butan-1-ol and pentane, all three substances having molar masses between 72 g mol^{-1} and 74 g mol^{-1}.

5 a Write the equation for the reaction between hydrogen cyanide and propanone.

 b Explain why this reaction does not take place unless a trace of alkali is added.

6 Give the formula of the organic products of the reaction, if any, between propanal and each of the following:

 a 2,4-dinitrophenylhydrazine solution

 b potassium dichromate(VI) in dilute sulphuric acid

 c Fehling's solution

 d a solution of silver nitrate in ammonia

 e a mixture of iodine and aqueous sodium hydroxide

In each case, state the observations that would be made.

7 Explain whether the product of the reaction of hydrogen cyanide with propanal at pH 8 would affect the plane of polarisation of polarised light.

8 A compound X of molecular formula $C_4H_{10}O$ was heated with a solution of potassium dichromate in sulphuric acid. The product, Y, was distilled off as it formed.

The compound Y gave a yellow precipitate with 2,4-dinitrophenylhydrazine. When Y was warmed with Fehling's solution, the Fehling's solution remained blue.

a Give the structural formulae of X and Y.
b What would you observe if X and Y were each warmed with a solution of iodine in aqueous sodium hydroxide?
c Write the equation for the reaction of Y with iodine in aqueous sodium hydroxide.
d A different compound, Z, also has the molecular formula $C_4H_{10}O$. When oxidised in the same way as X, it produced a product that also gave a yellow precipitate with 2,4-dinitro-phenylhydrazine, but which reacted with warm Fehling's solution, producing a red precipitate.

Give two possible structural formulae for Z and name the compounds.

9 Write the formula of the organic product of the reaction of $CH_2=CHCH_2CHO$ with each of the following:
a lithium tetrahydridoaluminate(III) in dry ether followed by the addition of dilute acid
b hydrogen gas with a platinum catalyst

10 Give details of how you would prepare a sample of butanone (boiling temperature 80 °C) from butan-2-ol (boiling temperature 100 °C). Include in your answer a diagram of the apparatus that you would use.

$$H_3C-\underset{\underset{O}{\|}}{C}-CH_2-CH_3 \qquad CH_3CH(OH)CH_2CH_3$$

butanone   butan-2-ol

11 a Define the terms 'nucleophile' and 'oxidation'.
b State the type of reaction between ethanal and each of the following:
   (i) hydrogen cyanide
   (ii) Fehling's solution
   (iii) ethylmagnesium bromide

12 Stating the reagents needed and the conditions required, outline the conversion of iodomethane into:
a ethanoic acid
b methane
c propan-2-ol

13 Explain why it is necessary to exclude all water during the preparation and the use of Grignard reagents.

14 Draw the full structural formulae of the isomers produced in the reactions of ethanal with:
a hydrogen cyanide
b ethylmagnesium bromide

15 Give details of the preparation of a solution of 1-propylmagnesium iodide. Include in your answer a diagram of the apparatus that you would use.

16 Search the internet and write a short account of the life of Victor Grignard.

Carboxylic acids and their derivatives

Chapter 7

Introduction

Carboxylic acids and their derivatives contain the group:

The nature of X varies as shown in Table 7.1.

Type of compound	Structure of X	Example Name	Formula
Carboxylic acid	O–H	Ethanoic acid	CH_3COOH
Ester	O–R*	Ethyl ethanoate	$CH_3COOC_2H_5$
Acid chloride	Cl	Ethanoyl chloride	CH_3COCl
Amide	NH_2	Ethanamide	CH_3CONH_2

* R stands for an alkyl group (e.g. CH_3, C_2H_5) or a benzene ring

Table 7.1 Carboxylic acids and their derivatives

The reactivity of the C=O group is considerably modified by the presence of the X group, so much so that, unlike aldehydes and ketones, carboxylic acids and their derivatives do not react with 2,4-dinitrophenylhydrazine.

The C=O group is polarised with the less electronegative carbon atom δ^+ and the more electronegative oxygen atom δ^-.

The mechanism for many of the reactions is for a nucleophile to attack the δ^+ carbon atom. This is then followed by the loss of the X group as an X^- ion:

This type of reaction is called an **addition–elimination** reaction. The ease of reaction depends on:

- the strength of the C–X bond. The weakest of these bonds is the C–Cl bond, so acid chlorides are the most susceptible to nucleophilic attack.
- the stability of the leaving group, X^-. The NH_2^- ion is too strong a base to be produced in aqueous solutions. This means that amides do not undergo addition–elimination reactions.

Carboxylic acids

Carboxylic acids contain the group:

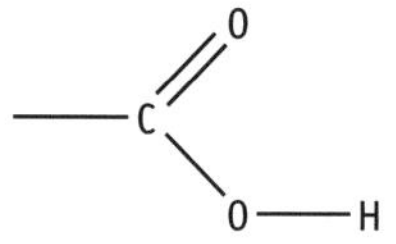

This is called the **carboxyl** group and consists of the *carb*onyl group, C=O, and the hydro*xyl* group, OH.

The names of some of the members of this homologous series, together with their melting and boiling temperatures, are given in Table 7.2.

Formula	Name	Melting temperature /°C	Boiling temperature /°C
HCOOH	Methanoic acid	8	101
CH_3COOH	Ethanoic acid	17	118
CH_3CH_2COOH	Propanoic acid	−21	141
$CH_3CH_2CH_2COOH$	Butanoic acid	−7	164
$CH_3CH(CH_3)COOH$	Methylpropanoic acid	−47	154

Table 7.2 Carboxylic acids

e Never write the formula of butanoic acid as C_3H_7COOH because this could also represent its isomer, methylpropanoic acid.

◄ Methanoic acid is also called formic acid; ethanoic acid is also called acetic acid.

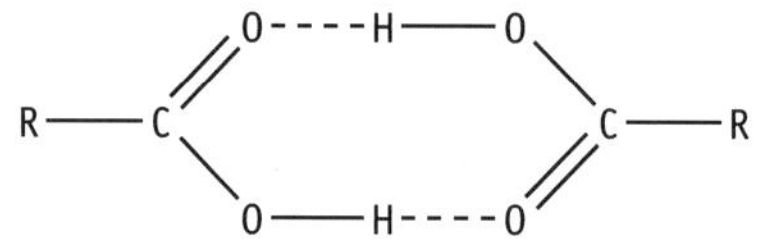

The melting temperatures of carboxylic acids do not fit the usual pattern of an increase with the number of electrons in the molecule. The reason for this is that with methanoic and ethanoic acids there is considerable hydrogen bonding. Pairs of acid molecules (dimers) are formed:

This occurs to a lesser extent with acids that have more carbon atoms, as the hydrogen bonding is inhibited by the zigzag chains of carbon atoms.

Methylpropanoic acid has fewer points of contact between adjacent molecules than does the straight chain butanoic acid, so the dispersion (temporary induced dipole–induced dipole) forces are weaker. This means that its melting and boiling temperatures are lower than those of butanoic acid, which is as expected with a branched-chain compound.

Names of carboxylic acids

The names of carboxylic acids are derived from the number of carbon atoms in the chain, *including* the carbon atom of the –COOH group. This carbon atom is regarded as the first carbon atom. Therefore, CH_2ClCH_2COOH is called 3-chloropropanoic acid and $CH_3CH(OH)COOH$ is called 2-hydroxypropanoic acid.

The old name for 2-hydroxypropanoic acid is lactic acid, which is still used in biochemistry.

Worked example
Name the compound that has the formula $CH_3CHClCH(CH_3)CH=CHCOOH$.

Answer
The carbon chain is six carbon atoms long (hex-). There is:
- a double bond on carbon number 2
- a $-CH_3$ group on carbon number 4
- a chlorine atom on carbon number 5

Its name is 5-chloro-4-methylhex-2-enoic acid.

Some organic acids have two –COOH groups. Examples are:
- HOOCCOOH (sometimes written $H_2C_2O_4$), which is ethanedioic acid
- HOOCCH=CHCOOH which exists as two geometric isomers, *cis*-butenedioic acid and *trans*-butenedioic acid

Aromatic acids contain a benzene ring.

The formula of benzenecarboxylic acid (benzoic acid) is:

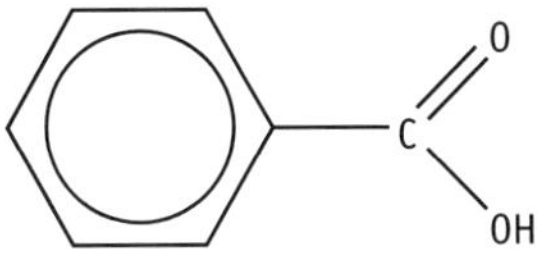

The formula of benzene-1,4-dicarboxylic acid (terephthalic acid) is:

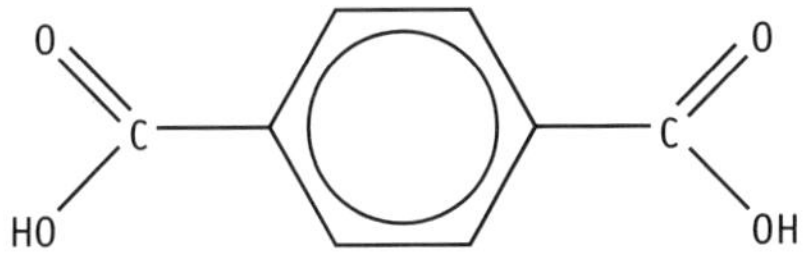

Physical properties

- The acids in the homologous series $C_nH_{2n+1}COOH$ are liquids up to $n = 9$.
- All carboxylic acids have strong smells. Vinegar is a dilute solution of ethanoic acid. The smell of rancid butter comes from butanoic acid formed by the action of bacteria on butter fat.
- Hydrogen bonding with water molecules enables those carboxylic acids with only a few carbon atoms to dissolve in water. Methanoic acid and ethanoic acid mix with water in all proportions.
- Benzoic acid, C_6H_5COOH, is a solid that melts at 122°C. It is sparingly soluble in cold water and soluble in hot water. This makes water a suitable solvent for purifying benzoic acid by recrystallisation (p. 298).

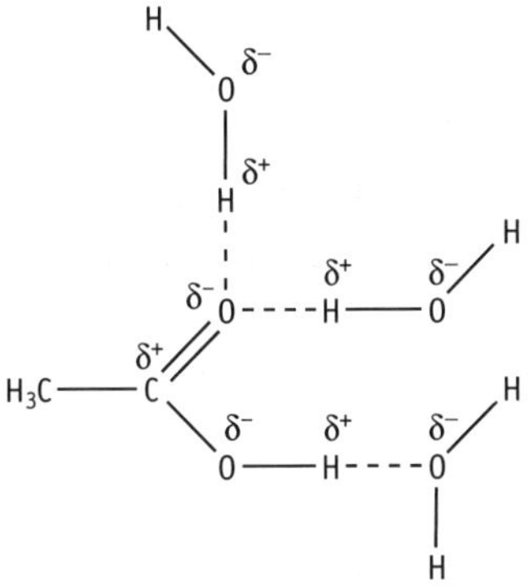

Preparation

Carboxylic acids can be prepared by:
- the oxidation of a primary alcohol. When heated under reflux with acidified potassium dichromate(VI), the primary alcohol is oxidised to a carboxylic acid, for example:

$$CH_3CH_2CH_2OH + 2[O] \rightarrow CH_3CH_2COOH + H_2O$$

- the oxidation of an aldehyde. Aldehydes are oxidised to carboxylic acids by the same reagent and under the same conditions as primary alcohols, for example:

$$CH_3CHO + [O] \rightarrow CH_3COOH$$

- the hydrolysis of an ester (p. 133)
- the hydrolysis of a nitrile (p. 153)
- the reaction of a Grignard reagent with carbon dioxide. Solid carbon dioxide (dry ice) is added to a Grignard reagent in dry ether (ethoxyethane) and the product is hydrolysed by dilute acid. A carboxylic acid, containing one *more* carbon atom than the Grignard reagent, is obtained. For example, ethylmagnesium bromide (C_2H_5MgBr) is converted into propanoic acid (CH_3CH_2COOH).
- the iodoform reaction of a methyl ketone or a secondary alcohol (p. 120). On addition of a solution of iodine in aqueous sodium hydroxide to a methyl ketone (such as butanone, $CH_3CH_2COCH_3$, the salt of the acid with one *fewer* carbon atoms (propanoic acid, CH_3CH_2COOH) is produced. The free carboxylic acid is formed by adding excess strong acid to the mixture.

Butan-2-ol, $CH_3CH_2CH(OH)CH_3$, would also produce propanoic acid in this reaction.

Chemical reactions

The reactions of carboxylic acids are illustrated using ethanoic acid as the example.

As an acid

Carboxylic acids are weak acids (p. 78).

Reaction with water

Carboxylic acids react reversibly with water:

$$CH_3COOH + H_2O \rightleftharpoons CH_3COO^- + H_3O^+$$

Aqueous solutions of ethanoic acid have pH $\approx$ 3.

The –OH group in carboxylic acids is more acidic than the –OH group in alcohols. There are two reasons for this. First, the C=O group pulls electrons away from the –OH group, making the hydrogen atom more δ^+ and therefore easier to remove as an H$^+$ ion:

Second, the carboxylate anion has the negative charge shared between two oxygen atoms. The p_z-orbital of the carbon atom (containing one electron), the p_z-orbital of the oxygen double-bonded to it (containing one electron), and the p_z-orbital of the other oxygen (containing its one electron and the one gained by the formation of the O$^-$ ion) all overlap. This can be shown as:

e Vinegar is a 3% solution of ethanoic acid. It is produced from ethanol, which is made by the fermentation of grains and sugars. Ethanol is then oxidised by the oxygen in the air in a reaction catalysed by enzymes in specific bacteria.

Reaction with bases

Carboxylic acids form salts with bases such as sodium hydroxide:

$$CH_3COOH + NaOH \rightarrow CH_3COONa + H_2O$$

Reaction with carbonates and hydrogencarbonates

Carboxylic acids produce carbon dioxide when added to a carbonate:

$$2CH_3COOH(aq) + Na_2CO_3 \rightarrow 2CH_3COONa(aq) + CO_2(g) + H_2O(l)$$

Similarly, with hydrogencarbonate:

$$CH_3COOH(aq) + NaHCO_3(s) \rightarrow CH_3COONa(aq) + CO_2(g) + H_2O(l)$$

Esterification

Carboxylic acids do not react readily with nucleophiles. However, they do react with alcohols in the presence of concentrated sulphuric acid (as a catalyst) in a reversible reaction to form esters:

$$acid + alcohol \rightleftharpoons ester + water$$

For example:

$$\underset{\text{ethanoic acid}}{CH_3COOH} + \underset{\text{ethanol}}{C_2H_5OH} \overset{H_2SO_4(l)}{\rightleftharpoons} \underset{\text{ethyl ethanoate}}{CH_3COOC_2H_5} + H_2O$$

The catalyst acts by protonating the ethanoic acid, which then loses a water molecule:

$$CH_3COOH + H_2SO_4 \rightarrow HSO_4^- + CH_3COOH_2^+ \rightarrow CH_3C^+O + H_2O$$

The lone pair of electrons on the oxygen of the alcohol bonds to the positive carbon atom in the CH_3C^+O ion and then an H^+ is removed, thus reforming the catalyst:

$$C_2H_5OH + CH_3C^+O \rightarrow CH_3COOC_2H_5 + H^+$$
$$H^+ + HSO_4^- \rightarrow H_2SO_4$$

Reduction

Carboxylic acids are reduced by lithium tetrahydridoaluminate(III), $LiAlH_4$, dissolved in dry ether (ethoxyethane). The H^- ion in the AlH_4^- is a very powerful nucleophile. It adds on to the $\delta+$ carbon atom in the –COOH group. A series of reactions takes place and the final product has to be hydrolysed by dilute acid. The carboxylic acid is reduced to a primary alcohol. The overall equation is:

$$CH_3COOH + 4[H] \rightarrow CH_3CH_2OH + H_2O$$

Carboxylic acids (unlike alkenes, which are reduced to alkanes) are *not* reduced by hydrogen gas in the presence of a catalyst of nickel or platinum.

$$CH_2{=}CHCOOH \overset{LiAlH_4}{\rightarrow} CH_2C{=}CHCH_2OH$$
$$CH_2{=}CHCOOH \overset{H_2/Pt}{\rightarrow} CH_3CH_2COOH$$

Formation of acid chloride

Ethanoic acid can be converted to ethanoyl chloride by adding solid phosphorus pentachloride to the dry acid:

$$CH_3COOH + PCl_5 \rightarrow CH_3COCl + POCl_3 + HCl$$

e The symbol [H] is used in organic reactions involving a reducing agent such as $LiAlH_4$, because the full equation is too complex. However, the equation must still balance, which is why 4[H] is written in this equation.

The H^- ion in $LiAlH_4$ attacks $\delta+$ sites. Therefore, $LiAlH_4$ will not reduce a C=C group as it has a high electron density.

This is a similar reaction to that between PCl_5 and an alcohol. In both reactions, the –OH group is replaced by a chlorine atom and clouds of misty fumes of hydrogen chloride are given off.

The conversion can also be performed using thionyl chloride, $SOCl_2$:

$$RCOOH + SOCl_2 \rightarrow RCOCl + SO_2 + HCl$$

The advantage of this reagent is that the inorganic products are gases, so only the acid chloride is left in the reaction flask.

Formation of a halogenoacid

If chlorine is bubbled into a boiling carboxylic acid in the presence of sunlight or ultraviolet (UV) light, a chlorine atom replaces one of the hydrogen atoms in the alkyl chain:

$$CH_3COOH + Cl_2 \rightarrow CH_2ClCOOH + HCl$$

This is an example of free-radical substitution. It is similar to the reaction of methane with chlorine in the presence of UV light.

If propanoic acid is used in place of ethanoic acid, the product is 2-chloro-propanoic acid, not 3-chloropropanoic acid:

$$CH_3CH_2COOH + Cl_2 \rightarrow CH_3CHClCOOH + HCl$$

Summary

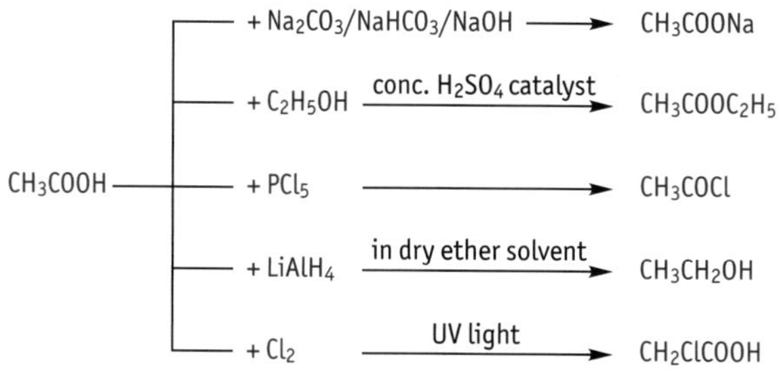

$$CH_3COOH$$

+ $Na_2CO_3/NaHCO_3/NaOH \longrightarrow CH_3COONa$

+ C_2H_5OH $\xrightarrow{\text{conc. } H_2SO_4 \text{ catalyst}}$ $CH_3COOC_2H_5$

+ PCl_5 $\longrightarrow CH_3COCl$

+ $LiAlH_4$ $\xrightarrow{\text{in dry ether solvent}}$ CH_3CH_2OH

+ Cl_2 $\xrightarrow{\text{UV light}}$ $CH_2ClCOOH$

Esters

Esters have the structural formula:

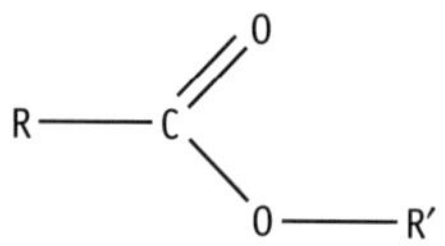

The group R can be a hydrogen atom or an organic residue, such as $-CH_3$. R′ must be a residue of an alcohol with a carbon atom attached to the oxygen of the ester linkage.

Esters are named after the alcohol residue, R′, followed by the name of the carboxylate group, RCOO:

- $HCOOCH_3$ is methyl methanoate.
- $CH_3COOCH_2CH_2CH_3$ is called 1-propyl ethanoate.

The prefix '1-' indicates the position of the ester linkage in the propyl chain.

e Note that the formula of an ester is written with the acid-derived group first, then the stem of the alcohol.

Physical properties

Most esters are liquids at room temperature. The names and boiling points of the first four members of the series of esters derived from ethanoic acid are shown in Table 7.3.

Name	Formula	Boiling temperature/°C
Methyl ethanoate	CH_3COOCH_3	57
Ethyl ethanoate	$CH_3COOC_2H_5$	77
1-propyl ethanoate	$CH_3COOCH_2CH_2CH_3$	102
2-propyl ethanoate	$CH_3COOCH(CH_3)_2$	93

Table 7.3 Esters derived from ethanoic acid

Solubility

Despite being polar molecules, all esters are insoluble in water. The reason for this is that they cannot form hydrogen bonds with water molecules because they do not have any δ^+ hydrogen atoms and the δ^- oxygen atoms are sterically hindered, preventing close approach by water molecules.

Preparation

Esters can be prepared by warming an alcohol and a carboxylic acid under reflux with a few drops of concentrated sulphuric acid:

$$C_2H_5OH + CH_3COOH \rightleftharpoons CH_3COOC_2H_5 + H_2O$$

A higher yield is obtained if the alcohol is reacted with an acid chloride at room temperature, because the reaction is not reversible:

$$C_2H_5OH + CH_3COCl \rightarrow CH_3COOC_2H_5 + HCl$$

Chemical reactions

Esters are inert to most chemicals. However, they are hydrolysed when heated under reflux with either aqueous acid or aqueous alkali:

$$CH_3COOC_2H_5 + H_2O \overset{H^+(aq)}{\rightleftharpoons} CH_3COOH + C_2H_5OH$$
$$CH_3COOC_2H_5 + NaOH \rightarrow CH_3COONa + C_2H_5OH$$

Note the difference between these two reactions. In the first, the acid is a catalyst and the reaction is reversible. Therefore, the yield of acid and alcohol is low.

The hydrolysis with aqueous alkali is not reversible, so there is a good yield of the salt of the carboxylic acid and the alcohol. If the organic acid is required, the solution is cooled and excess dilute strong acid, such as hydrochloric or sulphuric, is added:

$$CH_3COONa + HCl \rightarrow CH_3COOH + NaCl$$

Uses of esters

Esters are used as:
- perfumes and flavourings. Perfumes are complex mixtures of esters and ketones.
- solvents. Nail varnish contains some ethyl ethanoate, as the solvent of the varnish.

- anaesthetics. Benzocaine and procaine are esters and are used as local anaesthetics, the latter in dentistry.

Methyl esters of long-chain acids are used as fuels.

Polyesters

Polyesters are **condensation polymers**.

> A condensation polymer is formed when monomers join together with the elimination of a simple molecule, such as water or hydrogen chloride.

The monomers that condense must have two groups, one at each end of the molecule. For example, a dicarboxylic acid has two –COOH groups, a diacid chloride has two –COCl groups and a diol has two –OH groups in the molecule.

A polyester is formed if a dicarboxylic acid, such as benzene-1,4-dicarboxylic acid (terephthalic acid) reacts with a diol, such as ethane-1,2-diol, CH_2OHCH_2OH. One of the –COOH groups in the dicarboxylic acid reacts with one of the –OH groups in the diol. The remaining –OH group in the diol then reacts with one of the –COOH groups in a second diacid molecule. The remaining –COOH group then reacts with the –OH in a second diol molecule and so on, thousands of times.

The reaction also takes place with the dimethyl ester or a diacid chloride. An example is the formation of the polymer Terylene® or PET (**P**oly **E**thylene **T**erephthalate:

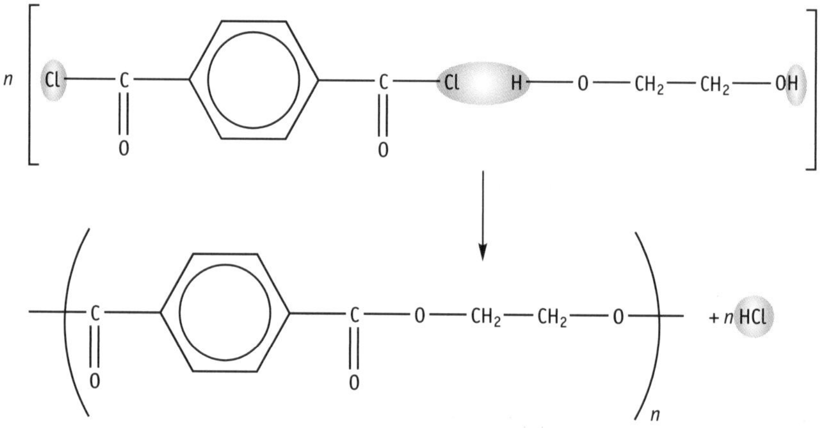

Uses of polyesters

Polyesters, such as Terylene, are used in the manufacture of synthetic fibres. Some shirts, sheets, socks and trousers are made from a mix of polyester and a natural fibre such as cotton or wool. The polyester gives the material strength and crease resistance; the natural fibre gives a softer feel and allows the material to absorb some perspiration from the wearer.

Polyesters are also excellent thermal insulators and can be used as fillings for duvets.

PET can be extruded into different shapes and is used to make bottles for fizzy drinks and water. The bottle does not allow the dissolved carbon dioxide to escape as gas and the material is shatterproof, so will not break if dropped.

Disposal of polyesters

Polyesters are not biodegradable because enzymes have not evolved that hydrolyse the ester linkages in the man-made fibres. This means that they do not rot in a landfill site. If burnt, toxic fumes are produced if the temperature and amount of air are not closely controlled.

Soaps and soapless detergents

Soaps

Soaps are made by the hydrolysis of animal fats, which are heated with aqueous sodium hydroxide solution. On cooling, the sodium stearate formed precipitates out. This reaction is known as **saponification**. Perfumes and oils are added to sodium stearate, which is then sold as soap.

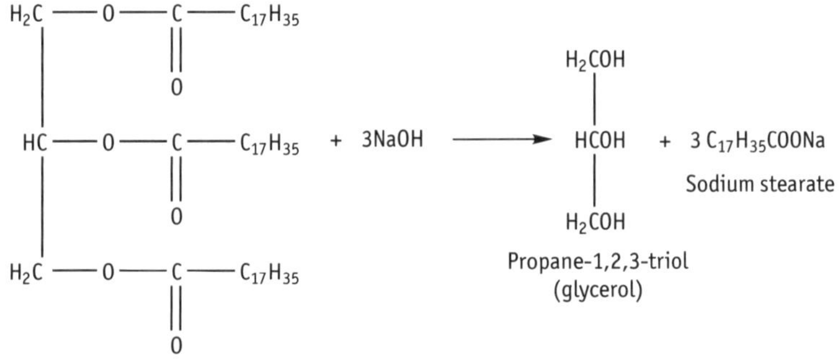

Uses of polyesters

$$
\begin{array}{c}
H_2C - O - \overset{\displaystyle O}{\underset{\displaystyle \|}{C}} - C_{17}H_{35} \\[2mm]
HC - O - \overset{\displaystyle O}{\underset{\displaystyle \|}{C}} - C_{17}H_{35} \quad + \quad 3NaOH \\[2mm]
H_2C - O - \overset{\displaystyle O}{\underset{\displaystyle \|}{C}} - C_{17}H_{35}
\end{array}
\quad \longrightarrow \quad
\begin{array}{c}
H_2COH \\[2mm]
HCOH \\[2mm]
H_2COH
\end{array}
\quad + \quad 3\,C_{17}H_{35}COONa
$$

Glyceryl tristearate

Sodium stearate

Propane-1,2,3-triol (glycerol)

Soaps consist of a hydrocarbon 'tail', shown in red, and an ionic 'head', shown in green:

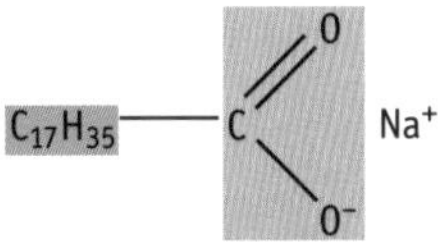

$$
C_{17}H_{35} - \overset{\displaystyle O}{\underset{\displaystyle O^-}{C}} \quad Na^+
$$

The tail dissolves in organic matter and the head dissolves in water. Dirt is held onto skin and clothing by a thin film of oil or grease. Soap makes this water soluble and it is lifted off the fabric or the skin, leaving it clean.

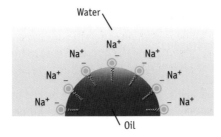

One problem with soaps occurs with hard water, which contains calcium ions in solution. Calcium stearate is insoluble in water and so, having gathered the dirt, it precipitates as a scum.

Soapless detergents

Soapless detergents are made from oil. They have a hydrocarbon tail that contains a benzene ring and an ionic head that is derived from sulphonic acid. They work in the same way as ordinary soaps. However, their calcium salts are more soluble and, therefore, do not form a scum in hard water.

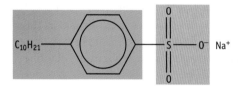

The nature of the side chain is important with respect to biodegradability of the detergent. Those with one or no branches in the alkyl chain are more biodegradable than those that are considerably branched.

Acid chlorides

These are also known as acyl chlorides and have the functional group:

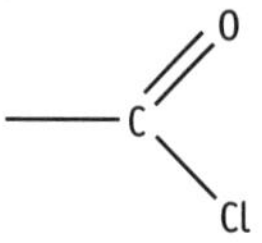

Physical properties

- Most acid chlorides are volatile liquids at room temperature.
- They are soluble in several organic solvents, but react with water.

The names, formulae and boiling temperatures of some acid chlorides are given in Table 7.4.

Name	Formula	Boiling temperature/°C
Ethanoyl chloride	CH_3COCl	51
Propanoyl chloride	CH_3CH_2COCl	80
Butanoyl chloride	$CH_3CH_2CH_2COCl$	102
Benzoyl chloride	C_6H_5COCl	197

Table 7.4 Some acid chlorides

Methanoyl chloride has never been isolated as it decomposes at room temperature into carbon monoxide and hydrogen chloride.

Preparation

Acid chlorides are prepared from carboxylic acids. The –OH group is replaced by a chlorine atom. The reagents that can be used are phosphorus pentachloride, phosphorus trichloride or thionyl chloride. Starting from ethanoic acid, the equations are:

$$CH_3COOH + PCl_5 \rightarrow CH_3COCl + POCl_3 + HCl$$
$$3CH_3COOH + PCl_3 \rightarrow 3CH_3COCl + H_3PO_3$$
$$CH_3COOH + SOCl_2 \rightarrow CH_3COCl + SO_2 + HCl$$

The organic product is ethanoyl chloride.

Chemical reactions

In acid chlorides, the carbon atom of the C=O group is δ^+; the C–Cl bond is not very strong and Cl^- is a good leaving group. Taken together, this makes the molecule susceptible to nucleophilic attack, in an addition–elimination reaction. The end result is a **substitution** in which the nucleophile replaces the chlorine atom.

Acid chlorides react much more quickly than carboxylic acids. The C–OH bond in carboxylic acids is stronger than the C–Cl bond and OH^- is a less good leaving group than Cl^-.

Reaction with water
Ethanoyl chloride reacts vigorously with water forming ethanoic acid and clouds of hydrogen chloride gas:

$$CH_3COCl + H_2O \rightarrow CH_3COOH + HCl$$

The first step is the addition of water. The oxygen atom in water has a lone pair of electrons. This makes it a nucleophile. The lone pair forms a bond with the δ^+ carbon atom in the C=O group. Simultaneously, the π-bond breaks and the C=O oxygen becomes O^-:

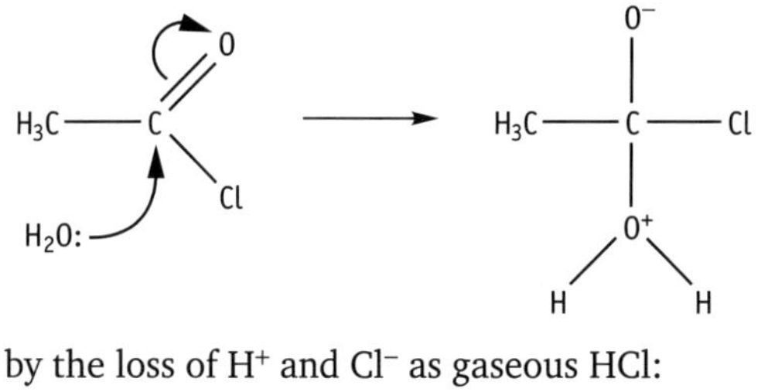

This is followed by the loss of H^+ and Cl^- as gaseous HCl:

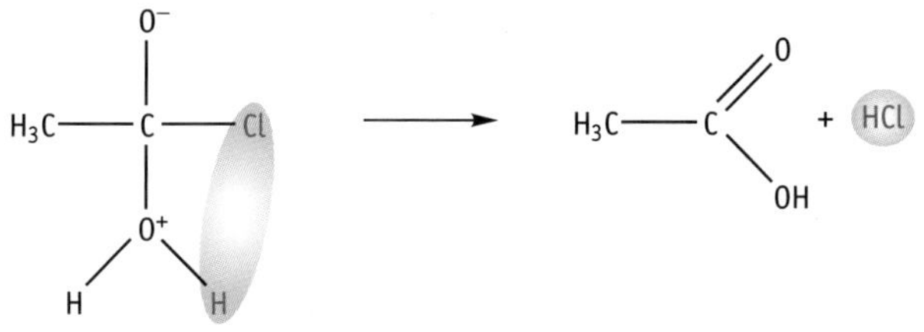

This rapid reaction with water means that when using ethanoyl chloride as a reactant, all reagents must be dry.

Benzoyl chloride is less reactive than ethanoyl chloride and reacts only slowly with water. Therefore, it can be used with reagents in aqueous solution.

Reaction with alcohols

Ethanoyl chloride reacts rapidly in a non-reversible reaction with alcohols. The products are an ester and misty fumes of hydrogen chloride vapour.

$$CH_3COCl + CH_3OH \rightarrow CH_3COOCH_3 + HCl$$
ethanoyl chloride   methanol   methyl ethanoate

The mechanism of this reaction is analogous to that of the reaction with water.

As this is a non-reversible reaction with a good yield, it is a more efficient method of making an ester than reacting the alcohol with a carboxylic acid. The latter reaction is reversible with a maximum possible yield of under 70%.

The alcohol must be dry, or the acid chloride will be hydrolysed by the water.

Reaction with ammonia

The nitrogen atom in ammonia has a lone pair of electrons, which is used in a nucleophilic attack on the C=O group. The product is an amide (p. 139), for example:

$$CH_3COCl + HNH_2 \rightarrow CH_3CONH_2 + HCl$$
ethanoyl chloride   ethanamide

Reaction with amines

Amines also have a lone pair of electrons on the nitrogen atom. They react with acid chlorides in the same way as ammonia. The product is a substituted amide, for example:

$$CH_3COCl + CH_3NH_2 \rightarrow CH_3CONHCH_3 + HCl$$
ethanoyl chloride   N-methylethanamide

The prefix *N-* indicates that the methyl group is attached to a nitrogen atom.

Reaction with lithium tetrahydridoaluminate(III)

Acid chlorides, like carboxylic acids and esters, are reduced by lithium tetrahydridoaluminate(III) in dry ether solution to form a primary alcohol, for example:

$$CH_3COCl + 4[H] \rightarrow CH_3CH_2OH + HCl$$

Reaction with aromatic compounds

Ethanoyl chloride reacts with benzene and with phenol (see pp. 239 and 246).

Summary

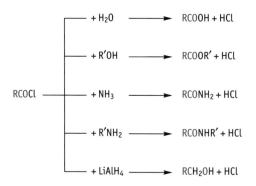

$$+ H_2O \longrightarrow RCOOH + HCl$$

$$+ R'OH \longrightarrow RCOOR' + HCl$$

$$RCOCl \quad + NH_3 \longrightarrow RCONH_2 + HCl$$

$$+ R'NH_2 \longrightarrow RCONHR' + HCl$$

$$+ LiAlH_4 \longrightarrow RCH_2OH + HCl$$

Amides

Amides contain the group:

$$\begin{array}{c} & & O \\ & & \parallel \\ \text{---} & C & \\ & & \backslash \\ & & NH_2 \end{array}$$

Physical properties

An amide molecule contains two δ^+ hydrogen atoms, a δ^- oxygen atom and a δ^- nitrogen atom. Therefore, the molecules can form several *inter*molecular hydrogen bonds. This means that amides have higher melting temperatures than acid chlorides derived from the same acid.

Name	Formula	Melting temperature/°C	Boiling temperature/°C
Ethanamide	CH_3CONH_2	82	222
Propanamide	$CH_3CH_2CONH_2$	79	222
Benzamide	$C_6H_5CONH_2$	132	290

Table 7.5
Some amides

Apart from those with a large hydrophobic group, for example benzamide, amides are water-soluble. This is because the molecules can form several hydrogen bonds with water molecules.

Preparation

Amides can be prepared by the reaction between ammonia and an acid chloride:

$$CH_3COCl + NH_3 \rightarrow CH_3CONH_2 + HCl$$

They can also be made by heating a carboxylic acid and ammonium carbonate mixture under reflux. The ammonium salt is formed, which dehydrates on heating:

$$2CH_3COOH + (NH_4)_2CO_3 \rightarrow 2CH_3COONH_4 + H_2O + CO_2$$
$$CH_3COONH_4 - H_2O \rightarrow CH_3CONH_2$$

Chemical reactions

Hydrolysis

When boiled under reflux with either aqueous acid or aqueous alkali, amides are hydrolysed.

For example, ethanamide is hydrolysed in acid solution to ethanoic acid and ammonium ions:

$$CH_3CONH_2 + H^+ + H_2O \rightarrow CH_3COOH + NH_4^+$$

With alkali, the salt of the carboxylic acid is formed and ammonia gas is evolved. For example, when hydrolysed by sodium hydroxide, benzamide gives sodium benzoate:

$$C_6H_5CONH_2 + OH^- \rightarrow C_6H_5COO^- + NH_3$$

If the carboxylic acid is required, the product of alkaline hydrolysis must be acidified with a solution of a strong acid:

$$C_6H_5COO^- + H^+ \rightarrow C_6H_5COOH$$

Benzoic acid is insoluble in cold water and so on cooling it precipitates out.

Dehydration

When an amide is heated with phosphorus(V) oxide, P_4O_{10}, it is dehydrated to a nitrile (p. 152):

$$C_2H_5CONH_2 - H_2O \rightarrow C_2H_5CN$$

Propanamide produces propanenitrile.

Hofmann degradation reaction

The Hofmann degradation reaction is one of the few examples of a reaction that shortens the carbon chain. The amide is mixed with liquid bromine and then aqueous sodium hydroxide is added. The amide is converted into an amine with one less carbon atom. For example, propanamide (three-carbon chain) is converted into ethylamine (two-carbon chain):

$$C_2H_5CONH_2 \xrightarrow{Br_2(l)/NaOH(aq)} C_2H_5NH_2$$
propanamide   ethylamine

Polyamides

The reaction between an acid chloride and an amine is described on page 138. If a compound that has two COCl groups reacts with a substance with two NH_2 groups a polyamide is formed.

The first commercial polyamide was nylon-6,6. This can be made in the laboratory by the reaction of hexane-1,6-dioyl dichloride, $ClOC(CH_2)_4COCl$ and 1,6-diamino-hexane. The former is soluble in 1,1,2-trichloroethane and the latter in water. If the two solutions are carefully added together so that the aqueous layer floats on top of the organic layer, a thread of nylon can be drawn from the interface of the two liquids.

CHARLES D. WINTERS/SPL

A thread of nylon being pulled from the interface of the two solutions

The equation for the reaction is:

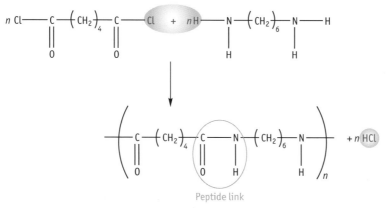

Peptide link

Nylon is a condensation polymer — a molecule of hydrogen chloride is eliminated as each acid chloride group reacts with an amino group.

The strength of nylon is increased by cold-drawing. This involves putting the threads under tension. The polymer chains become more aligned. This results in hydrogen bonding between the δ^- oxygen in the C=O groups and the δ^+ hydrogen atoms in the NH groups.

Uses of nylon

- Nylon fibres are used in stockings and carpets.
- Nylon is used to make a number of machine parts such as bearings and rollers. This is because it is a very tough material that has a melting point above 250°C.
- It has a high electrical resistance and so is used to make switches.

Other polyamides

Nomex® is a long straight-chain polymer with flame-resistant properties. The equation for its formation is:

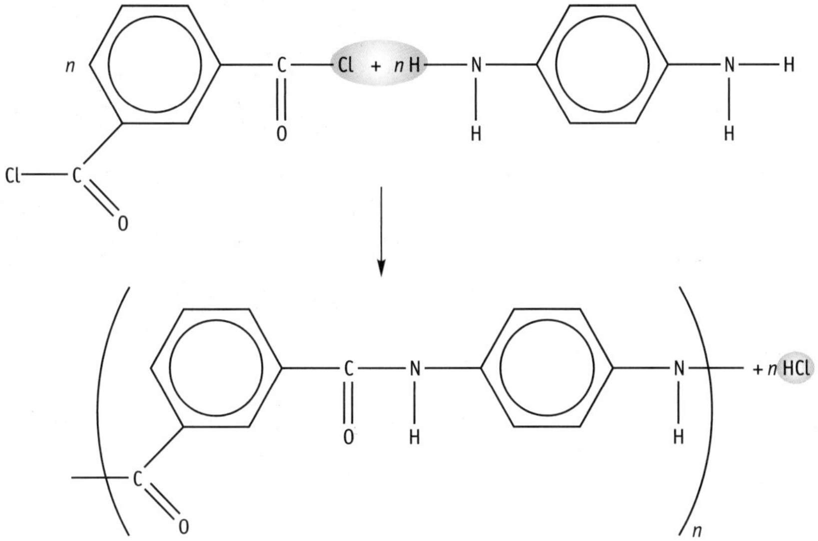

Kevlar® is another tough polyamide. It is used in bulletproof vests. The equation for its formation is:

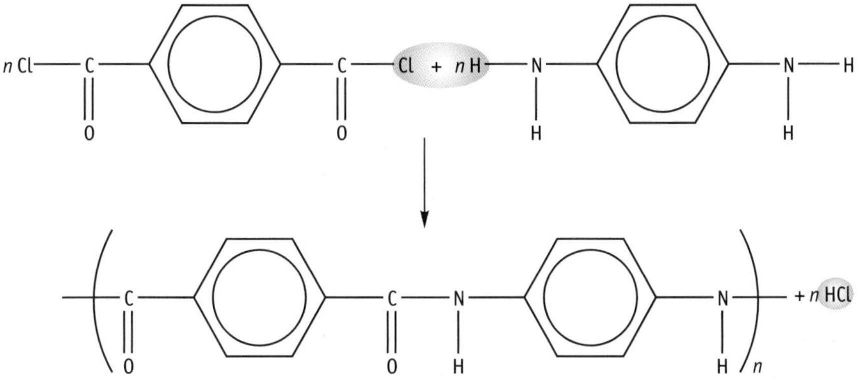

All polyamides contain the peptide link. This is the same link that joins α-amino acid residues in proteins.

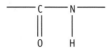

Questions

1 Name the following compounds:
   a $(CH_3)_2C(OH)COOH$
   b $CH_3CHClCOCl$
   c $C_2H_5COOCH(CH_3)_2$

2 Explain why propanoic acid is soluble in water whereas propane is insoluble.

3 If the molar mass of ethanoic acid is measured when dissolved in an organic solvent such as benzene, it is found to be 120 g mol⁻¹. Explain this.

4 Identify the organic product of the reaction of excess phosphorus pentachloride with 2-hydroxy-propanoic acid (lactic acid).

5 Identify the organic product obtained on reducing $CHOCH=CHCH(OH)COOH$ with:
   a lithium tetrahydridoaluminate(III) in dry ether followed by dilute hydrochloric acid
   b hydrogen gas and a platinum catalyst

6 Write equations for the reactions of propanoic acid with:
   a aqueous sodium hydroxide
   b magnesium
   c methanol

   State the conditions necessary for the reaction between propanoic acid and methanol.

7 Aspirin can be prepared by the reaction of ethanoyl chloride with:

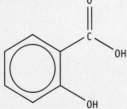

   Write the structural formula of aspirin.

8 Describe how you would prepare a pure, high-yield sample of benzoic acid, C_6H_5COOH, from ethyl benzoate, $C_6H_5COOC_2H_5$.

9 Describe how you would prepare a sample of propanoyl chloride from propanoic acid.

10 Write equations for the reaction of propanoyl chloride with:
   a ammonia
   b water
   c 2-aminoethanol, $NH_2CH_2CH_2OH$

11 Describe how propanamide can be converted into:
   a ethylamine
   b propanoic acid
   c propanenitrile

12 Outline how propanoic acid, CH_3CH_2COOH, can be converted into butanoic acid. The conversion requires several steps.

13 Explain how sodium palmitate, $CH_3(CH_2)_{14}COONa$, acts as a soap.

14 2-hydroxypropanoic acid can be polymerised. Draw the structure of two repeat units of this polymer.

15 Draw the structure of the peptide link.

16 Discuss the problems of disposal of items containing large quantities of polyamides, for example nylon carpets.

17 Write the equation for the polymerisation of butane-1,4-dioic acid with 1,5-diaminopentane. Make sure that, in the formula of the product, the structure of the link between the two monomers is clearly shown.

Organic nitrogen compounds

Chapter 8

Amines

Amines contain the group:

There are three types of amine:
- A **primary amine** has only one carbon atom bonded to the nitrogen atom and, therefore, has an $-NH_2$ group. Methylamine, CH_3NH_2, is an example.
- A **secondary amine** has two carbon atoms directly joined to the nitrogen atom. Dimethylamine, $(CH_3)_2NH$, is an example. All secondary amines have an $>NH$ group.
- A **tertiary amine** has three carbon atoms and no hydrogen atoms attached directly to the nitrogen atom. Trimethylamine, $(CH_3)_3N$, is an example.

The nitrogen atom in all amines has three σ-bonds and a lone pair of electrons. The four pairs of electrons are arranged in a tetrahedron around the nitrogen. Therefore, the three bonding pairs are arranged pyramidally, with the H–N–H bond angle less than the tetrahedral angle. This is because the lone pair/bond pair repulsion is greater than the bond pair/bond pair repulsion.

Amines can be named by:
- adding amine to the stem of the alkyl group. Thus, $C_2H_5NH_2$ is ethylamine and $CH_3CH_2CH_2NH_2$ is 1-propylamine; or
- adding the prefix amino- to the alkane from which the amine is derived. $C_2H_5NH_2$ is called aminoethane and $CH_3CH_2CH_2NH_2$ is 1-aminopropane.

Physical properties

Methylamine is a gas at room temperature and pressure. Ethylamine boils around room temperature and the next members of the homologous series of primary amines are liquids (Table 8.1).

Name	Formula	Boiling temperature/°C
Methylamine (aminomethane)	CH_3NH_2	−6
Ethylamine (aminoethane)	$CH_3CH_2NH_2$	+17
1-propylamine (1-aminopropane)	$CH_3CH_2CH_2NH_2$	+49
2-propylamine (2-aminopropane)	$CH_3CH(NH_2)CH_3$	+33
Dimethylamine	$(CH_3)_2NH$	+7
Trimethylamine	$(CH_3)_3N$	+4
Phenylamine (aminobenzene, aniline)	$C_6H_5NH_2$	+184

Table 8.1 Boiling temperatures of amines

Hydrogen bonding occurs between amine molecules:

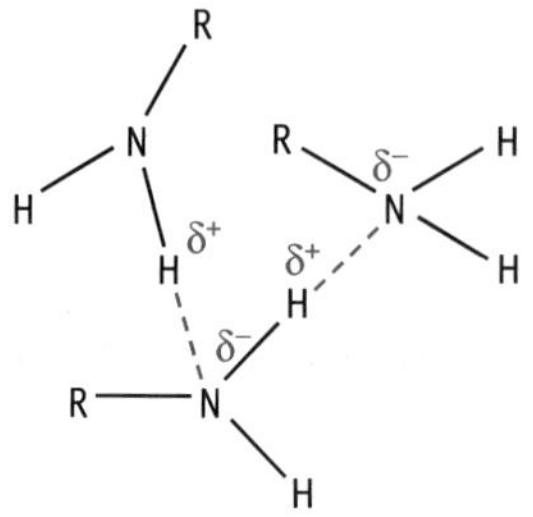

This explains why the boiling temperatures of amines are higher than those of the parent alkane. Methylamine (18 electrons) boils at −6°C whereas the non-hydrogen bonded ethane (also 18 electrons) boils at −89°C.

Amines are water-soluble because they form hydrogen bonds with water molecules. The nitrogen atom is δ^- and the hydrogen atom attached to it is δ^+:

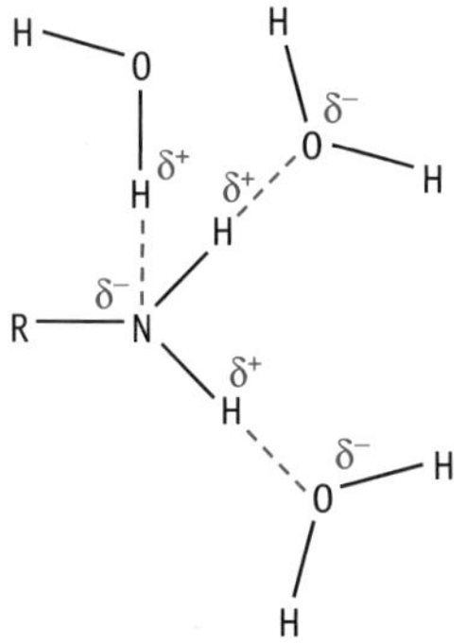

Preparation

There are three ways of preparing primary amines.

Reaction of ammonia with a halogenoalkane

If a halogenoalkane is mixed with excess concentrated ammonia in aqueous ethanolic solution and left for several minutes, a primary amine is obtained, for example:

$$C_2H_5Cl + 2NH_3 \rightarrow C_2H_5NH_2 + NH_4Cl$$

An excess of ammonia will yield the secondary amine.

Another condition for this reaction, often quoted in textbooks and accepted by examiners, is heating the mixture in a sealed tube.

> **e** When the base ammonia is a reactant, do not write an equation that has an acid such as HCl as a product. With excess ammonia, ammonium chloride is produced. If the ammonia is not in excess, the amine salt is formed (see the reaction of amines with acids on page 145).

Reduction of a nitrile or amide

A nitrile (e.g. ethanenitrile) or an amide (e.g. ethanamide) can be reduced by warming with a solution of lithium tetrahydridoaluminate(III) in dry ether

e Remember that the strength of the intermolecular dispersion (van der Waals) forces depends mainly on the total number of electrons in the molecules.

e Note that the angle around a hydrogen-bonded hydrogen atom is 180°.

(ethoxyethane), followed by hydrolysis of the adduct with dilute acid:

$$CH_3CN \quad + 4[H] \rightarrow CH_3CH_2NH_2$$
ethanenitrile $\qquad$ ethylamine

$$CH_3CONH_2 \quad + 4[H] \rightarrow CH_3CH_2NH_2 + H_2O$$
ethanamide $\qquad$ ethylamine

Nitriles, but not amides, can also be reduced by hydrogen in the presence of a heated nickel catalyst. However, the yield is not high because some rearrangement takes place and some secondary amines are produced.

Hofmann degradation of an amide

If liquid bromine and aqueous sodium hydroxide are added to an amide, an amine with one fewer carbon atoms than the amide is produced, for example:

$$CH_3CH_2CONH_2 + Br_2 + 4NaOH \rightarrow CH_3CH_2NH_2 + Na_2CO_3 + 2NaBr + 2H_2O$$

The yield of this reaction is high.

Chemical reactions

The nitrogen atom has a lone pair of electrons and this causes it to be a base and a nucleophile.

As a base

The base reactions of amines are similar to those of ammonia. Ammonia and amine molecules have a lone pair of electrons on the nitrogen atom that can be used to form a dative covalent bond with an H^+ ion.

Reaction with water

Amines react reversibly with water, for example:

$$C_2H_5NH_2 + H_2O \rightleftharpoons C_2H_5NH_3^+ + OH^-$$

As OH^- ions are produced, the solution is alkaline, with a pH of about 11.

This reaction is similar to:

$$NH_3 + H_2O \rightleftharpoons NH_4^+ + OH^-$$

The $-C_2H_5$ group pushes electrons slightly towards the nitrogen atom making it more δ^- than it is in ammonia. Therefore, ethylamine is a stronger base than ammonia:

- K_b of ethylamine = 5.6×10^{-4} mol dm^{-3}
- K_b of ammonia = 1.8×10^{-5} mol dm^{-3}

Diethylamine, $(C_2H_5)_2NH$, is a slightly stronger base than ethylamine because it contains two electron-pushing groups.

Reaction with acids

When an amine reacts with a strong acid, such as dilute hydrochloric acid, a salt (similar to an ammonium salt) is formed. For example, ethylamine and dilute hydrochloric acid produce ethylammonium chloride:

$$C_2H_5NH_2 + HCl \rightarrow C_2H_5NH_3^+Cl^-$$

This reaction can be reversed by adding a strong base, such as sodium hydroxide:

$$C_2H_5NH_3^+ + OH^- \rightarrow C_2H_5NH_2 + H_2O$$

e Sodium tetra-hydridoborate(III) is not a strong enough reducing agent to reduce either nitriles or amides.

e Ammonia reacts with acids to form ammonium salts such as ammonium chloride:
$$NH_3 + HCl \rightarrow NH_4^+Cl^-$$

The amine can then be distilled off from the mixture of the amine salt and sodium hydroxide.

Reaction with acid chlorides

The lone pair of electrons on the nitrogen atom in the amine acts as a nucleophile and attacks the δ^+ carbon atom in the acid chloride in an addition–elimination reaction. For example, when ethanoyl chloride is added to ethylamine, a secondary amide, *N*-ethylethanamide, and misty fumes of hydrogen chloride are produced:

$$C_2H_5NH_2 + CH_3COCl \rightarrow CH_3CONHC_2H_5 + HCl$$

Amines with two $-NH_2$ groups in the molecule form polyamides with acid chlorides with two $-COCl$ groups.

Reaction with halogenoalkanes

A primary amine reacts with a halogenoalkane to produce a mixture of the salts of a secondary and a tertiary amine:

$$C_2H_5NH_2 + C_2H_5Cl \rightarrow (C_2H_5)_2NH_2{}^+Cl^-$$
$$(C_2H_5)_2NH_2{}^+Cl^- + C_2H_5Cl \rightarrow (C_2H_5)_3NH^+Cl^- + HCl$$

The reagents are heated in a solution in ethanol in a sealed tube.

If the free amine is required, a strong base is added to the solution and any unreacted primary amine and the secondary and tertiary amines formed are separated by fractional distillation.

$$(C_2H_5)_2NH_2{}^+Cl^- + OH^- \rightarrow (C_2H_5)_2NH + H_2O + Cl^-$$
$$(C_2H_5)_3NH^+Cl^- + OH^- \rightarrow (C_2H_5)_3N + H_2O + Cl^-$$

Reaction with *d*-block metal ions

The lone pair of electrons on the amine group can form a bond with the empty orbital of some *d*-block metal ions. The reaction is similar to the formation of ammines with excess ammonia.

A precipitate of the metal hydroxide is produced first. With Co^{2+}, Ni^{2+}, Cu^+, Cu^{2+}, Zn^{2+} and Ag^+ ions the precipitate dissolves because a complex ion is formed. The colour of the complex is similar to that formed with ammonia solution (see p. 198).

The first reaction, forming the precipitate, is an example of a deprotonation reaction. For example, the reaction between hexaaquacopper(II) ions and methylamine produces a pale blue precipitate:

$$[Cu(H_2O)_6]^{2+}(aq) + 2CH_3NH_2(aq) \rightarrow [Cu(H_2O)_4(OH)_2](s) + 2CH_3NH_3{}^+(aq)$$

With excess methylamine solution, the soluble complex ion is formed:

$$[Cu(H_2O)_4(OH)_2](s) + 4CH_3NH_2(aq) \rightarrow$$
$$[Cu(NH_2CH_3)_4(H_2O)_2]^{2+}(aq) + 2OH^-(aq) + 2H_2O(l)$$

This complex is deep blue.

The equivalent equations with ammonia are:

$$[Cu(H_2O)_6]^{2+}(aq) + 2NH_3(aq) \rightarrow [Cu(H_2O)_4(OH)_2](s) + 2NH_4{}^+(aq)$$
$$[Cu(H_2O)_4(OH)_2](s) + 4NH_3(aq) \rightarrow$$
$$[Cu(NH_3)_4(H_2O)_2]^{2+}(aq) + 2OH^-(aq) + 2H_2O(l)$$

e Ammonia reacts with acid chlorides to give amides (p. 138).

Natural products containing the amine group

The bases in DNA and RNA contain a nitrogen atom with a lone pair of electrons. Each base is attached to a carbohydrate (deoxyribose in DNA) in the carbohydrate-phosphate chain and forms hydrogen bonds with a particular base in the opposite DNA strand. Adenine (A) always forms hydrogen bonds with thymine (T); guanine (G) always forms hydrogen bonds with cytosine (C). Therefore, if one DNA strand in the double helix has the base order ATGGAC, the opposite strand will have the order TACCTG. Hydrogen bonds between strands are shown in red in Figures 8.1 and 8.2. The bond that attaches the base to the carbohydrate is shown in green.

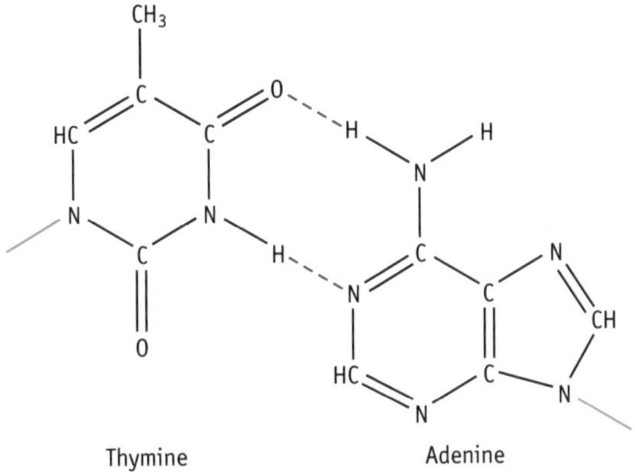

Thymine   Adenine

Figure 8.1 *The base pair thymine and adenine in DNA*

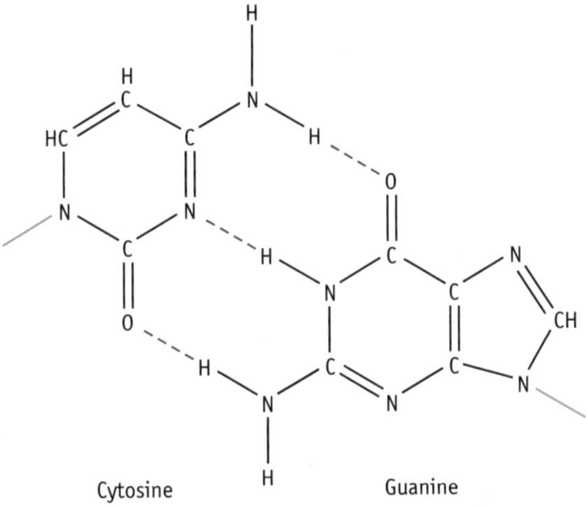

Cytosine   Guanine

Figure 8.2 *The base pair cytosine and guanine in DNA*

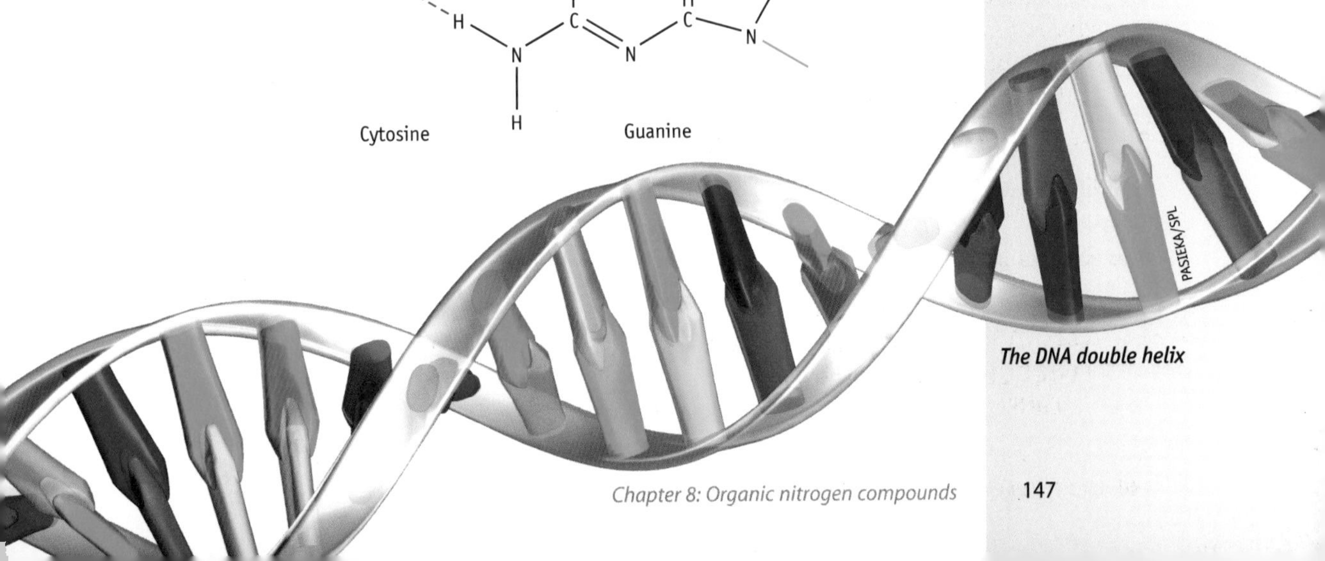

The DNA double helix

PASTEKA/SPL

In RNA, uracil replaces thymine and is found hydrogen-bonded to adenine. Thymine has a CH_3 group on one of the doubly bonded carbon atoms whereas uracil has a hydrogen atom.

The hormone adrenaline is a secondary amine:

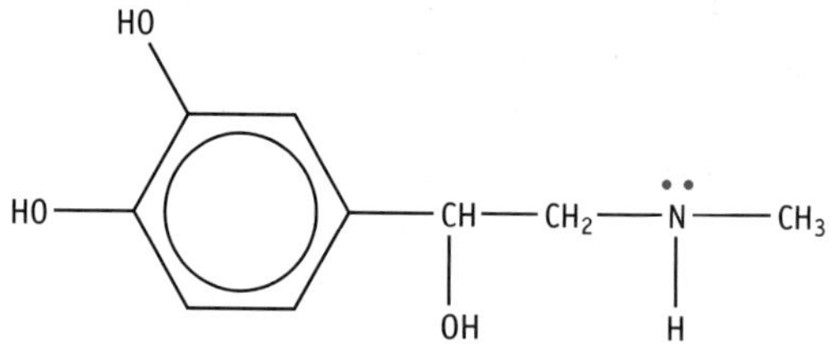

Other organic bases that contain an amine group include:
- the alkaloid poison, strychnine
- the painkillers, morphine and codeine
- the stimulants, caffeine and nicotine

Amino acids

Amino acid molecules contain at least one $-NH_2$ group and one $-COOH$ group. Those amino acids that are the building blocks of proteins have the $-NH_2$ group attached to the carbon atom next to the $-COOH$ group. These are called α-amino acids. The simplest is aminoethanoic acid (glycine), NH_2CH_2COOH.

Amino acids have the general formula:

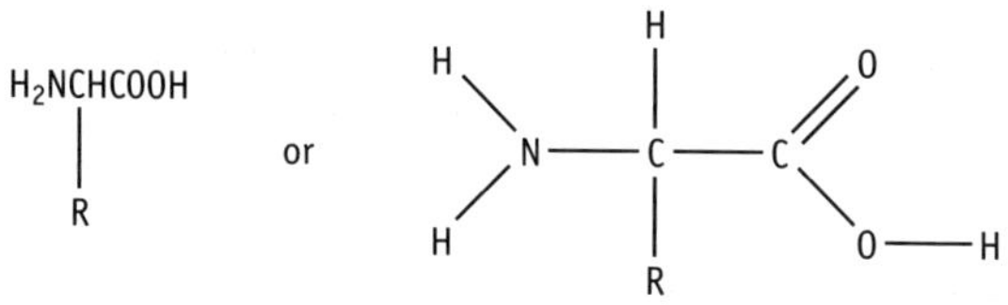

where R is either a hydrogen atom or an organic residue.

There are 20 amino acids that make up the proteins in the human body. Of these, twelve can be synthesised from other amino acids, but eight cannot. The latter are called **essential amino acids** and must be present in the diet. Two examples are valine and lysine.

Amino acids can be divided into three types:
- **neutral amino acids** — a molecule of a neutral amino acid contains only one basic $-NH_2$ group and one acidic $-COOH$ group
- **acidic amino acids** — a molecule of an acidic amino acid contains two $-COOH$ groups and one $-NH_2$ group
- **basic amino acids** — a molecule of a basic amino acid contains two $-NH_2$ groups and one $-COOH$ group

The salt of glutamic acid in which one hydrogen atom has been replaced by sodium is monosodium glutamate, the flavour enhancer added to some foods.

Table 8.2 Some amino acids

Type	Common name	Systematic name	Formula
Neutral	Glycine	Aminoethanoic acid	$CH_2(NH_2)COOH$
Neutral	Alanine	2-aminopropanoic acid	$CH_3CH(NH_2)COOH$
Neutral	Valine	2-amino-3-methylbutanoic acid	$(CH_3)_2CHCH(NH_2)COOH$
Neutral	Leucine	2-amino-4-methylpentanoic acid	$(CH_3)_2CHCH_2CH(NH_2)COOH$
Acidic	Cysteine	2-amino-3-sulphanylpropanoic acid	$HSCH_2CH(NH_2)COOH$
Acidic	Aspartic acid	2-aminobutane-1,4-dioic acid	$HOOCCH_2CH(NH_2)COOH$
Acidic	Glutamic acid	2-aminopentane-1,5-dioic acid	$HOOC(CH_2)_2CH(NH_2)COOH$
Basic	Lysine	2,6-diaminohexanoic acid	$NH_2CH_2CH_2CH_2CH_2CH(NH_2)COOH$

Physical properties

Amino acids are solids at room temperature. This is because the molecules form **zwitterions**. The –COOH group in one molecule protonates the –NH$_2$ group in another molecule, forming a species which has a positive charge at one end and a negative charge at the other. The positive charge on one zwitterion is strongly attracted to the negative charge of an *adjacent* zwitterion. The –COOH group is weakly acidic and the NH$_2$ group is weakly basic, so the formation of the zwitterion is reversible. Therefore, both the zwitterion and the neutral molecule are present. This can be represented for aminoethanoic acid (glycine) by the equation:

$$NH_2CH_2COOH \rightleftharpoons {}^+NH_3CH_2COO^-$$

where $^+NH_3CH_2COO^-$ is the zwitterion.

> **e** It is common practice to write the formula of an amino acid as an uncharged molecule, rather than as the zwitterion. However, it should be remembered that the position of this equilibrium is well to the right. Equations for reactions of amino acids should have the zwitterion on the left. However, an equation with the molecular species on the left will score full marks at A-level.

The full structural formula of the zwitterion of glycine is:

Chemical reactions

The two most important are the reactions of amino acids with acids and with bases.

Reaction with acids

The COO$^-$ group in the zwitterion acts as a base and accepts an H$^+$ ion from the acid:

$$^+NH_3CH_2COO^- + H^+ \rightarrow {}^+NH_3CH_2COOH$$

The name 'zwitterion' is derived from the German for the word 'mongrel', which is the offspring of two different breeds of dog. In the chemical sense, it is the mongrel of a cation and an anion.

This reaction can also be written with the uncharged molecule as the starting species:

$$NH_2CH_2COOH + H^+ \rightarrow {}^+NH_3CH_2COOH$$

The basic $-NH_2$ group reacts with the H^+ ions in a strong acid.

Reaction with bases

The NH_3^+ group in the zwitterion acts as an acid and protonates the base:

$$^+NH_3CH_2COO^- + OH^- \rightarrow NH_2CH_2COO^- + H_2O$$

The $-NH_3^+$ group, which is the conjugate acid of the weakly basic $-NH_2$ group, gives a proton to the OH^- ion.

The alternative equation shows the acidic $-COOH$ group in the uncharged molecule protonating hydroxide ions:

$$NH_2CH_2COOH + OH^- \rightarrow NH_2CH_2COO^- + H_2O$$

Other reactions as an acid

Amino acids have $-COO^-$ groups, rather than $-COOH$, because they exist mainly as zwitterions. This means that they do not undergo reactions of the $-OH$ group, unless the reaction is carried out in the presence of an acid. In this case the $-COO^-$ group becomes protonated, forming a $-COOH$ group. Thus amino acids can be esterified in the presence of concentrated sulphuric acid.

Other reactions as an amine

Amino acids have $-NH_3^+$ groups, rather than $-NH_2$ groups, because of the presence of zwitterions. This means that an amino acid molecule does not have a lone pair of electrons on the nitrogen atom and so will not act as a nucleophile, unless the pH of the reaction mixture is significantly above 7.

Stereoisomerism

All the natural amino acids, except glycine, are optically active. The carbon atom next to the $-COOH$ is a chiral centre because it has four different groups attached to it. Alanine (2-aminopropanoic acid) has two optical isomers (Figure 8.3). The isomers can be written as zwitterions or as uncharged molecules. The latter is more common, especially in biochemistry.

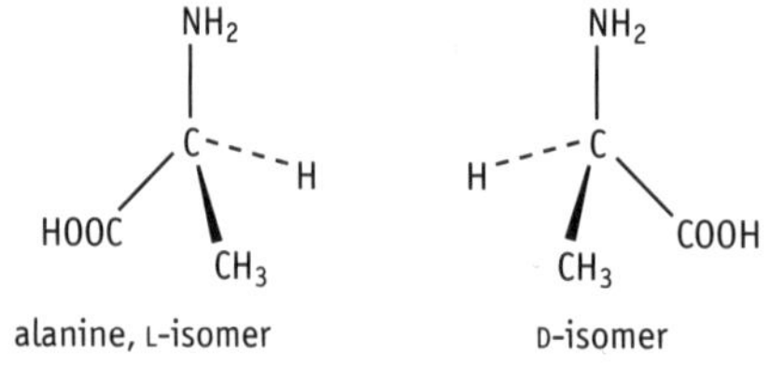

alanine, L-isomer   D-isomer

Alanine, which occurs in proteins, is only one of the two optical isomers shown in Figure 8.3. Alanine rotates the plane of polarisation of plane-polarised light clockwise.

Glycine (aminoethanoic acid, NH_2CH_2COOH) is optically inactive because it does not have a chiral centre. The carbon atom next to the $-COOH$ group has two hydrogen atoms bonded to it, so it cannot be chiral. Therefore, a solution of glycine has no effect on the plane of polarisation of plane-polarised light.

Figure 8.3 The two optical isomers of 2-aminopropanoic acid

> **e** A base is a species that accepts a proton. An acid is a species that protonates a base.

> **e** Almost all the amino acids in proteins have the same absolute configuration in space. This is the L-configuration, as shown in the diagram of alanine (Figure 8.3).

Proteins

Proteins consist of a number of amino acids joined together by peptide links.

If two amino acids join together, the product is called a **dipeptide**. The artificial sweetener aspartame is a dipeptide formed from phenylalanine and aspartic acid:

$$H_2N \underset{\overset{|}{\underset{\overset{|}{C_6H_5}}{CH_2}}}{-CH-} COOH \quad + \quad H_2N \underset{\overset{|}{\underset{\overset{|}{COOH}}{CH_2}}}{-CH-} COOH$$

$$H_2N \underset{\overset{|}{\underset{\overset{|}{C_6H_5}}{CH_2}}}{-CH-} \underset{\overset{||}{O}}{C} - \underset{\overset{|}{H}}{N} - \underset{\overset{|}{\underset{\overset{|}{COOH}}{CH_2}}}{CH-} COOH \quad + \quad H_2O$$

The peptide link is shown in red.

An amino acid in a peptide chain is called a **residue**. Thus, aspartame has the residues of phenylalanine and aspartic acid.

Natural proteins are **polypeptides**. Bovine insulin has 51 amino acids in one specific sequence. The number of different ways of arranging these 51 amino acids is about the same as there are atoms in the whole of the Milky Way galaxy, but only one way produces insulin.

It is remarkable that so few mutations occur to produce rogue polypeptides. However, sickle cell anaemia is a hereditary disease that results when two glutamic acid molecules (one in each β-polypeptide sequence in haemoglobin) are replaced by valine molecules. The resulting haemoglobin molecule is a much poorer oxygen carrier, which tends to shorten the life of the sufferer. However, this mutation does provide protection against malaria, and the gene is passed on from generation to generation in regions where malaria is endemic.

e The structural formula of an amino acid can also be written as $NH_2CHRCOOH$, where R is a hydrogen atom (in glycine) or an organic group.

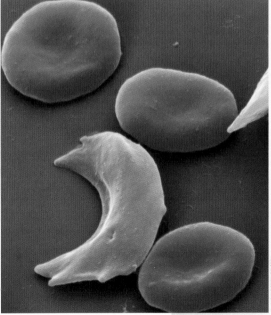

False-colour scanning electron micrograph of normal red blood cells (rounded) and sickle cells (crescent-shaped)

EYE OF SCIENCE/SPL

Structure of proteins

The **primary structure** is the order of the amino acids in the chain. This is specific to the protein. However, the peptide chains are not randomly arranged like a pile of spaghetti. They are organised into a **secondary structure**, of which there are two types:

- **α-helix** — the peptide is coiled in a spiral and the structure held together by *intramolecular* hydrogen bonds between a $>C=O$ group in one part of the chain and an $>NH$ group four residues away along the chain. There are also ionic bonds between the residues of basic and acidic amino acids. Myoglobin is an example of a protein with an α-helical structure.
- **β-pleated sheet** — the polypeptide chains are almost fully extended and are held by hydrogen bonds to other polypeptide chains. The result is rather like a stack of corrugated cardboard. Silk has this structure. A thread of silk is strong because of the many intermolecular hydrogen bonds between its polypeptide chains.

e Nylon is a polyamide in which all the pairs of residues are identical. Its secondary structure is a β-pleated sheet, which is why nylon is so strong.

Nitriles

Nitriles contain the $-C\equiv N$ group. They used to be called cyanides. However, unlike ionic cyanides such as KCN, they are not poisonous.

The names of nitriles depend on the longest carbon chain, including the carbon of the $-CN$ group. Therefore, CH_3CN is ethanenitrile and CH_3CH_2CN is propanenitrile.

Some nitriles contain another group as well as $-CN$. The product of the reaction of HCN with a carbonyl compound propanone — 2-hydroxy-2-methylpropanenitrile — is an example of this type of compound:

This is a nucleophilic addition reaction.

Preparation

Simple nitriles

Simple nitriles are prepared by the reaction between a halogenoalkane and potassium cyanide. For example, the product of the reaction between bromoethane and potassium cyanide is propanenitrile:

$$C_2H_5Br + KCN \rightarrow C_2H_5CN + KBr$$

This is a nucleophilic substitution reaction. The halogenoalkane and potassium cyanide are heated under reflux in a solution of ethanol and water.

Simple nitriles can also be prepared by the dehydration of an amide with phosphorus(V) oxide, P_4O_{10}:

$$CH_3CONH_2 - H_2O \rightarrow CH_3CN$$

Hydroxynitriles

Hydroxynitriles are made by the nucleophilic addition of HCN to an aldehyde or ketone, for example:

$$CH_3CHO + HCN \rightarrow CH_3CH(OH)CN$$

The pH of the solution must be maintained at about 8 so that there is a significant amount of CN^- for the first step of the addition, and enough HCN for the second step (p. 116). The conditions are either to add hydrogen cyanide, HCN, plus some base or to use a mixture of hydrogen cyanide and potassium cyanide.

Chemical reactions

Nitriles are not very reactive.

Hydrolysis with acid

Nitriles are hydrolysed by boiling under reflux with aqueous strong acid, such as dilute sulphuric acid. The reaction proceeds via the amide but cannot be stopped at that point because the amide is hydrolysed as soon as it is produced:

$$CH_3CN + H_2O \xrightarrow{H^+(aq)} CH_3CONH_2$$

$$CH_3CONH_2 + H_2O \xrightarrow{H^+(aq)} CH_3COOH + NH_4^+$$

The products are the carboxylic acid and ammonium ions, and the overall equation is :

$$CH_3CN + 2H_2O + H^+ \rightarrow CH_3COOH + NH_4^+$$

Hydrolysis with alkali

Nitriles are hydrolysed by heating under reflux with aqueous alkali, such as sodium hydroxide solution. The products in this hydrolysis are the salt of a carboxylic acid and ammonia, for example:

$$CH_3CN + NaOH + H_2O \rightarrow CH_3COONa + NH_3$$

As with acid hydrolysis, the reaction goes via the amide. If the amide is required as the product, the reaction is carried out using an alkaline solution of hydrogen peroxide at 40°C. The alkali is the hydrolysing reagent and the reaction is catalysed by the hydrogen peroxide, which does not catalyse the further hydrolysis of the amide:

$$CH_3CN + H_2O \rightarrow CH_3CONH_2$$

To prevent hydrolysis of the amide, the temperature must not be allowed to go above 45°C.

Reduction

Nitriles can be reduced to primary amines. This is achieved using lithium tetra-hydridoaluminate(III) in dry ether (ethoxyethane), followed by hydrolysis of the adduct with aqueous acid:

$$CH_3CN + 4[H] \rightarrow CH_3CH_2NH_2$$

The attack on the δ^+ carbon atom of the $C{\equiv}N$ group is by H^- from the AlH_4^- ion.

Questions

1 Name the reagents and conditions for the two-step preparation of ethylamine from ethene.

2 $C_4H_{11}N$ has several structural isomers. Write the structural formula of the isomer of $C_4H_{11}N$ that is:

  a a primary amine with a branched chain

  b a symmetrical secondary amine with a straight chain

  c a secondary amine with a branched chain

  d a tertiary amine

3 Give the H–N–H bond angle in methylamine. Justify your answer.

4 Give the N–C–C bond angle in ethanamide. Justify your answer.

5 Explain why ethylamine is soluble in water but chloroethane and ethane are both insoluble.

6 Explain why ethanoic acid, CH_3COOH, has a higher boiling point than 1-propylamine, $CH_3CH_2CH_2NH_2$, and why both these compounds have a higher boiling point than butane, $CH_3CH_2CH_2CH_3$.

7 Outline how the following compounds can be prepared from ethanoic acid by a three-step synthesis:

  a CH_3NH_2

  b $CH_3CH_2NH_2$

8 An organic compound contains 39.3% carbon, 11.5% hydrogen, 26.2% oxygen and 23.0% nitrogen by mass.

  a Calculate its empirical formula.

  b The molecular formula of this compound is the same as its empirical formula. It reacts with phosphorus pentachloride, giving off misty fumes. Suggest a structural formula for this compound.

9 Write equations for the reaction of 2-amino-ethanol, $NH_2CH_2CH_2OH$ with:

  a dilute hydrochloric acid

  b ethanoyl chloride

  c iodomethane

10 Explain why methylamine is a stronger base than ammonia.

11 Explain why aminoethanoic acid is a solid at room temperature and is soluble in water.

12 The formula of all naturally occurring amino acids can be written as $NH_2CHRCOOH$.

  a Rewrite this formula as the zwitterion.

  b Write an equation for the reaction of the zwitterion with aqueous acid.

  c Write an equation for the reaction of the zwitterion with aqueous alkali.

13 Suggest the formula of the organic product of the reactions, if any, of aminoethanoic acid with:

  a dilute hydrochloric acid

  b phosphorus pentachloride

  c ethanol and a few drops of concentrated sulphuric acid

  d ethanoyl chloride

  e lithium tetrahydridoaluminate(III) in dry ether (ethoxyethane) followed by aqueous acid

  f aqueous potassium hydroxide

14 Draw the two optical isomers of aminobutane-1,4-dioic acid. Identify which of the two is aspartic acid.

15 Name two essential amino acids.

16 Write a structure of the dipeptide formed from aminoethanoic acid and 2-aminopropanoic acid.

17 Outline the preparation of 2-hydroxypropanoic acid from ethanal.

18 State the reagents and the conditions for the preparation of ethylamine from ethanenitrile.

19 Outline how propanenitrile can be prepared from ethanol.

20 Identify the products of the reaction of butanenitrile with aqueous sodium hydroxide solution.

21 RNA contains the base uracil:

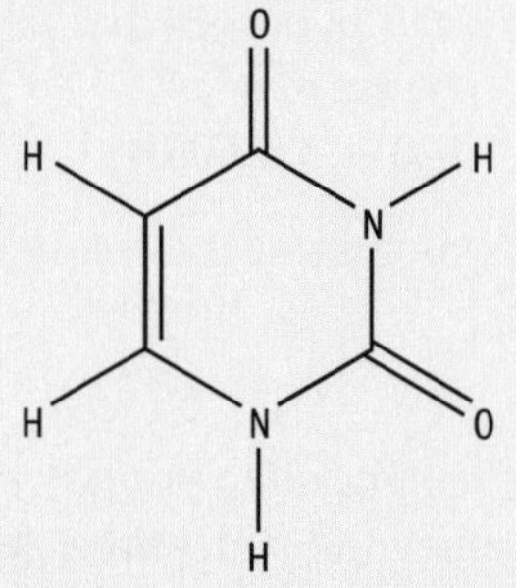

Draw a diagram of a uracil molecule in one strand of mRNA when hydrogen-bonded to an adenine molecule in a strand of DNA (see p. 147).

The information needed for questions 22–25 is not found in this textbook. You are advised to do your own research to find answers to these questions. Possible sources are the internet, biology textbooks and other students who are studying biochemistry.

22 Explain the link between a DNA molecule, an mRNA molecule and the polypeptide formed. What is the sequence of bases needed to put a leucine residue in a polypeptide?

23 Use the internet to find out about Chargaff's rule.

24 Write brief notes on the discoveries about DNA structure made by Wilkins and Franklin in London and Crick and Watson in Cambridge.

25 Write short notes on DNA fingerprinting.

Practice Unit Test 4

Time allowed: 1 hour 30 minutes

(1) (a) Write the equation for the reaction of calcium metal with:
    (i) water *(1 line)*   (1 mark)
    (ii) oxygen *(1 line)*   (1 mark)
  (b) The solubility of substances can be compared by using the values of their lattice energies and enthalpies of hydration. The lattice energy of barium sulphate is 253 kJ mol^{-1} less exothermic than that of calcium sulphate. The hydration enthalpy of $Ba^{2+}(g)$ is 290 kJ mol^{-1} less exothermic than that of $Ca^{2+}(g)$.
    (i) Define the term lattice energy. *(3 lines)*   (2 marks)
    (ii) Explain why the lattice energy of barium sulphate is less exothermic than the lattice energy of calcium sulphate. *(3 lines)*   (2 marks)
    (iii) Draw a labelled Hess's law cycle connecting the lattice energy of barium sulphate with its enthalpy of solution and the hydration energies of its ions. *(space)*   (2 marks)
    (iv) Use the differences in the lattice energies and hydration enthalpies to explain the difference in solubility of barium sulphate and calcium sulphate. *(4 lines)*   (2 marks)
                                                                   Total: 10 marks

(2) (a) Consider the following reaction scheme for producing propanoic acid from ethanal:

$$CH_3CHO \xrightarrow{\text{step 1}} CH_3CH_2OH \xrightarrow{\text{H}_2\text{SO}_4/\text{KBr}} CH_3CH_2Br \xrightarrow{\text{step 3}} CH_3CH_2MgBr \xrightarrow{\text{step 4}} CH_3CH_2COOH$$

Ethanal   Propanoic acid

Give the reagents and conditions for:
  (i) step 1 *(2 lines)*   (2 marks)
  (ii) step 3 *(2 lines)*   (2 marks)
  (iii) step 4 *(2 lines)*   (2 marks)
  (b) If hot propanoic acid is reacted with chlorine gas in the presence of ultraviolet light, 2-chloropropanoic acid, $CH_3CHClCOOH$, is produced.
    (i) Draw the two isomers of 2-chloropropanoic acid formed by this reaction. *(space)* (2 marks)
    (ii) 2-chloropropanoic acid can be converted to 2-aminopropanoic acid. Explain why this substance melts at a much higher temperature than 2-chloropropanoic acid. *(5 lines)*   (3 marks)
                                                                   Total: 11 marks

(3) (a) A compound, X, has the molecular formula C_4H_8O.
    (i) It reacts with a solution of 2,4-dinitrophenylhydrazine to form a yellow precipitate. What conclusion can be drawn from this? *(2 lines)*   (1 mark)
    (ii) When X is warmed with Fehling's solution, the blue colour remains. What conclusion can be drawn from this? *(2 lines)*   (1 mark)
    (iii) Write the structural formula of X. *(space)*   (1 mark)
    (iv) Write the equation for the reaction of X with 2,4-dinitrophenylhydrazine. *(1 line)* (2 marks)
  (b) A compound, Y, has the following percentage composition by mass:
Element % by mass: carbon 31.0%; hydrogen 2.6%; oxygen 20.6%; chlorine 45.8%

    (i) Use these data to calculate its empirical formula. *(space)*   (2 marks)

    (ii) The molar mass of compound Y is 155 g mol^{-1}. Calculate its molecular formula. Show your working. *(space)*   (2 marks)

    (iii) Compound Y reacts with ammonia, NH_3, to form a compound Z (molecular formula $C_4H_8O_2N_2$) and clouds of misty fumes of hydrogen chloride. Write the structural formula of $C_4H_8O_2N_2$. *(space)*   (2 marks)

(c) When 1,4-diaminobutane, $NH_2(CH_2)_4NH_2$, and butane-1,4-dioyl dichloride, $ClOC(CH_2)_2COCl$, are mixed, a condensation polymerisation reaction takes place.

    (i) Explain the meaning of the term condensation polymerisation. *(2 lines)*   (2 marks)

    (ii) Write the structure of the repeat unit of the polymer produced. *(space)*   (2 marks)

                                               Total: 15 marks

(4) Hydrogen chloride is a by-product of many industrial organic reactions. It can be converted to chlorine by the reaction:

$$4HCl(g) + O_2(g) \rightleftharpoons 2Cl_2(g) + 2H_2O(g) \quad \Delta H_r = -115 \text{ kJ mol}^{-1}$$

When 4.0 mol of hydrogen chloride and 1.0 mol of oxygen were allowed to reach equilibrium under certain conditions, 75% of the hydrogen chloride and oxygen were found to have reacted. The final pressure was 2.0 atm.

(a) (i) Write the expression for the equilibrium constant, K_p. *(space)*   (1 mark)

    (ii) Define the term partial pressure. *(2 lines)*   (1 mark)

    (iii) Calculate the value of the equilibrium constant under these conditions. *(space)*   (5 marks)

(b) Explain what would happen to the value of the equilibrium constant and hence the position of equilibrium if the temperature were to be increased. *(3 lines)*   (2 marks)

                                               Total: 9 marks

(5) (a) Chlorine reacts with water, according to the equation:

$$Cl_2 + H_2O \rightleftharpoons HClO + HCl$$

Explain, in terms of oxidation numbers, why this is a disproportionation reaction. *(3 lines)*   (2 marks)

(b) Chloric(I) acid, HClO, is a *weak* acid.

    (i) Explain the meaning of the word *weak* in this context. *(2 lines)*   (1 mark)

    (ii) A 0.10 mol dm^{-3} solution of chloric(I) acid has a pH of 4.22. Calculate the value of the acid dissociation constant, K_a, for chloric(I) acid. *(space)*   (3 marks)

(c) A buffer solution is made when 50 cm^3 of 0.10 mol dm^{-3} chloric(I) acid solution is mixed with 50 cm^3 of a 0.20 mol dm^{-3} solution of sodium chlorate(I), NaClO.

    (i) Calculate the pH of this buffer solution. *(space)*   (3 marks)

    (ii) Explain why the pH of this solution hardly alters when a small amount of hydroxide ions is added. *(5 lines)*   (4 marks)

(d) Explain why the enthalpy of neutralisation of chloric(I) acid by sodium hydroxide is less exothermic than the enthalpy of neutralisation of hydrochloric acid. *(3 lines)*   (2 marks)

                                               Total: 15 marks

(6) (a) Write the equation for the reactions of an aqueous acid, such as HCl(aq), and an aqueous alkali, such as NaOH(aq), with the following compounds that contain elements in period 3. If there is no reaction, state that fact.

    (i) sodium oxide, Na_2O *(2 lines)*   (2 marks)

(ii) aluminium hydroxide, $Al(OH)_3$ *(2 lines)*   (2 marks)

(iii) phosphorus(V) oxide, P_4O_{10} *(2 lines)*   (2 marks)

What trend in properties of the elements in period 3 do these reactions show? *(2 lines)*   (1 mark)

(b) State the effect of water on the following chlorides:

  (i) sodium chloride, NaCl *(2 lines)*   (1 mark)

  (ii) anhydrous aluminium chloride, $AlCl_3$ *(2 lines)*   (1 mark)

  (iii) silicon tetrachloride, $SiCl_4$ *(2 lines)*   (1 mark)

Explain the differences in these reactions in terms of the bonding of the chlorides. *(2 lines)*   (1 mark)

(c) Explain why silicon tetrachloride reacts rapidly with water at room temperature, but carbon tetrachloride does not react. *(5 lines)*   (4 marks)

Total: 15 marks

Paper total: 75 marks

Unit 5

Transition metals, quantitative kinetics and applied organic chemistry

Electrochemistry and redox equilibria

Chapter 9

Introduction

This topic assumes knowledge of the redox chemistry covered in the AS course. There are some important concepts that must be revisited before embarking on the new A2 work.

The definitions of oxidation and reduction are:

> Oxidation is loss of electrons by an atom, ion or molecule.

> Reduction is gain of electrons by an atom, ion or molecule.

e OIL RIG — oxidation is loss; reduction is gain.

Oxidation numbers

Oxidation numbers can be worked out using a series of rules:

- The oxidation number of an uncombined element is zero.
- The oxidation number of the element in a monatomic ion is the charge on the ion.
- The sum of the oxidation numbers of the atoms in a neutral compound is zero.
- The sum of the oxidation numbers in a polyatomic ion equals the charge on the ion.
- All group 1 metals have an oxidation number of +1 in their compounds, and all group 2 metals have an oxidation number of +2 in their compounds.
- Fluorine always has the oxidation number −1 in its compounds.
- Hydrogen has the oxidation number +1 in its compounds, apart from when it is combined with a metal, when the oxidation number is −1.
- Oxygen has the oxidation number −2 in its compounds, apart from in peroxides and superoxides or when it is combined with fluorine.

Half-equations

Ionic half-equations always have electrons on either the left-hand side or the right-hand side.

When zinc is added to dilute hydrochloric acid, the hydrogen ions are reduced to hydrogen. The half-equation is:

$$2H^+(aq) + 2e^- \rightleftharpoons H_2(g)$$

This is a reduction reaction, so the electrons are on the left-hand side of the half-equation.

The zinc atoms are oxidised to zinc ions:

$$Zn(s) \rightleftharpoons Zn^{2+}(aq) + 2e^-$$

This is oxidation, so the electrons are on the right-hand side of the equation.

e Half-equations must balance for charge as well as for numbers of atoms.

e State symbols must be used in half-equations.

Overall equations

When half-equations are combined to give the overall equation, the stoichiometry must be such that the numbers of electrons cancel. To do this, one or both half-equations must be multiplied by integers so that the number of electrons is the same in both. The two half-equations are then added together to get the overall equation.

The total change in oxidation number of the species being oxidised is equal to the total change in oxidation number of the species being reduced.

> *Worked example*
> **a** Write the half-equation for the oxidation of Sn^{2+} ions to Sn^{4+} ions in aqueous solution.
> **b** Write the half-equation for the reduction of MnO_4^- ions to Mn^{2+} ions in aqueous acidic solution.
> **c** Hence, write the overall equation for the oxidation of tin(II) ions by manganate(VII) ions in aqueous acidic solution.
>
> **Answer**
> **a** This is oxidation, so the electrons are on the right-hand side of the half-equation. The oxidation number of tin changes by 2, so there are two electrons in the half-equation:
> $$Sn^{2+}(aq) \rightarrow Sn^{4+}(aq) + 2e^-$$
> **b** This is reduction, so the electrons are on the left-hand side. Five electrons are needed because the oxidation number of manganese changes by 5 (from +7 to +2):
> $$MnO_4^-(aq) + 8H^+(aq) + 5e^- \rightarrow Mn^{2+}(aq) + 4H_2O(l)$$
> **c** Multiply the first equation by 5 and the second equation by 2 to obtain the same number of electrons in each equation. Then add the two equations and cancel the electrons. The overall equation is:
> $$5Sn^{2+}(aq) + 2MnO_4^-(aq) + 16H^+(aq) \rightarrow 5Sn^{4+}(aq) + 2Mn^{2+}(aq) + 8H_2O(l)$$

ⓔ You should make sure that both reactants are on the left-hand side of the overall equation.

ⓔ Tin changes oxidation number by $5 \times 2 = 10$ and manganese changes oxidation number by $2 \times 5 = 10$ as well.

Redox as electron transfer

When a piece of zinc is placed in a solution of copper(II) sulphate, a reaction takes place in which the zinc is oxidised to zinc ions and the copper ions are reduced to copper metal.

The two half-equations are:
$$Zn(s) \rightleftharpoons Zn^{2+}(aq) + 2e^-$$
$$Cu^{2+}(aq) + 2e^- \rightleftharpoons Cu(s)$$

In the reaction shown in the photograph, the copper ions collide with zinc atoms in the surface of the metal and remove two electrons from each zinc atom. However, this reaction can also occur without the copper ions and the zinc atoms coming into contact.

Reaction between zinc and copper(II) sulphate

MEGNA/FUNDAMENTAL PHOTOS/SPL

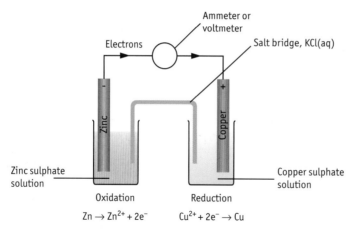

Figure 9.1
An electrochemical cell of Zn/Zn²⁺ and Cu/Cu²⁺

The zinc rod is in equilibrium with the solution of zinc ions:

$$Zn(s) \rightleftharpoons Zn^{2+}(aq) + 2e^-$$

The position of equilibrium is to the right-hand side, so electrons are produced making the zinc rod negatively charged relative to the solution.

Oxidation takes place at the zinc rod, which is called the anode.

The copper ions are in equilibrium with the copper rod:

$$Cu^{2+}(aq) + 2e^- \rightleftharpoons Cu(s)$$

The copper rod has given some of its delocalised electrons to the copper ions, so the rod becomes positively charged relative to the solution.

Reduction (of copper ions) takes place at the copper rod, which is called the cathode.

This sets up a **potential difference** (emf) between the two metal rods. A current will flow when the rods are connected by a wire and the solutions are connected by a **salt bridge**, which contains a concentrated solution of an inert electrolyte, such as potassium chloride or potassium nitrate. The current is carried in the salt bridge by the movement of the ions. The anions (Cl⁻ or NO_3^-) move towards the anode and the cations (K⁺) move towards the cathode. The current is carried in the wire by the flow of electrons from the zinc rod to the copper rod.

The convention for diagrams such as that in Figure 9.1 is to put the electrode at which oxidation is taking place on the left.

Cell diagrams

The representation of all the parts of a cell in Figure 9.1 can be replaced by a cell diagram. There is a set convention for this:

- A single vertical line is used to show where there is a phase boundary, for example between Zn(s) and Zn^{2+}(aq).
- The anode compartment is written on the left-hand side and the cathode compartment on the right-hand side.
- Oxidation takes place at the anode. Therefore, the formula of the reactant being oxidised is written first, then the formula of its oxidised form.

e Oxidation and anode begin with a vowel.

e Reduction and cathode begin with a consonant.

e The ions in the salt bridge must *not* react with the ions in the cells.

e Note that the reactants are written first in each cell compartment. In the worked example, the reactants are Zn(s) and Cu^{2+}(aq).

- The salt bridge is represented by two short vertical lines.
- Reduction takes place at the cathode Therefore, the formula of the reagent being reduced is written first, then the formula of its reduced form.
- State symbols are added to the formulae of all species.

Worked example

Write the cell diagram for a cell consisting of zinc in a solution of zinc ions connected via a salt bridge to a copper rod dipping into a solution of copper(II) ions.

Answer

Zinc reduces copper ions to copper and is itself oxidised to Zn^{2+} ions. The anode is the Zn/Zn^{2+} system where oxidation of zinc takes place. Zn is the reduced form and Zn^{2+} is the oxidised form. Cu^{2+} is the oxidised form and Cu the reduced form. The cell diagram is:

$Zn(s) \mid Zn^{2+}(aq) \parallel Cu^{2+}(aq) \mid Cu(s)$

---

e The reactants are on the left of each pair in the two cells and the products on the right of each pair. In this example, zinc reacts to form zinc ions and copper ions react to form copper.

If a platinum electrode has to be used, its formula is written at the beginning of the anode compartment and at the end of the cathode compartment. It is separated from the formulae of the reactants by a single vertical line.

Worked example

Write a cell diagram to represent the oxidation of iodide ions by manganate(VII) ions in acid solution.

The reduction half-equations are:

$MnO_4^-(aq) + 8H^+(aq) + 5e^- \rightleftharpoons Mn^{2+}(aq) + 4H_2O(l)$
$I_2(s) + 2e^- \rightleftharpoons 2I^-(aq)$

Answer

A platinum electrode has to be used in both compartments as an electrical conductor. The reactants are MnO_4^-, H^+ and I^-, so they are on the left in each electrode compartment. The cell diagram is:

$Pt \mid \{MnO_4^-(aq), H^+(aq)\}, \{Mn^{2+}(aq), H_2O(l)\} \parallel I^-(aq) \mid I_2(s) \mid Pt$

---

e All the species in the half-equations must appear in the cell diagram. If there are several species on either side of the half-equation, they are separated by a comma in the cell diagram, with the oxidised form next to the electrode.

Electrode potentials

Standard electrode potential, $E^{\ominus}$

Standard electrode potential is also called the standard *reduction* potential, because the equation is normally written as a reduction half-equation with the electrons on the left.

A zinc rod dipped into a solution of zinc ions generates a potential relative to the solution. However, this cannot be measured. To avoid this problem, electrode potentials are measured against another electrode. By convention, the standard electrode potential of hydrogen is defined as zero.

The term *standard* means that:
- All solutions are at a concentration of 1.0 mol dm^{-3}.
- All gases are at a pressure of 1.0 atm.
- The system is at a stated temperature, usually 298 K (25°C).

For zinc, the standard reduction potential is for a piece of zinc dipping into a 1.0 mol dm^{-3} solution of zinc ions. It is written either as:

$$Zn^{2+}(aq) + 2e^- \rightleftharpoons Zn(s) \quad E^\circ = -0.76 \text{ V}$$

or as:

$$Zn^{2+}(aq)/Zn(s) \quad E^\circ = -0.76 \text{ V}$$

◀ The oxidised form of the couple is written on the left, followed by a slash and then the reduced form.

If the substance is a gas, such as hydrogen or chlorine, the electrode consists of a platinum plate dipping into a 1.0 mol dm^{-3} solution of ions of the element with the gaseous element, at 1.0 atm pressure, bubbling over the surface of the platinum.

Types of electrode

Standard hydrogen electrode (SHE)

A **standard hydrogen electrode** consists of hydrogen gas at 1.0 atm pressure bubbling over a platinum plate which is dipping into a solution that is 1.0 mol dm^{-3} in H$^+$ ions (such as 1.0 mol dm^{-3} HCl), at a temperature of 298 K.

$$H^+(aq) + e^- \rightleftharpoons \tfrac{1}{2}H_2(g) \quad E^\circ = 0 \text{ V}$$

or

$$H^+(aq)/H_2(g), \text{Pt} \quad E^\circ = 0 \text{ V}$$

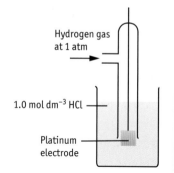

Figure 9.2 A standard hydrogen electrode

Hydrogen gas at 1 atm

1.0 mol dm^{-3} HCl

Platinum electrode

Calomel electrode

A standard hydrogen electrode is not easy to use, so a secondary standard is normally used as the reference electrode. This is a **calomel electrode**, which consists of mercury in contact with a saturated solution of mercury(I) chloride. This has a reduction potential of +0.27 V.

For a Zn/Zn^{2+} electrode joined to a calomel electrode:

$$E_{cell} = E(\text{calomel}) - E^\circ(Zn^{2+}/Zn)$$

where $E^\circ(Zn^{2+}/Zn)$ is the standard *reduction* potential of zinc ions to zinc and $E_{cell} = 1.03$ V.

$$E^\circ(Zn^{2+}/Zn) = E(\text{calomel}) - E_{cell} = +0.27 - 1.03 = -0.76 \text{ V}$$

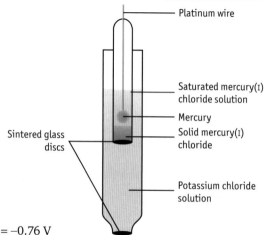

Figure 9.3 A calomel electrode

Platinum wire

Saturated mercury(I) chloride solution

Mercury

Solid mercury(I) chloride

Sintered glass discs

Potassium chloride solution

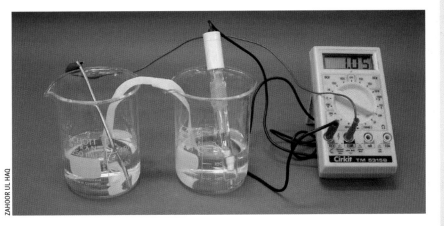

ZAHOOR UL HAQ

Glass electrode

A pH meter utilises a half-cell that is based on the reduction of hydrogen ions:

$$H^+(aq) + e^- \rightleftharpoons \tfrac{1}{2}H_2(g)$$

which is linked to a reference electrode, such as a calomel electrode.

The potential of the H^+/H_2 half-cell depends on the concentration of H^+ ions. This means that the voltage produced is a measure of $[H^+]$ and therefore of the pH of the solution. The hydrogen half-cell, which acts as an H^+/H_2 system, is called a **glass electrode**

Measurement of electrode potentials

Standard electrode potential of a metal

The standard electrode potential of a metal is measured using the system illustrated in Figure 9.4.

CHARLES D. WINTERS/SPL

Using a pH meter to measure the pH of methanoic acid

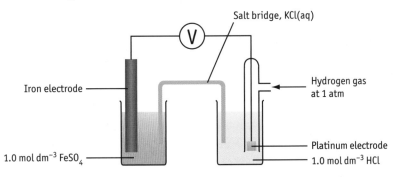

Salt bridge, KCl(aq)

Iron electrode

Hydrogen gas at 1 atm

Platinum electrode

1.0 mol dm^{-3} FeSO$_4$

1.0 mol dm^{-3} HCl

Figure 9.4
Measurement of the standard electrode potential of iron

The metal is dipping into a 1.0 mol dm^{-3} solution of its ions with a salt bridge to a standard hydrogen electrode, SHE, or a calomel electrode. The two are connected externally by a high-resistance voltmeter or a potentiometer. Using the apparatus shown in Figure 9.4, the voltmeter would read 0.44 V.

$$E_{cell} = E^{\ominus}(\text{standard hydrogen electrode}) - E^{\ominus}(Fe^{2+}(aq)/Fe(s))$$

So the standard electrode potential of iron is:

$$E^{\ominus}(Fe^{2+}(aq)/Fe(s)) = E^{\ominus}(SHE) - E_{cell} = 0 - (+0.44) = -0.44 \text{ V}$$

This information can be written as a half-equation:

$$Fe^{2+}(aq) + 2e^- \rightleftharpoons Fe(s) \quad E^{\ominus} = -0.44 \text{ V}$$

or as:

$$E^{\ominus}(Fe^{2+}(aq)/Fe(s)) = -0.44 \text{ V}$$

Copper and other metals below hydrogen in the electrochemical series have positive standard electrode potentials.

If a calomel electrode ($E = +0.27$ V) is used in place of a standard hydrogen electrode, the cell potential, E_{cell}, is +0.71 V.

The standard electrode potential is calculated as:

$$E^{\ominus}(Fe^{2+}(aq)/Fe(s)) = +0.27 \text{ V} - E_{cell} = +0.27 - (+0.71) = -0.44 \text{ V}$$

Standard electrode potential of a gas

If the standard electrode potential of a gas such as chlorine is required, the iron electrode compartment in Figure 9.4 is replaced by a compartment with a platinum plate dipping into a 1.0 mol dm^{-3} solution of sodium chloride, with chlorine gas, at 1.0 atm pressure, bubbling over the platinum.

$$\tfrac{1}{2}Cl_2(g) + e^- \rightleftharpoons Cl^-(aq) \quad E^{\ominus} = +1.36 \text{ V}$$

Standard electrode potential of an ion pair

Manganate(VII) is a powerful oxidising agent in acid solution. The half-equation is:

$$MnO_4^-(aq) + 8H^+(aq) + 5e^-$$
$$\rightleftharpoons Mn^{2+}(aq) + 4H_2O(l)$$

One electrode compartment is made of a piece of platinum dipping into a solution which is 1.00 mol dm^{-3} in MnO_4^-, H^+ and Mn^{2+} ions. This is connected to a standard hydrogen or calomel electrode, as in Figure 9.5.

$$MnO_4^-(aq), H^+(aq)/Mn^{2+}(aq), Pt \quad E^{\ominus} = +1.52 \text{ V}$$

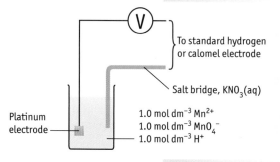

To standard hydrogen or calomel electrode

Salt bridge, $KNO_3(aq)$

Platinum electrode

1.0 mol dm^{-3} Mn^{2+}
1.0 mol dm^{-3} MnO_4^-
1.0 mol dm^{-3} H^+

Figure 9.5
Measurement of the standard electrode potential of MnO_4^-/Mn^{2+}

> **e** A potential can never be measured, only a potential difference. This is why the Fe^{2+}(aq)/Fe(s) cell is coupled to a standard hydrogen (or calomel) electrode.

Comparative values of $E^{\ominus}$

Standard electrode potentials can be listed either in alphabetical order or in numerical order. Alphabetical order has the advantage of easy use in a long list of data. Numerical order lists the electrode potentials with the most negative first, then in order of increasing value, finishing with the most positive. The numerical-order method means that the weakest oxidising agent is the left-hand species at the top of the list (Li$^+$(aq) in Table 9.1) and the strongest reducing agent is the right-hand species at the top of the list (Li(s) in Table 9.1). Similarly, the strongest oxidising agent is the left-hand species at the bottom of the list (F$_2$(g) in Table 9.1) and the weakest reducing agent is the right-hand species at the bottom of the list (F$^-$(aq) in Table 9.1).

Alphabetical list		Numerical list	
Electrode reaction	$E^\ominus$/V	**Electrode reaction**	$E^\ominus$/V
$Ag^+(aq) + e^- \rightleftharpoons Ag(s)$	+0.80	$Li^+(aq) + e^- \rightleftharpoons Li(s)$	−3.04
$Al^{3+}(aq) + 3e^- \rightleftharpoons Al(s)$	−1.66	$Ba^{2+}(aq) + 2e^- \rightleftharpoons Ba(s)$	−2.90
$Ba^{2+}(aq) + 2e^- \rightleftharpoons Ba(s)$	−2.90	$Ca^{2+}(aq) + 2e^- \rightleftharpoons Ca(s)$	−2.87
$\frac{1}{2}Br_2(l) + e^- \rightleftharpoons Br^-(aq)$	+1.07	$Al^{3+}(aq) + 3e^- \rightleftharpoons Al(s)$	−1.66
$Ca^{2+}(aq) + 2e^- \rightleftharpoons Ca(s)$	−2.87	$Zn^{2+}(aq) + 2e^- \rightleftharpoons Zn(s)$	−0.76
$\frac{1}{2}Cl_2(g) + e^- \rightleftharpoons Cl^-(aq)$	+1.36	$Fe^{2+}(aq) + 2e^- \rightleftharpoons Fe(s)$	−0.44
$HOCl(aq) + H^+(aq) + e^- \rightleftharpoons \frac{1}{2}Cl_2(g) + H_2O(l)$	+1.64	$Cr^{3+}(aq) + e^- \rightleftharpoons Cr^{2+}(aq)$	−0.41
$Cr^{3+}(aq) + e^- \rightleftharpoons Cr^{2+}(aq)$	−0.41	$Sn^{2+}(aq) + 2e^- \rightleftharpoons Sn(s)$	−0.14
$Cr_2O_7^{2-}(aq) + 14H^+(aq) + 6e^- \rightleftharpoons 2Cr^{3+}(aq) + 7H_2O(l)$	+1.33	$H^+(aq) + e^- \rightleftharpoons \frac{1}{2}H_2(g)$	0.00
$Cu^+(aq) + e^- \rightleftharpoons Cu(s)$	+0.52	$S(s) + 2H^+(aq) + 2e^- \rightleftharpoons H_2S(g)$	+0.14
$Cu^{2+}(aq) + 2e^- \rightleftharpoons Cu(s)$	+0.34	$Cu^{2+}(aq) + e^- \rightleftharpoons Cu^+(aq)$	+0.15
$Cu^{2+}(aq) + e^- \rightleftharpoons Cu^+(aq)$	+0.15	$Sn^{4+}(aq) + 2e^- \rightleftharpoons Sn^{2+}(aq)$	+0.15
$\frac{1}{2}F_2(g) + e^- \rightleftharpoons F^-(aq)$	+2.87	$Cu^{2+}(aq) + 2e^- \rightleftharpoons Cu(s)$	+0.34
$Fe^{2+}(aq) + 2e^- \rightleftharpoons Fe(s)$	−0.44	$Cu^+(aq) + e^- \rightleftharpoons Cu(s)$	+0.52
$Fe^{3+}(aq) + e^- \rightleftharpoons Fe^{2+}(aq)$	+0.77	$\frac{1}{2}I_2(s) + e^- \rightleftharpoons I^-(aq)$	+0.54
$H^+(aq) + e^- \rightleftharpoons \frac{1}{2}H_2(g)$	0.00	$MnO_4^-(aq) + e^- \rightleftharpoons MnO_4^{2-}(aq)$	+0.56
$\frac{1}{2}I_2(s) + e^- \rightleftharpoons I^-(aq)$	+0.54	$MnO_4^{2-}(aq) + 2H_2O(l) + 2e^- \rightleftharpoons MnO_2(s) + 4OH^-(aq)$	+0.59
$Li^+(aq) + e^- \rightleftharpoons Li(s)$	−3.04	$O_2(g) + 2H^+(aq) + 2e^- \rightleftharpoons H_2O_2(aq)$	+0.68
$MnO_4^-(aq) + 8H^+(aq) + 5e^- \rightleftharpoons Mn^{2+}(aq) + 4H_2O(l)$	+1.52	$Fe^{3+}(aq) + e^- \rightleftharpoons Fe^{2+}(aq)$	+0.77
$MnO_4^-(aq) + e^- \rightleftharpoons MnO_4^{2-}(aq)$	+0.56	$Ag^+(aq) + e^- \rightleftharpoons Ag(s)$	+0.80
$MnO_4^{2-}(aq) + 2H_2O(l) + 2e^- \rightleftharpoons MnO_2(s) + 4OH^-(aq)$	+0.59	$\frac{1}{2}Br_2(l) + e^- \rightleftharpoons Br^-(aq)$	+1.07
$\frac{1}{2}H_2O_2(aq) + H^+(aq) + e^- \rightleftharpoons H_2O(l)$	+1.77	$\frac{1}{2}O_2(g) + 2H^+(aq) + 2e^- \rightleftharpoons H_2O(l)$	+1.23
$\frac{1}{2}O_2(g) + 2H^+(aq) + 2e^- \rightleftharpoons H_2O(l)$	+1.23	$Cr_2O_7^{2-}(aq) + 14H^+(aq) + 6e^- \rightleftharpoons 2Cr^{3+}(aq) + 7H_2O(l)$	+1.33
$O_2(g) + 2H^+(aq) + 2e^- \rightleftharpoons H_2O_2(aq)$	+0.68	$\frac{1}{2}Cl_2(g) + e^- \rightleftharpoons Cl^-(aq)$	+1.36
$Pb^{4+}(aq) + 2e^- \rightleftharpoons Pb^{2+}(aq)$	+1.69	$MnO_4^-(aq) + 8H^+(aq) + 5e^- \rightleftharpoons Mn^{2+}(aq) + 4H_2O(l)$	+1.52
$Sn^{2+}(aq) + 2e^- \rightleftharpoons Sn(s)$	−0.14	$HOCl(aq) + H^+(aq) + e^- \rightleftharpoons \frac{1}{2}Cl_2(g) + H_2O(l)$	+1.64
$Sn^{4+}(aq) + 2e^- \rightleftharpoons Sn^{2+}(aq)$	+0.15	$Pb^{4+}(aq) + 2e^- \rightleftharpoons Pb^{2+}(aq)$	+1.69
$S(s) + 2H^+(aq) + 2e^- \rightleftharpoons H_2S(g)$	+0.14	$\frac{1}{2}H_2O_2(aq) + H^+(aq) + e^- \rightleftharpoons H_2O(l)$	+1.77
$Zn^{2+}(aq) + 2e^- \rightleftharpoons Zn(s)$	−0.76	$\frac{1}{2}F_2(g) + e^- \rightleftharpoons F^-(aq)$	+2.87

increasing strength as an oxidising agent →

Table 9.1 *Standard reduction potential values at 298 K*

Non-standard conditions

If the conditions are not standard, the value of the electrode potential will alter. The direction of change can be predicted using Le Chatelier's principle.

Change in concentration

Consider the redox half-equation:

$$Cr_2O_7^{2-}(aq) + 14H^+(aq) + 6e^- \rightleftharpoons 2Cr^{3+}(aq) + 7H_2O(l) \quad E^\ominus = +1.33\ V$$

If the concentrations of dichromate(VI) ions and hydrogen ions are increased above 1.0 mol dm^{-3}, the position of equilibrium is driven to the right. This causes the value of the electrode potential, E, to be higher than the standard value: $E > +1.33$ V.

Consider the redox equilibrium:

$$\frac{1}{2}Cl_2(g) + e^- \rightleftharpoons Cl^-(aq) \quad E^\ominus = +1.36\ V$$

If the concentration of chloride ions is increased, the equilibrium position will shift to the left. This causes the value of the electrode potential, E, to be lower than the standard value: $E < +1.36$ V.

This can have a serious effect on the spontaneity of a reaction.

Change in pressure

A change in pressure affects gaseous reactants only. Oxygen acting as an oxidising agent has the redox half-equation:

$$O_2(g) + 2H_2O(l) + 4e^- \rightleftharpoons 4OH^-(aq) \qquad E^\circ = +0.40 \text{ V}$$

This assumes that the pressure of oxygen is 1.0 atm. In air, this is not the case. The partial pressure of oxygen in air is about 0.2 atm. This drives the redox equilibrium to the left, making $E < +0.40$ V. Therefore, oxygen in the air is a less good oxidising agent than pure oxygen. Conversely, a scuba diver's air tank has oxygen at a partial pressure much greater than 1 atm. So, if damp air is pumped into the tank, internal rusting will occur more than it does with iron in normal air.

Change in temperature

The effect of a change in temperature depends on whether the redox half-equation is exothermic or endothermic. If it is exothermic, an increased temperature drives the position of equilibrium to the left (in the endothermic direction). This makes the value of the electrode potential less positive (or more negative).

Chlorine is reduced exothermically in aqueous solution. Therefore, an increase in temperature makes the new electrode potential less than +1.36 V.

Altering a reduction potential equation

Changing direction

If the electrode equation is reversed, its sign must also be reversed, for example:

$$Zn^{2+}(aq) + 2e^- \rightleftharpoons Zn(s) \qquad E^\circ = -0.76 \text{ V}$$
$$Zn(s) \rightleftharpoons Zn^{2+}(aq) + 2e^- \qquad E^\circ = -(-0.76) = +0.76 \text{ V}$$

$$\tfrac{1}{2}Cl_2(g) + e^- \rightleftharpoons Cl^-(aq) \qquad E^\circ = +1.36 \text{ V}$$
$$Cl^-(aq) \rightleftharpoons \tfrac{1}{2}Cl_2(g) + e^- \qquad E^\circ = -(+1.36) = -1.36 \text{ V}$$

> **e** This is similar to enthalpy calculations — if the equation of a reaction is reversed, the sign of ΔH has to be changed.

Multiplying by integers

The units of E are volts *not* volts per mole, so multiplying a redox half-equation has *no* effect on the value of E:

$$\tfrac{1}{2}Cl_2(g) + e^- \rightleftharpoons Cl^-(aq) \quad E^\circ = +1.36 \text{ V}$$
$$Cl_2(g) + 2e^- \rightleftharpoons 2Cl^-(aq) \quad E^\circ = +1.36 \text{ V}$$

> **e** This is *unlike* ΔH calculations, where the units are kJ mol^{-1} and the value depends on the number of moles in the equation as written.

Feasibility of reaction

A redox reaction is thermodynamically feasible if the value of the cell potential is positive.

The standard cell potential, $E^{\ominus}_{cell}$, can be calculated from standard electrode potential data. Since these data are normally given as reduction potentials, the two reactants must be identified. One reactant will be on the left-hand side of one half-equation and the other on the right-hand side of the second half-equation.

The half-equation with the reactant on the right-hand side must be reversed. This alters the sign of its $E^{\ominus}$ value. If necessary, the two half-equations are multiplied by integers to give the same number of electrons in each equation. The overall equation is obtained by adding these half-equations together. The altered $E^{\ominus}$ value is then added to the $E^{\ominus}$ value of the unchanged half-equation to give the value of $E^{\ominus}_{cell}$. If this value is positive, then the reaction is feasible (the products are thermodynamically stable relative to the reactants).

Worked example 1

Use the data below to predict whether Fe^{3+} ions will oxidise I^- ions in aqueous solution. Write the overall equation.

$$Fe^{3+}(aq) + e^- \rightleftharpoons Fe^{2+}(aq) \quad E^{\ominus} = +0.77 \text{ V}$$
$$\tfrac{1}{2}I_2(s) + e^- \rightleftharpoons I^-(aq) \quad E^{\ominus} = +0.54 \text{ V}$$

Answer

The reactants are Fe^{3+} and I^-. so the second equation has to be reversed and the sign of its $E^{\ominus}$ value changed.
Both equations have one electron, so no multiplying is needed.

$$Fe^{3+}(aq) + e^- \rightleftharpoons Fe^{2+}(aq) \quad E^{\ominus} = +0.77 \text{ V}$$
$$I^-(aq) \rightleftharpoons \tfrac{1}{2}I_2(s) + e^- \quad E^{\ominus} = -(+0.54) = -0.54 \text{ V}$$

These two equations and their $E^{\ominus}$ values are then added together:

$$Fe^{3+}(aq) + I^-(aq) \rightarrow Fe^{2+}(aq) + \tfrac{1}{2}I_2(s) \quad E^{\ominus}_{cell} = +0.77 + (-0.54) = +0.23 \text{ V}$$

$E^{\ominus}_{cell}$ is positive, so the reaction is feasible.

Worked example 2

Use the data below to predict if the dichromate(VI) ions in acidified potassium dichromate(VI) will react with chloride ions in hydrochloric acid.

$$Cr_2O_7{}^{2-}(aq) + 14H^+(aq) + 6e^- \rightleftharpoons 2Cr^{3+}(aq) + 7H_2O(l) \quad E^{\ominus} = +1.33 \text{ V}$$
$$\tfrac{1}{2}Cl_2(g) + e^- \rightleftharpoons Cl^-(aq) \quad E^{\ominus} = +1.36 \text{ V}$$

Answer

The reactants are $Cr_2O_7{}^{2-}$ and Cl^-, so the second equation has to be reversed and the sign of its $E^{\ominus}$ value changed.

To get the overall equation, the number of electrons must be the same in both half-equations, so the second equation has to be multiplied by 6. This does not alter the $E^{\ominus}$ value. The half-equations are then added together.

$$Cr_2O_7{}^{2-}(aq) + 14H^+(aq) + 6e^- \rightleftharpoons 2Cr^{3+}(aq) + 7H_2O(l) \quad E^{\ominus} = +1.33 \text{ V}$$
$$6Cl^-(aq) \rightleftharpoons 3Cl_2(g) + 6e^- \quad E^{\ominus} = -1.36 \text{ V}$$
$$\overline{Cr_2O_7{}^{2-}(aq) + 14H^+(aq) + 6Cl^-(aq) \rightleftharpoons 2Cr^{3+}(aq) + 7H_2O(l) + 3Cl_2(g)}$$

$E^{\ominus}_{cell} = 1.33 + (-1.36) = -0.03 \text{ V}$

$E^{\ominus}_{cell}$ is negative, so the reaction is not feasible under standard conditions.

This is the safest way to predict the feasibility of a redox reaction. It also generates the overall equation.

There are other methods, but they pose particular difficulties:

- The 'anticlockwise rule' works only if the data are presented in increasing numerical order.
- The rule '$E_{cell} = E_{oxidising\ agent} - E_{reducing\ agent}$' can be misremembered and also does not give the overall equation. In addition, it requires correct identification of the oxidising agent and the reducing agent. The reducing agent is found on the right of the reduction potential half-equation, and $E_{reducing\ agent}$ is the value of the reduction potential.

In worked example 2 above, the oxidising agent is dichromate(VI) and the reducing agent is the Cl^- ions.

Thus $E_{cell}^{\ominus} = E_{oxidising\ agent}^{\ominus} - E_{reducing\ agent}^{\ominus} = +1.33 - (+1.36) = -0.03$ V

Actuality of reaction

A reaction may be thermodynamically feasible ($E_{cell}^{\ominus}$ positive) but might not take place. The reasons for this can be kinetic or connected with non-standard conditions.

Kinetic reasons

The sign of $E_{cell}^{\ominus}$ enables the prediction of whether a reaction is thermodynamically feasible. However, thermodynamic feasibility is no guarantee that the reaction will take place under standard conditions. The reaction may have such a high activation energy that it is too slow to be observed at room temperature. For example, $E_{cell}^{\ominus}$ for the reaction $H_2(g) + \frac{1}{2}O_2(g) \rightarrow H_2O(l)$ is +1.23 V, but a mixture of hydrogen and oxygen will not react unless heated or unless a catalyst is present.

The reaction between persulphate ions, $S_2O_8^{2-}$ and iodide ions, I^-, is thermodynamically feasible as $E_{cell}^{\ominus} = +1.47$ V. However, it does not occur unless a catalyst of iron ions (either Fe^{2+} or Fe^{3+}) is added. The activation energy is high because of the need for two negative ions to collide in the uncatalysed route.

Non-standard conditions

The data provided are always *standard* electrode potentials. If the concentration of a reactant or product is not 1 mol dm^{-3}, the value of E_{cell} will differ from that of $E_{cell}^{\ominus}$.

This might result in a reaction taking place that is predicted to be unfeasible.

> **Worked example**
> Consider the redox reaction:
> $$Cu^{2+}(aq) + 2I^-(aq) \rightarrow CuI(s) + \tfrac{1}{2}I_2(s)$$
> Explain why this reaction will take place, given that:
> $$Cu^{2+}(aq) + e^- \rightleftharpoons Cu^+(aq) \quad E^{\ominus} = +0.15\ V$$
> $$\tfrac{1}{2}I_2(s) + e^- \rightleftharpoons I^-(aq) \quad E^{\ominus} = +0.54\ V$$

Answer

The reactants are Cu^{2+} and I^- ions. The feasibility is predicted by reversing the sign of the $E^\ominus$ value of the second equation and adding the two $E^\ominus$ values together.

$E^\ominus_{cell} = +0.15 + (-0.54) = -0.39\,V$

The negative value predicts that the reaction will not take place under standard conditions where the concentrations of Cu^+ and I^- ions are both $1.0\,mol\,dm^{-3}$. However, this is not the case in this reaction because copper(I) iodide is precipitated and so $[Cu^+]$ is almost zero. This drives the equilibrium of the Cu^{2+}/Cu^+ reaction to the right, increasing its electrode potential and making the value of the non-standard cell potential positive. The reaction is now feasible and, as the activation energy is low, the reaction takes place rapidly.

Disproportionation reactions

If an element exists in three different oxidation states (which could include the zero state of the uncombined element), disproportionation becomes a possibility. The feasibility of such a reaction can be predicted from standard electrode potential data.

Worked example

Predict whether or not copper(I) ions will disproportionate into copper metal and copper(II) ions. If so, write the overall equation.

$$Cu^{2+}(aq) + e^- \rightleftharpoons Cu^+(aq) \quad E^\ominus = +0.15\,V$$
$$Cu^+(aq) + e^- \rightleftharpoons Cu(s) \quad E^\ominus = +0.52\,V$$

Answer

As this is a disproportionation reaction, a single species is both reduced and oxidised at the same time. In this example that species is the Cu^+ ion, so the first equation must be reversed and added to the second equation to give the overall equation:

$$Cu^+(aq) \rightleftharpoons Cu^{2+}(aq) + e^- \quad E^\ominus = -0.15\,V$$
$$Cu^+(aq) + e^- \rightleftharpoons Cu(s) \quad E^\ominus = +0.52\,V$$

$$\overline{2Cu^+(aq) \rightleftharpoons Cu^{2+}(aq) + Cu(s) \quad E^\ominus_{cell} = -0.15 + (+0.52) = +0.37\,V}$$

The value of $E^\ominus_{cell}$ is positive, so the disproportionation reaction is feasible.

This is a disproportionation reaction because copper in the +1 state is simultaneously oxidised to copper in the +2 state and reduced to copper in the zero state.

Practical aspects of electrochemistry

Batteries

Batteries are cells in which chemical energy is converted to electrical energy.

Disposable batteries

Standard AA batteries consist of a zinc anode and a cathode of a carbon rod packed round with granules of manganese(IV) oxide. The electrolyte is a paste of ammonium chloride. The zinc loses electrons to form zinc ions. At the cathode, manganese(IV) oxide is reduced to a manganese(III) compound.

An AA alkaline battery

Alkaline batteries are similar, except that the electrolyte is sodium hydroxide. Here, the anode reaction is:

$$Zn(s) + 2OH^-(aq) \rightarrow Zn(OH)_2(s) + 2e^-$$

The cathode reaction is

$$2MnO_2(s) + 2H_2O(l) + 2e^- \rightarrow 2MnO(OH)(s) + 2OH^-(aq)$$

Since the concentration of ions remains constant, the voltage does not fall until all the zinc has been used, at which point the battery becomes flat.

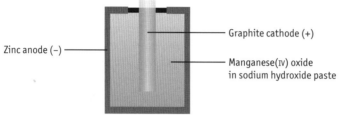

Zinc anode (–)

Graphite cathode (+)

Manganese(IV) oxide in sodium hydroxide paste

Figure 9.6 An alkaline battery

Mercury batteries can be used in watches, cameras and heart pacemakers. The anode is zinc and the cathode is a paste of mercury(II) oxide in an electrolyte of alkali.

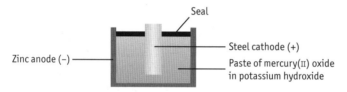

Seal

Zinc anode (–)

Steel cathode (+)

Paste of mercury(II) oxide in potassium hydroxide

Figure 9.7 A mercury button battery

Other button batteries are made of lithium and manganese(IV) oxide, or zinc and silver oxide with suitable electrolytes.

Rechargeable batteries

The lead–acid battery is used in cars. Each cell consists of two lead plates. The cathode is coated with solid lead(IV) oxide. The electrolyte is a fairly concentrated solution of sulphuric acid.

The anode reaction is:

$$Pb(s) + SO_4^{2-}(aq) \rightarrow PbSO_4(s) + 2e^-$$

The cathode reaction is:

$$PbO_2(s) + 4H^+(aq) + SO_4^{2-}(aq) + 2e^- \rightarrow PbSO_4(s) + 2H_2O(l)$$

The overall discharging reaction is:

$$Pb(s) + PbO_2(s) + 4H^+(aq) + 2SO_4^{2-}(aq) \rightarrow 2PbSO_4(s) + 2H_2O(l)$$

The potential of each cell is +2.0 V. Normally, six cells are arranged in series creating a battery with a potential of 12 V.

When all the lead(IV) oxide has been reduced, the battery is flat.

The discharging reaction is reversible. If an external potential greater than 12 V is applied, the reaction is driven backwards and the plates restored to their original composition.

A car battery

The overall charging reaction is:

$$2PbSO_4(s) + 2H_2O(l) \rightarrow Pb(s) + PbO_2(s) + 4H^+(aq) + 2SO_4^{2-}(aq)$$

Many digital cameras contain rechargeable lithium cells that use a solid polymer electrolyte. There are several types with different materials for the anode and cathode. One type of battery has a lithium anode and a titanium(IV) sulphide cathode. The reactions are:

$$Li(s) \rightleftharpoons Li^+ + e^-$$
$$TiS_2 + e^- \rightleftharpoons TiS_2^-$$

The Li^+ and the TiS_2^- ions then form solid $LiTiS_2$.

The main principles of storage (rechargeable) cells are that:

- The chemical reactions at both electrodes must be able to be reversed when an electrical potential is applied.
- The oxidised and reduced forms of the anode and cathode must be solid.

Fuel cells

Manned spacecraft are powered by hydrogen–oxygen fuel cells. These cells are also being developed for commercial use. Some London buses have such a fuel cell. The electricity it produces powers the electric motor of the bus. The buses are advertised as 'zero-emission' buses because when they are operating only water, and no carbon dioxide, is produced.

A zero-emission London bus

The principle behind a hydrogen–oxygen fuel cell is that hydrogen gas, in an alkaline solution of potassium hydroxide, is oxidised at the anode and oxygen is reduced at the cathode.

The electrodes act both as electrical conductors and as catalysts for the reactions. They are made from metals such as platinum, nickel or rhodium and must be very porous to allow the gases to pass through and come into contact with the electrolyte.

The two *reduction* half-equations are:

$$2H_2O(l) + 2e^- \rightleftharpoons H_2(g) + 2OH^-(aq) \quad E^\ominus = -0.83\ V$$
$$\tfrac{1}{2}O_2(g) + H_2O(l) + 2e^- \rightleftharpoons 2OH^-(aq) \quad\quad E^\ominus = +0.40\ V$$

The overall equation and the cell potential are obtained by reversing the first half-equation and adding it to the second half-equation. This gives:

$$H_2(g) + \tfrac{1}{2}O_2(g) \rightleftharpoons H_2O(g) \quad E^\ominus_{cell} = +0.40 - (-0.83) = +1.23\ V$$

Steam can be seen from the exhaust pipe near the roof on zero-emission buses. This is the water that has been produced by the reaction of the hydrogen fuel with oxygen.

Figure 9.8
A hydrogen fuel cell

Hydrogen out ← | → Oxygen in

Catalytic anode (−) | Catalytic cathode (+)

Electrolyte (KOH)

Hydrogen in → | → Oxygen out

The statement that there are no emissions (implying no CO_2) is misleading. The hydrogen is produced by electrolysis, which consumes 96 million coulombs of electricity per tonne of hydrogen. This is equivalent to a current of 26 000 amp h^{-1}. This electricity will almost certainly have been produced by burning fossil fuels such as coal, oil or gas. Therefore, although the bus does not produce carbon dioxide, it is created at the power station. Carbon dioxide is produced in approximately the same amount as if the bus had been powered by a diesel engine. The only way that a hydrogen–oxygen fuel cell could be rightly described as having 'zero emissions' is if the electricity had been produced by nuclear power or some form of renewable energy.

Research is being carried out into designing a fuel cell that will use ethanol, rather than hydrogen. The two half-equations are:

$$C_2H_5OH(l) + 4OH^-(aq) \rightleftharpoons 2CO_2(g) + 5H_2O(l) + 4e^-$$
$$O_2(g) + 2H_2O(l) + 4e^- \rightleftharpoons 4OH^-(aq)$$

Ethanol could be made by fermenting surplus sugar grown in the EU. The CO_2 photosynthesised by the sugar beet would be converted into ethanol and then back to CO_2 in the fuel cell. This would be truly 'carbon-neutral'.

> This would have the added benefit of preventing surplus sugar being dumped by rich countries on the world market, which harms sugar farmers in the developing world.

Corrosion

Corrosion is the electrolytic oxidation of metals by air. Rusting of iron and the tarnishing of silver objects are examples.

The conditions for the rusting of iron are that the metal must be in contact with both air and water. The reactants are oxygen, water and iron. The half-equations and standard reduction potentials are:

$$\tfrac{1}{2}O_2(g) + H_2O(l) + 2e^- \rightleftharpoons 2OH^-(aq) \quad E^\ominus = +0.40 \text{ V}$$
$$Fe^{2+}(aq) + 2e^- \rightleftharpoons Fe(s) \quad E^\ominus = -0.44 \text{ V}$$

At the interface between air and water, the oxygen in the air becomes reduced:

Half-equation 1: $\tfrac{1}{2}O_2(g) + H_2O(l) + 2e^- \rightleftharpoons 2OH^-(aq)$ $\quad E^\ominus = +0.40 \text{ V}$

A part of the iron acts as the anode and becomes oxidised:

Half-equation 2: $Fe(s) \rightleftharpoons Fe^{2+}(aq) + 2e^-$ $\quad E^\ominus = +0.44 \text{ V}$

The electrons travel through the metal to where the oxygen is being reduced, for example the edge of a drop of water.

The Fe^{2+} ions migrate away from the surface of the metal and become oxidised further by dissolved oxygen.

$$2Fe^{2+}(aq) + 4OH^-(aq) + \tfrac{1}{2}O_2(aq) + H_2O(l) \rightarrow 2Fe(OH)_3(s)$$

The iron(III) hydroxide then starts to dehydrate forming hydrated iron(III) oxide — rust.

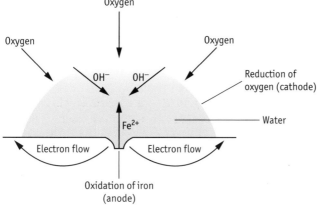

Figure 9.9 The mechanism of rusting

The equation for the initial overall reaction and its cell potential are obtained by adding the two half-equations 1 and 2:

$$\tfrac{1}{2}O_2(g) + H_2O(l) + Fe(s) \rightleftharpoons Fe^{2+}(aq) + 2OH^-(aq)$$
$$E^{\ominus}_{cell} = +0.40 + (+0.44) = +0.84\ V$$

The cell potential is positive and so the reaction will take place under standard conditions. However, natural conditions are not standard. The partial pressure of oxygen in the air is only about 0.2 atm and the pH of rainwater is approximately 5, not 14, as for the standard conditions for half-equation 1. These conditions cause the electrode potential of the O_2, H_2O/OH^- system to increase to +0.66 V.

This makes the cell potential +0.66 + (+0.44) = +1.10 V. Therefore, rusting is more likely in a slightly acidic medium than at a high pH.

If a drop of solution containing potassium hexacyanoferrate(III) and a little phenolphthalein is placed on a piece of mild steel, the edge of the drop goes pink because of the formation of OH^- ions as oxygen is reduced. Blue spots appear inside the drop. These are a precipitate of iron(II) hexacyanoferrate(III), which shows that Fe^{2+} ions are formed as iron corrodes.

Formation of Fe^{2+} ions when iron corrodes

ZAHOOR UL-HAQ

Prevention of corrosion

Physical barriers

The simplest method of preventing corrosion is to place a barrier between the iron and the environment. This can be done in a number of ways:

- The object can be painted. Car bodies are dipped in baths of paint. However, if the paintwork of the car becomes scratched, the body panels will begin to rust.

- The object can be sprayed with oil or covered in grease. Water and oil do not mix and oil is a non-electrolyte, so corrosion cannot take place. The disadvantage is that oil collects dirt and it also evaporates.
- The object can be coated with a thin layer of an unreactive metal. Baked-bean cans are made of mild steel that has been coated in tin. The tin does not corrode and, as long as the tin coating is not broken, the iron will not rust nor will it be attacked by the acids in food.
- The iron can be alloyed with chromium. The result is stainless steel. The chromium is oxidised in dry air to form an invisible impermeable layer of chromium oxide. This separates the iron atoms from the air. If this layer is scratched, another chromium oxide layer immediately forms.

Cathodic protection

Iron can be coated with a sacrificial metal, such as zinc. This is called **galvanising**. Since the Zn^{2+}/Zn reduction potential is more negative than the Fe^{2+}/Fe potential, the zinc is more easily oxidised than the iron. Under corrosion conditions, the zinc acts as the anode and is oxidised preferentially to the iron. Car bodies are now zinc-dipped before they are painted. This increases the lifespan of a car considerably.

Another cathodic method is to put blocks of magnesium at intervals along an iron object. Oil pipelines are protected this way. The Mg^{2+}/Mg potential is more negative than the Fe^{2+}/Fe potential, so the magnesium corrodes rather than the iron.

Alternative materials

Aluminium, like chromium, spontaneously forms a protective layer of oxide and, therefore, does not corrode. When alloyed with small amounts of magnesium, aluminium has a high strength-to-weight ratio. These two properties make it excellent for the construction of aircraft and lightweight drink cans. The use of aluminium as a structural material in ordinary situations is limited by its high cost in comparison with iron.

Synthetic polymers are now being used increasingly. Sailing boats are made of fibreglass (a composite of resin and glass fibres). Carbon fibre and Kevlar are used in the aircraft industry and the shafts of golf clubs are now made from carbon fibre rather than steel.

Electrolysis

Electrolysis occurs when an electric current is passed through a conducting liquid. The current causes oxidation to occur at the anode and reduction to occur at the cathode.

In the examples given so far, chemical reactions have produced electrons, which generate electricity if the system is set up as an electrolytic cell. The reverse of this can occur — electricity can be passed through a solution and cause a chemical reaction. This process is called **electrolysis**.

An example of this is the charging cycle of the lead–acid battery (pp. 172–173). The extraction of aluminium and the manufacture of chlorine are industrial examples of electrolysis.

Never buy a can that has a dent in it. The distortion may have caused the tin layer to break, exposing the food to the iron.

Stainless steel contains up to 30% chromium and nickel with small amounts of manganese and carbon.

The anode removes electrons and is, therefore, connected to the positive terminal of the source of electricity. The cathode supplies electrons and is connected to the negative terminal.

Aluminium manufacture

Purified aluminium oxide is dissolved in molten cryolite, Na_3AlF_6, and electricity is passed into the cell via carbon electrodes.

Oxidation takes place at the positive anode:

$$2O^{2-} \rightarrow O_2 + 4e^-$$

The oxygen produced reacts with the carbon anode forming carbon dioxide. Over time, this eats away the anode, which, therefore, has to be replaced periodically.

Aluminium ions are reduced at the negative cathode:

$$Al^{3+} + 3e^- \rightarrow Al$$

Chlorine manufacture

A concentrated solution of sodium chloride is electrolysed.

Oxidation takes place at the titanium anode:

$$2Cl^-(aq) \rightarrow Cl_2(g) + 2e^-$$

The standard oxidation potential for this reaction is -1.36 V ($[Cl^-] = 1$ mol dm^{-3}). However, the sodium chloride used has a concentration greater than 5 mol dm^{-3}. This causes the oxidation potential to change to -1.32 V.

Water is reduced to hydrogen at the steel cathode:

$$2H_2O(l) + 2e^- \rightarrow H_2(g) + 2OH^-(aq)$$

The reduction potential for this reaction is -0.83 V.

This means that to make these two reactions take place, a potential greater than 2.15 V must be applied.

Electrolysis of water

Water is not sufficiently ionic to be a reasonable conductor of electricity. Therefore, either acid or alkali is added to provide the ions necessary for conduction.

The electrode reactions and potentials for the electrolysis of acidified water at pH 0 are:

Anode: $H_2O(l) \rightarrow \frac{1}{2}O_2(g) + 2H^+(aq) + 2e^-$ $E^\ominus = -1.23$ V
Cathode: $2H^+(aq) + 2e^- \rightarrow H_2(g)$ $E^\ominus = 0.00$ V

Therefore, a potential greater than 1.23 V is necessary for electrolysis.

The electrode reactions and potentials for the electrolysis of water containing alkali (KOH or NaOH) at pH = 14 are:

Anode: $2OH^-(aq) \rightarrow \frac{1}{2}O_2(g) + H_2O(l) + 2e^-$ $E^\ominus = -0.40$ V
Cathode: $2H_2O(l) + 2e^- \rightarrow H_2(g) + 2OH^-(aq)$ $E^\ominus = -0.83$ V

A potential of at least 1.23 V is also necessary for electrolysis under these conditions.

The overall reaction is the sum of the two half-equations. The potential needed for electrolysis is the same in acidic or alkaline conditions, because the overall reactions are the same.

$$H_2O(l) \rightarrow H_2(g) + \frac{1}{2}O_2(g)$$

Hydrogen and oxygen are produced in the volume ratio 2:1.

Oxidising and reducing agents

Oxidising agents

An oxidising agent is a species that removes electrons from another species, thus oxidising it. It is itself reduced by the gain of electrons.

Some oxidising agents, the species produced when they react and their standard reduction potentials are given in Table 9.2.

e The oxidation number of an element in the oxidising agent decreases (becomes less positive or more negative). The oxidation number of an element in the species being oxidised increases (becomes more positive or less negative).

Oxidising agent	Oxidising species	Reduced species	$E^{\ominus}$/V
Ozone	O_3 in H^+(aq)	O_2, H_2O	+2.07
Persulphate ions	$S_2O_8^{2-}$	SO_4^{2-}	+2.01
Hydrogen peroxide	H_2O_2 in H^+(aq)	H_2O	+1.77
Chloric(I) acid	HOCl in H^+(aq)	Cl_2, H_2O	+1.64
Manganate(VII) ions	MnO_4^- in H^+(aq)	Mn^{2+}, H_2O	+1.52
Lead(VI) oxide	PbO_2 in H^+(aq)	Pb^{2+}, H_2O	+1.47
Chlorine	Cl_2	Cl^-	+1.36
Dichromate(VI) ions	$Cr_2O_7^{2-}$ in H^+(aq)	Cr^{3+}, H_2O	+1.33
Manganese(IV) oxide	MnO_2 in H^+(aq)	Mn^{2+}, H_2O	+1.23
Oxygen	O_2 in H^+(aq)	H_2O	+1.23
Iodate(V) ions	IO_3^- in H^+(aq)	I_2, H_2O	+1.19
Bromine	Br_2	Br^-	+1.07
Iron(III) ions	Fe^{3+}	Fe^{2+}	+0.77
Iodine	I_2	I^-	+0.54
Tetrathionate ions	$S_4O_6^{2-}$	$S_2O_3^{2-}$	+0.09

Table 9.2 Common oxidising agents, listed in order of decreasing power

All oxidising agents should oxidise the reduced form of any species below them in the table. For example, lead(IV) oxide will oxidise chloride ions to chlorine. A laboratory preparation of chlorine is to warm concentrated hydrochloric acid with lead(IV) oxide.

Worked example

Show that iodate(V) ions in acid solution should oxidise iodide ions and write the overall equation for the reaction.

Answer

The two reduction half-equations are:

$$IO_3^-(aq) + 6H^+(aq) + 5e^- \rightleftharpoons \tfrac{1}{2}I_2(s) + 3H_2O(l) \quad E^{\ominus} = +1.19\,V$$
$$\tfrac{1}{2}I_2(s) + e^- \rightleftharpoons I^-(aq) \quad E^{\ominus} = +0.54\,V$$

Iodate(V) ions and iodide ions are the reactants. The overall equation is obtained by reversing the second equation, multiplying it by 5 and then adding it to the first equation:

$$IO_3^-(aq) + 6H^+(aq) + 5I^-(aq) \rightarrow 3I_2(s) + 3H_2O(l)$$
$$E^{\ominus}_{cell} = +1.19 + (-0.54) = +0.65\,V$$

The $E^{\ominus}_{cell}$ value is positive, so the redox reaction is feasible.

Estimation of the concentration of a solution of an oxidising agent

As can be seen from Table 9.2, all the oxidising agents (apart from tetrathionate ions) in the list should oxidise iodide ions to iodine.

> **Worked example**
>
> Write the equation for the oxidation of thiosulphate ions by iodine and calculate the standard cell potential.
>
> **Answer**
>
> The two reduction half-equations are:
>
> $$\tfrac{1}{2}I_2(s) + e^- \rightleftharpoons I^-(aq) \quad E^\circ = +0.54 \text{ V}$$
> $$\tfrac{1}{2}S_4O_6{}^{2-} + e^- \rightleftharpoons S_2O_3{}^{2-} \quad E^\circ = +0.09 \text{ V}$$
>
> The overall equation is obtained by reversing the second equation and adding it to the first. The overall equation is multiplied by 2, to remove the halves.
>
> $$I_2(s) + 2S_2O_3{}^{2-}(aq) \rightarrow 2I^-(aq) + S_4O_6{}^{2-}(aq) \quad E^\circ_{cell} = +0.54 + (-0.09) = +0.45 \text{ V}$$

This reaction in the worked example above is fundamental to the method for estimating the concentrations of solutions of oxidising agents.

The standard method is as follows:

- A known volume, usually 25.0 cm^3, of the solution of the oxidising agent is pipetted into a conical flask.
- A similar volume of dilute sulphuric acid is added, followed by excess solid potassium iodide. The mixture is swirled to ensure that all the oxidising agent reacts.
- A burette is filled with a standard solution of sodium thiosulphate.
- Sodium thiosulphate solution is steadily added to the conical flask from the burette. As this is done, the colour of the iodine in the solution fades.
- When the solution in the flask is a pale straw colour, a few drops of starch solution are added. This reacts reversibly with the iodine to form a dark blue-black substance.
- Sodium thiosulphate is then added dropwise, until the solution is decolourised.
- The experiment is repeated until two consistent titres are obtained.

The reactions are:

$$\text{Oxidising agent} + \text{Excess iodide ions} \rightarrow \text{Iodine}$$
$$I_2 + 2Na_2S_2O_3 \rightarrow 2NaI + Na_2S_4O_6$$

The oxidising agent produces x mol of I_2, which reacts with $2x$ mol of sodium thiosulphate.

> **Worked example**
>
> 25.0 cm^3 of a solution of potassium iodate(v) was pipetted into a conical flask. 25 cm^3 of dilute sulphuric acid and 2 g of potassium iodide (an excess) were added. The iodine liberated was titrated with $0.104 \text{ mol dm}^{-3}$ sodium thiosulphate solution using starch as an indicator. The mean titre was 23.2 cm^3. Calculate the concentration of the potassium iodate(v) solution.

Answer

The equations are:

$I_2 + 2Na_2S_2O_3 \rightarrow 2NaI + Na_2S_4O_6$

$KIO_3 + 3H_2SO_4 + 5KI \rightarrow 3I_2 + 3K_2SO_4 + 3H_2O$

amount of sodium thiosulphate $= 0.104$ mol dm$^{-3} \times 0.0232$ dm$^3 = 0.002413$ mol

Since 1 mol I_2 reacts with 2 mol $S_2O_3^{2-}$:

amount of iodine liberated $= 0.00243$ mol $Na_2S_2O_3 \times \frac{1}{2} = 0.001206$ mol

Since 1 mol of KIO_3 gives 3 mol of I_2:

amount of KIO_3 in 25.0 cm$^3 = 0.001206$ mol $I_2 \times \frac{1}{3} = 0.000402$ mol

concentration of KIO_3 solution $= \dfrac{0.000402 \text{ mol}}{0.0250 \text{ dm}^3} = 0.0161$ mol dm^{-3}

e Use the ratio of the stoichiometric numbers when converting moles of one substance to moles of another. The number of the substance being determined goes on top of the ratio.

Reducing agents

A reducing agent is a species that gives electrons to another species, thus reducing it. It is itself oxidised by loss of electrons.

Some reducing agents, the species produced when they react and their standard reduction potentials are given in Table 9.3.

Reducing agent	Oxidised form	$E^{\ominus}$ /V	
$(COO)_2^{2-}$	$2CO_2$	−0.49	
H_2S	S	+0.14	
Sn^{2+}	Sn^{4+}	+0.15	
I^-	$\frac{1}{2}I_2$	+0.54	Decreasing strength as a reducing agent ↓
H_2O_2	O_2	+0.68	
Fe^{2+}	Fe^{3+}	+0.77	
Br^-	$\frac{1}{2}Br_2$	+1.07	
Pb^{2+}	PbO_2 (Pb^{4+})	+1.47	

Table 9.3 Common reducing agents

Reducing agents become oxidised, so the standard reduction potential of +0.54 V in Table 9.3 is the potential for the half-reaction:

$\frac{1}{2}I_2(s) + e^- \rightleftharpoons I^-(aq)$ $E^{\ominus} = +0.54$ V

so

$I^-(aq) \rightleftharpoons \frac{1}{2}I_2(s) + e^-$ $E^{\ominus} = -0.54$ V

A reducing agent will reduce the oxidised form of a species that has a more positive reduction potential. For example, Fe^{2+} reduces bromine to bromide ions: $E^{\ominus}$ for $Br_2/Br^- = +1.07$ V.

◀ The reducing agent is on the *right-hand* side of the standard reduction potential half-equation.

e The oxidation number of an element in the reducing agent increases (becomes more positive or less negative). The oxidation number of an element in the species being reduced decreases (becomes less positive or more negative).

Estimation of the concentration of a reducing agent

As can be seen from Table 9.3 and the $E^{\ominus}$ value of the MnO_4^-, H^+/Mn^{2+} system, all the reducing agents in the table will reduce manganate(VII) ions in acidic

9

Worked example

Show that hydrogen peroxide should reduce manganate(VII) ions in acid solution. Write the overall equation for the reaction.

Answer

$$O_2(g) + 2H^+(aq) + 2e^- \rightleftharpoons H_2O_2(aq) \qquad E^{\ominus} = +0.68 \text{ V}$$
$$MnO_4^-(aq) + 8H^+(aq) + 5e^- \rightleftharpoons Mn^{2+}(aq) + 4H_2O(l) \quad E^{\ominus} = +1.52 \text{ V}$$

The reactants are H_2O_2 and MnO_4^-, so the first equation has to be reversed. To achieve the same number of electrons in each equation, multiply the first equation by 5 and the second equation by 2. This gives ten electrons in each equation, which will cancel when the equations are added.

$$5H_2O_2(aq) \rightleftharpoons 5O_2(g) + 10H^+(aq) + 10e^- \quad E^{\ominus} = -0.68 \text{ V}$$
$$2MnO_4^-(aq) + 16H^+(aq) + 10e^- \rightleftharpoons 2Mn^{2+}(aq) + 8H_2O(l) \qquad E^{\ominus} = +1.52 \text{ V}$$

$$5H_2O_2(aq) + 2MnO_4^-(aq) + 6H^+(aq) \rightleftharpoons 5O_2(g) + 2Mn^{2+}(aq) + 8H_2O(l)$$
$$E^{\ominus}_{reaction} = +0.84 \text{ V}$$

The value of $E^{\ominus}_{reaction}$ is positive, so hydrogen peroxide should reduce manganate(VII) ions in acid solution.

solution. This is the basis of the determination of the concentration of a reducing agent. The method is:

- A sample of known volume, usually 25.0 cm³, of the reducing agent is pipetted into a conical flask.
- Approximately 25 cm³ of dilute sulphuric acid is added.
- A burette is filled with a standard solution of potassium manganate(VII).
- Potassium manganate(VII) solution is added steadily, with swirling, until the purple colour disappears slowly.
- The potassium manganate(VII) is then added dropwise, until the solution becomes slightly pink.
- The titration is repeated until at least two consistent titres are obtained.

There is no need to add an indicator because the manganate(VII) solution is so intensely coloured. The titration is stopped when the smallest excess of MnO_4^- ions cause a faint pink colour to be visible.

ZAHOOR UL-HAQ

Titration of Fe(II) with manganate(VII)

Worked example

A sample of impure iron(II) sulphate of mass 3.87 g was dissolved in water and the solution made up to 250 cm³. 25.0 cm³ of this solution was pipetted into a conical flask and 25 cm³ of dilute sulphuric acid was added from a measuring cylinder. This mixture was then titrated with a 0.0205 mol dm⁻³ solution of potassium manganate(VII) until a faint pink colour remained. The titration was repeated and the mean titre was found to be 23.4 cm³.

Calculate the percentage purity of the iron(II) sulphate.

Answer

amount (moles) of MnO_4^- in titre = 0.0205 mol dm^{-3} × 0.0234 dm^3

= 0.0004797 mol

The equation for the reaction is:

$5Fe^{2+}(aq) + MnO_4^-(aq) + 8H^+(aq) \rightarrow 5Fe^{3+}(aq) + Mn^{2+}(aq) + 8H_2O(l)$

amount (moles) of Fe^{2+} in 25 cm^3 of solution = 0.0004797 mol MnO_4^- × 5/1

= 0.002399 mol

amount (moles) of Fe^{3+} in 250 cm^3 of solution = 10 × 0.002399 = 0.02399 mol

molar mass of $FeSO_4$ = 56 + 32 + (4 × 16) = 152 g mol^{-1}

mass of $FeSO_4$ in sample = 152 g mol^{-1} × 0.02399 = 3.65 g

purity = $\frac{3.65}{3.87}$ × 100 = 94.3 %

ℯ Use the ratio of the stoichiometric numbers when converting moles of one substance to moles of another. The number of the substance being determined goes on top of the ratio.

Questions

Refer to Table 9.1 on page 167 for standard reduction potential values.

1 Give the oxidation number of oxygen in:
  a O^{2-}
  b O_2^{2-}
  c O_2^-
  d OF_2

2 Give the oxidation number of sulphur in:
  a H_2S
  b SO_4^{2-}
  c S_2Cl_2
  d H_2SO_3

3 Write the half-equations for:
  a the reduction of $Cr_2O_7^{2-}$ ions in acid solution to Cr^{3+} ions and water
  b the reduction of chlorine to chloride ions
  c the oxidation of iodide ions to iodine
  d the oxidation of Fe^{2+} ions to Fe^{3+} ions

4 Use your answers to question 3 to write overall equations for:
  a the reaction between acidified dichromate(VI) ions and iodide ions
  b the reaction between chlorine and Fe^{2+} ions

5 Write the cell diagram for the oxidation of Fe^{2+} ions to Fe^{3+} ions by acidified dichromate(VI) ions.

6 Draw a labelled diagram of the apparatus that you would use to measure the standard reduction potential of acidified potassium manganate(VII).

7 Explain how the potential of the standard hydrogen electrode would alter if the pressure of hydrogen gas were to be increased.

8 Refer to Table 9.1 and select:
  a the strongest oxidising agent
  b the weakest oxidising agent
  c the strongest reducing agent
  d the weakest reducing agent

9 Calculate the cell potential for the following and suggest whether the reaction is feasible or not:
  a a reaction between lead(IV) ions and chloride ions
  b a reaction between tin(IV) ions and Fe^{2+} ions
  c a reaction between iodide ions and Fe^{3+} ions
  d Write equations for any of the reactions in **a–c** that are feasible.

10 $E^\ominus$ values predict that potassium manganate(VII) in acid solution will oxidise chloride ions to chlorine. Suggest how the conditions could be altered to make this less likely to happen.

11 a Define the term 'disproportionation'.
  b Explain why an element must have at least three different oxidation states to be able to undergo a disproportionation reaction.
  c Use the $E^\ominus$ values in Table 9.1 to predict whether manganate(VI) ions, MnO_4^{2-}, will disproportionate into manganate(VII) ions, MnO_4^-, and manganese(IV) oxide, MnO_2.
  d Predict the effect of altering the pH of the solution on the feasibility of this disproportionation.

12 a Write the half-equations for the reactions that take place at the anode and at the cathode when a lead–acid battery produces electricity.
  b Explain what happens to the concentration of sulphuric acid during this discharge.

13 Explain why iron corrodes to a lesser extent in oxygenated water if the pH of the water is increased by the addition of alkali.

14 Explain why coating an iron object with tin will no longer protect the iron from rusting if the tin coating becomes scratched, whereas rusting does not occur if a zinc coating over iron is damaged.

15 Calculate E°_{cell} for the oxidation by oxygen of iron in aqueous solution. Write the overall equation for this reaction.

16 a Predict whether ferrate(VI) ions, FeO_4^{2-}, will be reduced to Fe^{3+} or to Fe^{2+} ions by hydrogen peroxide in an acidic solution.

$$FeO_4^{2-}(aq) + 8H^+(aq) + 3e^- \rightleftharpoons$$
$$Fe^{3+}(aq) + 4H_2O(l) \quad E^{\circ} = +2.20\,V$$

$$Fe^{3+}(aq) + e^- \rightleftharpoons Fe^{2+}(aq) \quad E^{\circ} = +0.77\,V$$

$$O_2(g) + 2H^+(aq) + 2e^- \rightleftharpoons$$
$$H_2O_2(aq) \quad E^{\circ} = +0.68\,V$$

b Write the overall equation for the reaction that takes place.

17 Describe how the concentration of a solution of sodium chlorate(I), NaClO, could be found experimentally.

18 Iron(II) sulphate contains water of crystallisation and its formula can be written as $FeSO_4.xH_2O$. Describe an experiment that would enable you to find the value of x. The method must involve a titration. Your answer should include what you would do, what measurements you would make and show how you would use your measurements to calculate the value of x. (Heating the hydrated solid would decompose the iron(II) sulphate, so this is not an acceptable method.)

19 Write a brief account of the methods used to prevent iron from rusting.

20 Search the internet to find details of the composition of rechargeable lithium cells that are used in cameras and camcorders.

Transition metals and the *d*-block elements

Introduction

The *d*-block elements lie between the *s*-block metals and the *p*-block non-metals in the periodic table. They are shown in Table 10.1.

Sc	Ti	V	Cr	Mn	Fe	Co	Ni	Cu	Zn
Scandium	Titanium	Vanadium	Chromium	Manganese	Iron	Cobalt	Nickel	Copper	Zinc
Y	Zr	Nb	Mo	Tc	Ru	Rh	Pd	Ag	Cd
Yttrium	Zirconium	Niobium	Molybdenum	Technetium	Ruthenium	Rhodium	Palladium	Silver	Cadmium
La	Hf	Ta	W	Re	Os	Ir	Pt	Au	Hg
Lanthanum	Hafnium	Tantalum	Tungsten	Rhenium	Osmium	Iridium	Platinum	Gold	Mercury

Table 10.1 The d-block elements

Electron configuration

Neutral atoms

Argon has the electron configuration $1s^2\, 2s^2\, 2p^6\, 3s^2\, 3p^6$. The next lowest energy level is the 4*s*-orbital, so it fills before the 3*d*. Therefore, potassium has the electron configuration [Ar] $3d^0\, 4s^1$ and calcium [Ar] $3d^0\, 4s^2$.

After calcium, the *d*-block starts and the 3*d*-orbitals begin to be filled. The general configuration for a *d*-block element is [Ar] $3d^x\, 4s^2$ where x is the number of the column along the *d*-block. Scandium is the first *d*-block element, so its configuration is [Ar] $3d^1\, 4s^2$, vanadium is the third, so its configuration is [Ar] $3d^3\, 4s^2$ and iron is the sixth so its configuration is [Ar] $3d^6\, 4s^2$.

In the fourth period, Sc to Zn, there are two exceptions to this rule. There is a slight gain in stability in having a full or half-full set of *d*-orbitals. Thus chromium, the fourth *d*-block element, has the electron configuration [Ar] $3d^5$ $4s^1$ *not* [Ar] $3d^4\, 4s^2$; copper has the configuration [Ar] $3d^{10}\, 4s^1$ *not* [Ar] $3d^9\, 4s^2$.

> **ⓔ** The stability of a full or half-full set of orbitals only applies to *p*- and *d*-orbitals. The reason for the stability is a quantum-mechanical factor called **exchange energy**. This stabilisation is because of the different numbers of ways in which electrons in the same energy level with *parallel* spins can be considered two at a time. There are three ways of pairing up the three electrons in a p^3 configuration ($p_x^1 + p_y^1$, $p_x^1 + p_z^1$ and $p_y^1 + p_z^1$), but only one for a p^2 configuration ($p_x^1 + p_y^1$).

Positive ions

When a *d*-block element in period 4 loses electrons and forms a positive ion, the outer *s*-electrons are always lost before any *d*-electrons. Losing all the 4*s*-electrons makes the ion smaller than if it had lost its 3*d*-electrons. This means that the lattice energy and the hydration energy are more exothermic. Therefore, in a reaction the overall ΔH is energetically more favourable than if the $3d$-electrons had been lost.

The electron configurations of d-block elements in period 4 and their 2+ and 3+ ions are shown in Table 10.2.

Table 10.2 *Period 4 d-block elements*

| Element | Electron configuration | | |
	Atom	M^{2+} ion	M^{3+} ion
Sc	[Ar] $3d^1\ 4s^2$	Does not exist	[Ar] $3d^0\ 4s^0$
Ti	[Ar] $3d^2\ 4s^2$	[Ar] $3d^2\ 4s^0$	[Ar] $3d^1\ 4s^0$
V	[Ar] $3d^3\ 4s^2$	[Ar] $3d^3\ 4s^0$	[Ar] $3d^2\ 4s^0$
Cr	[Ar] $3d^5\ 4s^1$	[Ar] $3d^4\ 4s^0$	[Ar] $3d^3\ 4s^0$
Mn	[Ar] $3d^5\ 4s^2$	[Ar] $3d^5\ 4s^0$	[Ar] $3d^4\ 4s^0$
Fe	[Ar] $3d^6\ 4s^2$	[Ar] $3d^6\ 4s^0$	[Ar] $3d^5\ 4s^0$
Co	[Ar] $3d^7\ 4s^2$	[Ar] $3d^7\ 4s^0$	[Ar] $3d^6\ 4s^0$
Ni	[Ar] $3d^8\ 4s^2$	[Ar] $3d^8\ 4s^0$	[Ar] $3d^7\ 4s^0$
Cu	[Ar] $3d^{10}\ 4s^1$	[Ar] $3d^9\ 4s^0$	Does not exist
Zn	[Ar] $3d^{10}\ 4s^2$	[Ar] $3d^{10}\ 4s^0$	Does not exist

Transition metals

The d-block elements are those between the s-block and the p-block. All d-block elements have an outer electron configuration of nd^x, $(n + 1)s^y$, where x is any number from 1 to 10 and y is 0, 1 or 2.

Transition metals are defined differently:

A transition metal has one or more *unpaired d*-electrons in one of its *ions*.

- Scandium forms Sc^{3+} as its only ion. This has no d-electrons and so scandium is not a transition metal.
- Titanium forms a Ti^{3+} ion, which has one unpaired d-electron, and Ti^{2+}, which has two unpaired electrons. Therefore, titanium is a transition metal.
- Iron has four unpaired electrons in a Fe^{2+} ion (two of the six d-electrons are paired in one of the d-orbitals) and five in a Fe^{3+} ion. Therefore, iron is a transition metal.
- Zinc does not form a Zn^{3+} ion. Zn^{2+} has ten d-electrons that are all paired in five full d-orbitals. Therefore, zinc is not a transition metal.

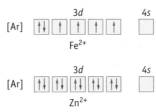

Figure 10.1 *Electron configurations of Fe^{2+} and Zn^{2+} ions*

The arrangements of electrons in Fe^{2+} and Zn^{2+} ions are shown in Figure 10.1.

Ionisation energies

First ionisation energies

In period 3, ionisation energies follow a general upward trend from sodium across to argon. This is caused by an increase in the nuclear charge without an increase in the number of shielding electrons in the inner orbits. The effective nuclear charge increases considerably, and this causes a large increase in the first ionisation energies. The first ionisation energy of sodium is 494 kJ mol^{-1} and that of argon is 1520 kJ mol^{-1}.

The pattern is different across the *d*-block. The outer electron that is removed in the reaction:

$$M(g) \rightarrow M^+(g) + e^-$$

is a 4s-electron, and it is shielded by the inner 3*d*-electrons (as well as by the 1*s*-, 2*s*-, 2*p*-, 3*s*- and 3*p*-electrons). Although the nuclear charge increases across the block from scandium to zinc, the number of inner shielding 3*d*-electrons increases as well. This means that the first ionisation energies of the *d*-block elements in period 4 are fairly similar. This is shown in Figure 10.2.

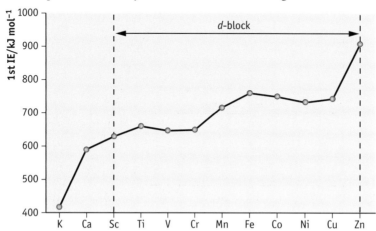

Figure 10.2 First ionisation energies of period 4 elements from potassium to zinc

Successive ionisation energies

There is normally a big jump between successive ionisation energies as a new quantum shell loses an electron. For example, there is a big jump between the second and third ionisation energies of magnesium (electron structure: $1s^2\ 2s^2\ 2p^6\ 3s^2$) because the third electron has to come from the second orbit. This electron is subjected to a much stronger pull from the nucleus as it is much less shielded.

The energy levels of the 3*d*- and the 4*s*-electrons are very similar in *d*-block elements and so the big jump comes after all the 4*s*- and 3*d*-electrons have been removed. There is no big jump between removing both the 4*s*-electrons and starting to remove the 3*d*-electrons.

Melting temperature and hardness

Metallic bonding can be described as the attraction between the delocalised electrons and the positive ions formed when the metal atoms lose their valence electrons into the cloud of delocalised electrons. This bonding is moderately strong and depends on the ionic radius and the number of electrons delocalised. The strength of the bond determines the melting temperature of the metal and its tensile strength. For example, potassium has a large ionic radius and only one delocalised electron. Its melting temperature is 64°C and it is so soft that it can be cut with a knife.

In the *d*-block metals, both the *d*-electrons and *s*-electrons are used in bonding. Therefore, the melting temperatures of *d*-block metals are significantly higher than those of *s*-block metals. The metals are also much harder and stronger.

Another effect of the stronger metallic bonding is that the enthalpy of atomisation of the metal is increased considerably. For example, ΔH_a of calcium is $+193 \text{ kJ mol}^{-1}$ whereas ΔH_a of iron is $+418 \text{ kJ mol}^{-1}$.

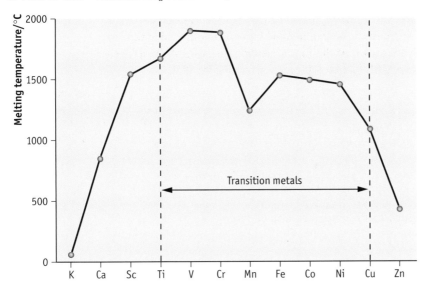

Figure 10.3 *Melting temperatures of the period 4 elements from potassium to zinc*

Common chemical properties of transition metals

Variable oxidation states

The metals in the *s*-block exist in only one oxidation state in their compounds — for example, sodium is always +1 and magnesium is always +2.

The non-transition *d*-block metals also have a single oxidation state. Zinc is always +2 in its compounds and scandium is always +3.

The transition metals exist in several different oxidation states. For example, manganese has stable compounds such as $MnSO_4$ (+2), MnO_2 (+4), K_2MnO_4 (+6) and $KMnO_4$ (+7). It also forms compounds in the +3 and +5 states.

Table 10.3 *Oxidation states of the d-block metals*

Sc	Ti	V	Cr	Mn	Fe	Co	Ni	Cu	Zn
				+7					
			+6	+6	+6				
		+5		+5					
	+4	+4	+4	+4					
+3	+3	+3	+3	+3	+3	+3	+3		
	+2	+2	+2	+2	+2	+2	+2	+2	+2
								+1	

Oxidation states in red are the stable states; those in blue are less stable.

Bonding

In most compounds, in the +2 and +3 oxidation states, the transition metals are ionically bonded. For example, iron(II) sulphate, $FeSO_4$, is ionic, as is chromium(III) sulphate, $Cr_2(SO_4)_3$. Anhydrous chlorides, bromides and iodides are usually covalent, but are ionic when hydrated.

When the transition metal is in an oxidation state of +4 or higher, it is covalently bonded, often in an anion. For example, the manganese atom in an MnO_4^- ion is covalently bonded to the four oxygen atoms by one single and three double bonds:

e Never state that there are Mn^{7+} ions. An oxidation state of +7 is different from an Mn^{7+} ion.

Different cation charges

The extra energy required to remove a third electron from an Fe^{2+} ion (the third ionisation energy) to form Fe^{3+} is only +2960 kJ mol^{-1}. This can be recovered either from lattice energy, if it forms a solid, or from hydration energy of the cation, if it goes into solution.

This is not the case with calcium, where removal of a third electron would have to be from an inner shell. The third ionisation energy of calcium is +4940 kJ mol^{-1}, which is too large to be recovered from lattice or hydration energy.

Number of covalent bonds

For each covalent bond to be formed, the element must have an unpaired electron in its valence shell. For transition metals, the valence shell consists of the occupied 4s- and 3d-orbitals and the unoccupied 4p-orbitals. All these are at a similar energy level and so can be used for bonding. For example, the valence electron configuration of manganese is:

When it forms seven covalent bonds, as in the MnO_4^- ion, it has to have seven unpaired electrons. This is achieved by promoting an electron from the 4s-orbital into an empty 4p-orbital. These seven unpaired electrons are then used to form seven covalent bonds:

As the energy levels of the 3d-, 4s- and 4p-orbitals are similar, little energy is required for promotion and this is recouped from the bond energy released. This means that the *overall* energy change through losing electrons followed by hydration of the ions (or placing ions into a lattice) and the *overall* energy change for promotion of electrons followed by covalent bond formation are both exothermic and, therefore, thermodynamically feasible.

Zinc has a stable d^{10} configuration. The energy needed to promote any of these electrons would not be regained from the energy released by covalent bond

◀ ↑ represents an Mn electron; ↓ represents an O electron

formation. Therefore, zinc does not show variable oxidation states and is not classed as a transition metal.

Formation of aqua ions

When d-block cations are dissolved in water they become hydrated. The oxygen atom in a water molecule has a lone pair of electrons that forms a bond with an empty $3d$- or $4p$-orbital in the metal ion.

The exact nature of the bonding is not understood. One theory is that it is an electrostatic attraction between the δ^- oxygen atoms and the positive metal ion. The accepted A-level theory is that a dative covalent bond forms with the oxygen atom as the donor atom. A more accurate theory is that the lone pair of electrons from all the water molecules and the valence electrons of the metal ion form molecular orbitals using the $3d$-, $4s$- and $4p$-orbitals of the d-block ion.

An example of an aqua ion is the hydrated iron(III) ion, which has the formula $[Fe(H_2O)_6]^{3+}$.

- The water molecules are called **ligands**.
- One of the lone pairs of electrons on the oxygen atom of each water molecule forms a dative covalent bond with an empty orbital in the Fe^{3+} ion.
- Six dative bonds form, so the hydrated ion has the **coordination number** 6.
- The ion, with its water molecules bonded to the central metal ion, is called a **complex ion**.

The shape of the complex ion can be predicted using valence-shell electron-pair repulsion (VSEPR) theory. There are six dative bonds, each containing a pair of electrons. These six pairs of bonding electrons repel each other to the position of minimum repulsion, which is also the position of maximum separation. The shape is, therefore, octahedral:

All complex ions with coordination number 6 are octahedral.

Formation of other complex ions

There are many molecules and anions that can form complex ions with transition metal cations:

- Ammonia, NH_3, and organic amines such as methylamine, CH_3NH_2, form complexes. An example is the complex of Cu^{2+} and ammonia, which has the formula $[Cu(NH_3)_4(H_2O)_2]^{2+}$.
- Anions such as Cl^- and CN^- also form complexes:
  - $[Fe(CN)_6]^{4-}$ is a complex between an Fe^{2+} ion and six CN^- ions.
  - $[CuCl_4]^{2-}$ is a complex between a Cu^{2+} ion and four Cl^- ions.

It is energetically unfavourable to fit six large ligands around a small cation. The Cl^- ion is much larger than a Cu^{2+} ion and the complex formed has a coordination number of 4. The shape of the ion is tetrahedral, with a bond angle of $109.5°$.

e Molecular orbital theory is beyond the scope of A-level chemistry. The most appropriate theory for you to learn is the formation of dative bonds.

These examples of complexing species, and also water, are **monodentate ligands**, in which the ion or molecule uses *one* lone pair of electrons to form a dative bond with the *d*-block ion.

Some more complex molecules or ions have lone pairs in different places and can form two dative bonds with the central metal ion. The geometry has to be correct for this to happen, as a ring is formed. Such ligands are called **bidentate ligands**. Two examples are 1,2-diaminoethane, $NH_2CH_2CH_2NH_2$, and ethanedioate ions, $^-OOCCOO^-$.

Other species can form five or six dative bonds with the central metal ion. These are called **polydentate ligands**. One of the best reagents for forming complexes of this type is the disodium salt of EDTA. EDTA loses two further H^+ ions to give an ion with two amine groups and four carboxylate groups:

EDTA stands for ethylenediamine-tetraacetic acid.

Therefore, EDTA can form six dative bonds.

In the haemoglobin molecule, the iron ions are complexed with an organic species that can form five bonds to the metal. The sixth position is taken up either by an oxygen molecule (arterial blood) or by a water molecule (venous blood).

Some common ligands are listed in Table 10.4.

Ligand type	Name	Formula
Neutral	Water	H_2O
	Ammonia	NH_3
	Methylamine	CH_3NH_2
Negative ions	Fluoride	F^-
	Chloride	Cl^-
	Cyanide	CN^-*
	Thiocyanate	SCN^-
	Hydroxide	OH^-
	Sulphate	SO_4^{2-}
Bidentate	1,2-diaminoethane	$NH_2CH_2CH_2NH_2$
	Ethanedioate	

*Table 10.4
Common ligands*

* The cyanide ion normally bonds through the carbon atom.

- Iron in both the +2 and +3 states forms many complexes, for example:
  - When a solution of cyanide ions is added to a solution of hydrated iron(II) ions, the hexacyano complex is formed:

$$[Fe(H_2O)_6]^{2+} + 6CN^- \rightarrow [Fe(CN)_6]^{4-} + 6H_2O$$

  - When thiocyanate ions, SCN^-, are added to a solution of hydrated iron(III) ions, a blood-red complex is formed:

$$[Fe(H_2O)_6]^{3+} + SCN^- \rightarrow [Fe(H_2O)_5(NCS)]^{2+} + H_2O$$

This reaction can be used as a test for the presence of iron(III) ions in solution.
- Chromium in the +3 oxidation state forms many complexes. For example, when excess sodium hydroxide is added to a suspension of chromium(III) hydroxide, a green solution of the hexahydroxy complex is formed:

$$[Cr(H_2O)_3(OH)_3] + 3OH^- \rightarrow [Cr(OH)_6]^{3-} + 3H_2O$$

Catalytic activity

Transition metals and their compounds are good catalysts. This is particularly true of the elements at the right-hand side of the *d*-block.

Heterogeneous catalysts

A heterogeneous catalyst is in a different phase from the reactants. Many industrial processes use transition metals or their compounds as heterogeneous catalysts. For example, in the Haber process iron in the solid state is used to catalyse the reaction between hydrogen and nitrogen gases.

Metal catalysts work by providing active sites onto which the reactant molecules can bond (adsorb). The sequence of reaction is:

Step 1 (fast): gaseous reactants + active site → adsorbed reactants

Step 2 (slow): adsorbed reactants → adsorbed product

Step 3 (fast): adsorbed product → gaseous product + empty active site

The cycle is then repeated.

A transition metal can act as a catalyst because its energetically available *d*-orbitals can accept electrons from a reactant molecule or its *d*-electrons can form a bond with a reactant molecule. This can be illustrated by the catalytic hydrogenation of an alkene. The alkene bonds to an active site by its π-electrons becoming involved with an empty *d*-orbital in the catalyst. The σ-bond in the hydrogen molecule breaks and each hydrogen atom forms a bond through a *d*-electron on an atom in the catalyst. The two hydrogen atoms then bond with the partially broken π-bond in the alkene and the alkane formed is released from the surface of the catalyst.

Some heterogeneous catalysts work because of the variable oxidation state of the transition metal. For example, vanadium(V) oxide is used as the catalyst in the oxidation of sulphur dioxide to sulphur trioxide in the manufacture of sulphuric acid. The sulphur dioxide is oxidised by the vanadium(V) oxide, which is reduced to vanadium(IV) oxide:

$$SO_2(g) + V_2O_5(s) \rightarrow SO_3(g) + 2VO_2(s)$$

The oxygen then oxidises the vanadium(IV) oxide back to vanadium(V) oxide:

$$\tfrac{1}{2}O_2(g) + 2VO_2(s) \rightarrow V_2O_5(s)$$

The overall equation is:

$$SO_2(g) + \tfrac{1}{2}O_2(g) \rightarrow SO_3(g)$$

Homogeneous catalysts

Homogeneous catalysts are in the same phase as the reactants. They always work via an intermediate compound or ion. For example, Fe^{2+} ions catalyse the oxidation of iodide ions by persulphate ions in aqueous solution:

$$2I^-(aq) + S_2O_8{}^{2-}(aq) \rightarrow I_2(s) + 2SO_4{}^{2-}(aq)$$

The two reactants are negative ions and so repel each other, making the reaction very slow. When positively charged Fe^{2+} ions are added, they are oxidised by the negatively charged persulphate ions:

$$S_2O_8{}^{2-}(aq) + 2Fe^{2+}(aq) \rightarrow 2SO_4{}^{2-}(aq) + 2Fe^{3+}(aq)$$

The Fe^{3+} ions are then reduced by iodide ions, regenerating the Fe^{2+} catalyst.

$$2Fe^{3+}(aq) + 2I^-(aq) \rightarrow 2Fe^{2+}(aq) + I_2(s)$$

Transition metal oxides as acids and bases

- Oxides of transition metals in the +2 oxidation state are bases. They react with acids to form salts that are in solution and which contain M^{2+} ions, for example:

$$CuO + H_2SO_4 \rightarrow CuSO_4 + H_2O$$

The ionic equation is:

$$CuO(s) + 2H^+(aq) \rightarrow Cu^{2+}(aq) + H_2O(l)$$

- Oxides of transition metals in the +3 oxidation state are either bases or amphoteric. Iron(III) oxide, for example, is a base:

$$Fe_2O_3(s) + 6H^+(aq) \rightarrow 2Fe^{3+}(aq) + 3H_2O(l)$$

Chromium(III) oxide is amphoteric and, if freshly prepared, reacts with both acids and strong bases:

$$Cr_2O_3(s) + 6H^+(aq) \rightarrow 2Cr^{3+}(aq) + 3H_2O(l)$$
$$Cr_2O_3(s) + 6OH^-(aq) + 3H_2O(l) \rightarrow 2[Cr(OH)_6]^{3-}(aq)$$

- Oxides of transition metals in the +4 state are inert to aqueous acids and bases.
- Oxides of transition metals in the +5, +6 and +7 states are acidic and react with bases to form anions. For example, chromium(VI) oxide, CrO_3, reacts with strong alkali to form chromate(VI) ions:

$$CrO_3(s) + 2OH^-(aq) \rightarrow CrO_4{}^{2-}(aq) + H_2O(l)$$

Common physical properties of transition metal ions

Coloured ions

The d-orbitals in a transition metal ion are all at the same energy level, but they point in different direction. Three of the orbitals point between the x, y and z axes and two point along these axes.

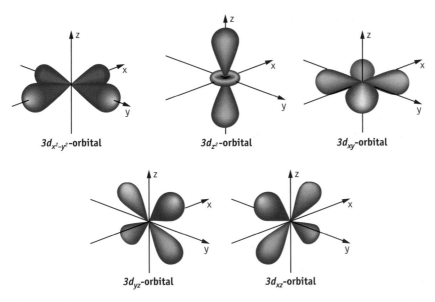

Figure 10.4 *Shapes of the d-orbitals*

$3d_{x^2-y^2}$-orbital $3d_{z^2}$-orbital $3d_{xy}$-orbital

$3d_{yz}$-orbital $3d_{xz}$-orbital

When six ligands approach the ion, they do so along the x, y and z axes. This causes greater repulsion with the two d-orbitals that point along the x, y and z axes than with the three that point between the axes. The energy levels of the d-orbitals are split into a lower group of three and an upper group of two (Figure 10.5).

$$E \Big| 3d \quad - - - - - - \quad \Big\langle \begin{array}{c} - \ - \\ \\ - \ - \end{array} \Big\uparrow \Delta_O$$

no ligand   with six ligands

Figure 10.5 *Splitting of d-orbitals by six ligands*

The energy difference Δ_O between these two sets of d-orbitals in a typical complex ion is equal to the energy of a photon in the visible region of the spectrum.

When white light shines through a solution of a complex ion of a transition metal, photons of a particular frequency are absorbed and their energy promotes an electron from the lower energy level to the upper energy level. This is called a d–d transition. A colour is *removed* from the white light and the solution has the complementary colour to the light absorbed.

Light

E

Light being absorbed   State after light absorbed

Figure 10.6 *Absorption of light energy*

(e) Ions with no d-electrons are not coloured simply because they do not have any d-electrons to promote. Therefore, Sc^{3+} and Ti^{4+} are colourless as both have the electron configuration of [Ar] $3d^0 4s^0$.

Within a fraction of a second the ion with an electron in the upper level collides with another ion. The electron drops down and energy is released as heat. The complex ion is once again in the ground state, able to absorb more light energy.

The colour wheel shown in Figure 10.7 shows the relationship between the colour of the light absorbed and the complementary colour of the complex ion. These colours are diametrically opposite each other.

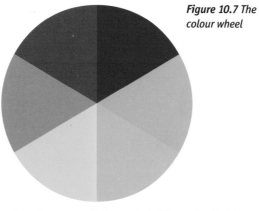

Figure 10.7 The colour wheel

The $[Cu(H_2O)_6]^{2+}$ ion absorbs orange light, so it is blue. The $[Ni(H_2O)_6]^{2+}$ ion absorbs red light, so it is green.

e The sequence of events for the colour of transition metal complexes is:

light energy absorbed removing colour from white light →
electron promoted to higher level

With flame colours, the opposite takes place:

heat from Bunsen → electron promoted →
electron falls back emitting coloured light

These two processes must not be confused.

Solutions of some complex metal ions (left to right: $[Ti(H_2O)_6]^{3+}$, $[Co(H_2O)_6]^{2+}$, $[Ni(H_2O)_6]^{2+}$ and $[Cu(H_2O)_6]^{2+}$)

Effect of ligand on colour

Some ligands interact more strongly than others with the *d*-electrons and so cause a greater splitting. The relative strength of ligands is shown in Figure 10.8.

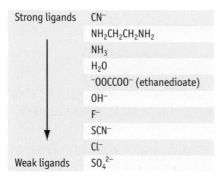

Strong ligands	CN^-
	$NH_2CH_2CH_2NH_2$
	NH_3
	H_2O
	$^-OOCCOO^-$ (ethanedioate)
	OH^-
	F^-
	SCN^-
	Cl^-
Weak ligands	SO_4^{2-}

Figure 10.8 Relative strength of ligands

ZAHOOR UL-HAQ

A strong ligand splits the *d*-orbitals in the complex ion to a greater extent than a weak ligand does.

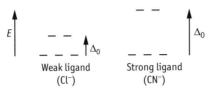

Figure 10.9 *Splitting of d-orbitals by different ligands*

If a stronger ligand replaces a weaker ligand, the colour absorbed moves towards the violet end of the spectrum. This can be shown by the addition of excess ammonia solution to aqueous copper sulphate. The reaction is:

$$[Cu(H_2O)_6]^{2+}(aq) + 4NH_3(aq) \rightarrow [Cu(NH_3)_4(H_2O)_2]^{2+}(aq) + 4H_2O(l)$$

Relatively weaker H_2O ligands have been replaced by stronger NH_3 ligands. The absorption moves from orange towards yellow and the colour of the complex changes from blue to violet-blue.

When concentrated HCl is added to a solution of copper(II) chloride, the equilibrium:

$$[Cu(H_2O)_6]^{2+} + 4Cl^-(aq) \rightleftharpoons [CuCl_4]^{2-}(aq) + 6H_2O(l)$$
$$\text{blue} \qquad\qquad\qquad \text{yellow}$$

is driven to the right. The colour changes from blue via green to yellow. The green colour is when both $[Cu(H_2O)_6]^{2+}$ and $[CuCl_4]^{2-}$ are present. The light absorbed changes from orange (causing the ion to be blue) to violet (causing the ion to be yellow).

Oxidation state of the transition metal ion

An ion with a high charge density will attract a ligand strongly, so the splitting of the *d*-orbitals will be greater. The $[Fe(H_2O)_6]^{2+}$ ion absorbs red light which means that it is green. The $[Fe(H_2O)_6]^{3+}$ ion absorbs yellow light and is amethyst (pale purple-violet).

Summary

■ The colour of transition metal complexes is caused by the ligand splitting the *d*-orbitals into two different sets of energy levels. Light is absorbed and an electron promoted. The colour of the complex is the complementary colour to that absorbed.

■ The *d*-orbital splitting of the transition metal, and hence the colour of the complex, depends on the nature of the ligand and on the oxidation state of the transition metal.

Magnetic properties

Some transition metals and their compounds are strongly magnetic. Iron, cobalt and nickel can be magnetised, as can the oxides Fe_3O_4 and CrO_2. These are known as **ferromagnetic** substances.

Most transition metal complexes are very slightly magnetic, and a needle made of their crystals will lie parallel to a strong magnetic field. This property is called **paramagnetism** and is caused by the ion having one or more unpaired *d*-electrons.

Reactions of *d*-block ions

Deprotonation

When a base is added to a solution of hydrated *d*-block ions, **deprotonation** takes place to a greater or lesser extent depending on the strength of the base.

> Deprotonation is a reaction in which the base removes a proton (H^+ ion) from the species.

Water is a weak base and only significantly deprotonates 3+ aqua ions such as $[Fe(H_2O)_6]^{3+}$:

$$[Fe(H_2O)_6]^{3+}(aq) + H_2O(l) \rightleftharpoons [Fe(H_2O)_5(OH)]^{2+}(aq) + H_3O^+(aq)$$
$$\text{amethyst} \qquad\qquad\qquad \text{yellow-brown}$$

The formation of the H_3O^+ ion makes a solution of an iron(III) compound acidic and changes the colour of the solution from the amethyst of the solid to yellow-brown. Further deprotonation is not extensive.

The charge density on the Fe^{2+} ion is lower, so it attracts the ligand electrons less and the hydrogen atoms in the water ligands are less δ^+. This means that very little deprotonation takes place with hydrated iron(II) ions and water.

All hydrated *d*-block ions are deprotonated when stronger bases, such as sodium hydroxide or ammonia are added. The deprotonation is so extensive that a neutral and hence insoluble species is produced, for example:

$$[Fe(H_2O)_6]^{3+}(aq) + 3OH^-(aq) \rightarrow [Fe(H_2O)_3(OH)_3](s) + 3H_2O(l)$$
$$[Fe(H_2O)_6]^{3+}(aq) + 3NH_3(aq) \rightarrow [Fe(H_2O)_3(OH)_3](s) + 3NH_4^+(aq)$$

Metals in the +2 oxidation state also form precipitates of the hydrated hydroxides, for example:

$$[Fe(H_2O)_6]^{2+}(aq) + 2OH^-(aq) \rightarrow [Fe(H_2O)_4(OH)_2](s) + 2H_2O(l)$$
$$[Fe(H_2O)_6]^{2+}(aq) + 2NH_3(aq) \rightarrow [Fe(H_2O)_4(OH)_2](s) + 2NH_4^+(aq)$$

$$[Cu(H_2O)_6]^{2+}(aq) + 2OH^-(aq) \rightarrow [Cu(H_2O)_4(OH)_2](s) + 2H_2O(l)$$
$$[Cu(H_2O)_6]^{2+}(aq) + 2NH_3(aq) \rightarrow [Cu(H_2O)_4(OH)_2](s) + 2NH_4^+(aq)$$

With some *d*-block metal ions, if an excess of a very strong base is added, further deprotonation can take place. These are the amphoteric hydroxides that dissolve in excess sodium hydroxide solution, for example:

$$[Cr(H_2O)_3(OH)_3](s) + 3OH^-(aq) \rightarrow [Cr(OH)_6]^{3-}(aq) + 3H_2O(l)$$

$$[Zn(H_2O)_2(OH)_2](s) + 2OH^-(aq) \rightarrow [Zn(OH)_4]^{2-}(aq) + 2H_2O(l)$$

The colour of the hydrated hydroxide formed with sodium hydroxide solution and whether or not the precipitate dissolves in excess can be used to identify a transition metal and its oxidation state. The colours are listed in Table 10.5.

Ion	Colour of precipitate	Effect of adding excess NaOH
Cr^{3+} in $[Cr(H_2O)_6]^{3+}$	Green	Forms green solution
Mn^{2+} in $[Mn(H_2O)_6]^{2+}$	Off-white*	None
Fe^{2+} in $[Fe(H_2O)_6]^{2+}$	Green†	None
Fe^{3+} in $[Fe(H_2O)_6]^{3+}$	Red-brown	None
Co^{2+} in $[Co(H_2O)_6]^{2+}$	Pink‡	None
Ni^{2+} in $[Ni(H_2O)_6]^{2+}$	Green	None
Cu^{2+} in $[Cu(H_2O)_6]^{2+}$	Blue	None
Zn^{2+} in $[Zn(H_2O)_6]^{2+}$	White	Forms colourless solution

* The precipitate with Mn(II) salts darkens on exposure to air as it is slowly oxidised to manganese(IV) oxide. Darkening is much more rapid if an oxidising agent (e.g. H_2O_2) is added to the precipitate.

† The precipitate with Fe(II) salts goes brown on exposure to air as it is oxidised to iron(III) hydroxide. Darkening is much more rapid if an oxidising agent (e.g. H_2O_2) is added to the precipitate. Very pure solutions of Fe^{2+} ions give a pale green (almost white) precipitate of hydrated iron(II) hydroxide.

‡ The precipitate of $Co(OH)_2$ turns pink on standing as some water molecules are lost from the hydrated hydroxide.

When sodium hydroxide is added to a solution of a silver salt, deprotonation of the $[Ag(H_2O)_2]^+$ ions takes place followed by dehydration of the hydroxide to form a brown precipitate of silver oxide:

$$2[Ag(H_2O)_2]^+(aq) + 2OH^-(aq) \rightarrow$$
$$Ag_2O(s) + 5H_2O(l)$$

Ligand exchange reactions

In most complex ions, the ligands are not irreversibly bound and so can be replaced.

■ One test for Fe^{3+} ions is to add a solution of potassium thiocyanate, KSCN. An intense blood-red complex is formed with hydrated iron(III) ions:

$$[Fe(H_2O)_6]^{3+} + SCN^- \rightarrow [Fe(H_2O)_5NCS]^{2+} + H_2O$$

One water ligand is exchanged for one SCN^- ligand.

■ If some cobalt(II) chloride is dissolved in a minimum quantity of water and then ethanol is added drop by drop to dehydrate the solution, ligand exchange takes place and the solution turns from red to blue:

$$[Co(H_2O)_6]^{2+} + 4Cl^- \rightleftharpoons [CoCl_4]^{2-} + 6H_2O$$
$$\text{Red} \qquad\qquad\qquad \text{Blue}$$

On addition of water, the reaction is reversed and the blue colour changes back to red.

■ Potassium hexacyanoferrate(II) can be prepared by adding potassium cyanide to a solution of hydrated iron(II) ions:

$$[Fe(H_2O)_6]^{2+} + 6CN^- \rightarrow [Fe(CN)_6]^{4-} + 6H_2O$$

The cyano complex is so stable that solutions of it are not poisonous.

ANDREW LAMBERT PHOTOGRAPHY/SPL

Hydroxides of, from left: iron(II), iron(III), copper(II) and nickel(II)

An immediate dose of iron(II) sulphate is an antidote to cyanide poisoning.

Addition of ammonia

The addition of excess ammonia solution to some ions results in ligand exchange. These are the ions that dissolve in excess ammonia to form an ammine. All transition metal ions are first deprotonated by basic ammonia forming precipitates of hydrated hydroxides. The hydroxides of cobalt(II), nickel(II), copper(II), zinc(II) and silver(I) readily form an ammine by ligand exchange. The precipitate of chromium(III) hydroxide partially reacts very slowly to form an ammonia complex.

The blue precipitate of hydrated copper(II) hydroxide redissolves in excess ammonia solution:

$$[Cu(H_2O)_4(OH)_2](s) + 4NH_3(aq) \rightarrow$$
$$[Cu(NH_3)_4(H_2O)_2]^{2+} + 2OH^-(aq) + 2H_2O(l)$$

The results of gradually adding ammonia solution to hydrated ions of some d-block elements until it is in excess are shown in Table 10.6.

Ion	Colour of precipitate	Effect of adding excess ammonia
Mn^{2+} in $[Mn(H_2O)_6]^{2+}$	Off-white*	None
Fe^{2+} in $[Fe(H_2O)_6]^{2+}$	Green*	None
Cr^{3+} in $[Cr(H_2O)_6]^{3+}$	Green	†Dissolves slightly to form a green solution
Fe^{3+} in $[Fe(H_2O)_6]^{3+}$	Red-brown	None
Co^{2+} in $[Co(H_2O)_6]^{2+}$	Pink	Dissolves to form a brown solution
Ni^{2+} in $[Ni(H_2O)_6]^{2+}$	Green	Dissolves to form a pale blue solution
Cu^{2+} in $[Cu(H_2O)_6]^{2+}$	Blue	Dissolves to form a deep blue solution
Zn^{2+} in $[Zn(H_2O)_6]^{2+}$	White	Dissolves to form a colourless solution
Ag^+ in $[Ag(H_2O)_2]^+$	Brown‡	Dissolves to form a colourless solution

Table 10.6 Effect of adding ammonia solution

* The precipitates of $Mn(OH)_2$ and $Fe(OH)_2$ darken as they oxidise in air.

† The ammonia complex with chromium hydroxide forms very slowly. If liquid ammonia is added to solid hydrated chromium(III) chloride, the ammonia molecules take the place of water molecules around the chromium ion:

$$[Cr(H_2O)_6]Cl_3 + 6NH_3 \rightarrow [Cr(NH_3)_6]Cl_3 + 6H_2O$$

‡ The brown precipitate of silver oxide is often not seen because the ammonia complex forms so easily. Adding ammonia solution to a precipitate of AgCl or AgBr also makes this silver complex:

$$AgCl(s) + 2NH_3(aq) \rightarrow [Ag(NH_3)_2]^+(aq) + Cl^-(aq)$$

AgBr is so insoluble that concentrated ammonia is required. AgI is even more insoluble and the complex does not form, even with concentrated ammonia.

Redox reactions

It is because transition metals have variable oxidation states that redox reactions are very common.

The ease with which a transition metal ion is oxidised or reduced is given by its standard reduction potential, $E^{\ominus}$.

- The more negative this potential, the worse the ion on the left-hand side of the half-equation is as an oxidising agent and the better the ion on the right-hand side of the half-equation is as a reducing agent.

e It is usual to write the hydrated ion as $M^{x+}(aq)$ (or even just M^{x+}) rather than write out all the water ligands in the formula. This is acceptable if ligand exchange or deprotonation does not take place.

- The more positive the value of E°, the better the ion on the left-hand side of the half-equation is as an oxidising agent and the worse the ion on the right-hand side is as a reducing agent.

For example:

$$V^{3+} + e^- \rightleftharpoons V^{2+} \qquad E^\circ = -0.26 \text{ V}$$
$$Fe^{3+} + e^- \rightleftharpoons Fe^{2+} \qquad E^\circ = +0.77 \text{ V}$$
$$\tfrac{1}{2}Cr_2O_7^{2-} + 7H^+ + 3e^- \rightleftharpoons Cr^{3+} + 3\tfrac{1}{2}H_2O \quad E^\circ = +1.33 \text{ V}$$

Dichromate(VI) ions are the best oxidising agent and vanadium(III) ions are the worst.

Chromium(III) ions are the worst reducing agent and vanadium(II) ions are the best.

The feasibility of a redox reaction is indicated by the value of the standard potential of the cell, E°_{cell}.

Feasibility is worked out by first reversing the half-equation that has one of the reactants on the right-hand side and changing the sign of its E° value. This half-equation is then added to the half-equation that has the other reactant on the left-hand side. The sum of the E° values for the two half-equations gives E°_{cell}. If the value is positive, the reaction is thermodynamically feasible.

> ### Worked example
> Will V^{2+} ions reduce Fe^{3+} ions to Fe^{2+}?
>
> **Answer**
> $$V^{3+} + e^- \rightleftharpoons V^{2+} \qquad E^\circ = -0.26 \text{ V}$$
> $$Fe^{3+} + e^- \rightleftharpoons Fe^{2+} \qquad E^\circ = +0.77 \text{ V}$$
> Reverse the first half-equation and then add it to the second half-equation:
> $$V^{2+} \rightleftharpoons V^{3+} + e^- \quad E^\circ = -(-0.26) = +0.26 \text{ V}$$
> $$Fe^{3+} + e^- \rightleftharpoons Fe^{2+} \qquad E^\circ = +0.77 \text{ V}$$
> $$E^\circ_{cell} = +0.26 + (+0.77) = +1.03 \text{ V}$$
> E°_{cell} is positive, so the reaction is feasible and the **reactants are thermodynamically unstable** relative to the products.

In some cases the activation energy of the reaction could be too high for the reaction to take place rapidly enough to be observed at room temperature. The reactants are then said to be **kinetically stable** relative to the products.

The standard reduction potentials of some transition metal ions, arranged in order of increasing oxidising power, are given in Table 10.7. The ion on the top right (Cr^{2+}) is the best reducing agent in the list and that at the bottom right (Fe^{3+}) is the worst reducing agent.

Notice the effect of the ligand on the value of E°:
- The reduction potential of the hydrated iron(II) ion is more positive than that of the hexacyanoferrate(III) ion. This means that the +3 oxidation state

becomes stabilised relative to the +2 state by the change to the strong cyanide ligand. Therefore, hydrated iron(III) is a stronger oxidising agent than hexa-cyanoiron(III).

Half-equation	$E^{\ominus}$/V
$Cr^{3+} + e^- \rightarrow Cr^{2+}$	−0.74
$V^{3+} + e^- \rightarrow V^{2+}$	−0.26
$CrO_4^{2-} + 4H_2O + 3e^- \rightarrow Cr(OH)_3 + 5OH^-$	−0.13
$[Co(NH_3)_6]^{3+} + e^- \rightarrow [Co(NH_3)_6]^{2+}$	+0.10
$Cu^{2+} + e^- \rightarrow Cu^+$	+0.15
$VO^{2+} + 2H^+ + e^- \rightarrow V^{3+} + H_2O$	+0.34
$[Fe(CN)_6]^{3-} + e^- \rightarrow [Fe(CN)_6]^{4-}$	+0.36
$Cu^+ + e^- \rightarrow Cu$	+0.52
$MnO_4^{2-} + 2H_2O + 2e^- \rightarrow MnO_2 + 4OH^-$	+0.59
$Fe^{3+} + e^- \rightarrow Fe^{2+}$	+0.77
$VO_2^+ + 2H^+ + e^- \rightarrow VO^{2+} + H_2O$	+1.00
$MnO_2 + 4H^+ + 2e^- \rightarrow Mn^{2+} + 2H_2O$	+1.23
$Cr_2O_7^{2-} + 14H^+ + 6e^- \rightarrow 2Cr^{3+} + 7H_2O$	+1.33
$MnO_4^- + 8H^+ + 5e^- \rightarrow Mn^{2+} + 4H_2O$	+1.51
$Co^{3+} + e^- \rightarrow Co^{2+}$	+1.81
$FeO_4^{2-} + 8H^+ + 3e^- \rightarrow Fe^{3+} + 4H_2O$	+2.20

Table 10.7 Standard reduction potentials for some transition metal ions

◀ In Table 10.7, the water ligands have been omitted to simplify the equations. Ligands other than H_2O are included in the formulae.

■ This is even more noticeable with cobalt(III). Almost nothing will oxidise hydrated Co^{2+} ions to hydrated Co^{3+} ions, but if the Co^{2+} is complexed with ammonia, the oxidation can take place.

Notice also the effect of pH. The definition of standard reduction potential assumes that all soluble species are at a concentration of 1 mol dm^{-3}. Therefore, if OH$^-$ appears on either side of a half-equation, the solution is assumed to be at pH 14; if H$^+$ is in the equation, the pH is assumed to be 0.

If it is required to oxidise chromium from the +3 state to +6, it is easier if the solution is alkaline. The *oxidation* potentials are the negative of the reduction potentials:

$$Cr(OH)_3 + 5OH^- \rightarrow CrO_4^{2-} + 4H_2O + 3e^- \quad E^{\ominus} = -(-0.13) = +0.13 \text{ V}$$
$$Cr^{3+} + 3\tfrac{1}{2}H_2O \rightarrow \tfrac{1}{2}Cr_2O_7^{2-} + 7H^+ + 3e^- \quad E^{\ominus} = -(+1.33) = -1.33 \text{ V}$$

In alkaline conditions (pH 14), an oxidising agent with a reduction potential greater than −0.13 V will oxidise chromium hydroxide to chromate(VI) ions.

In acid conditions (pH 0), an oxidising agent with a reduction potential greater than +1.33 V will oxidise Cr^{3+} ions to dichromate(VI).

ⓔ A reduction potential measures the ease of reduction of a substance. The more positive the reduction potential, the more likely it is that the substance will be reduced and, therefore, the stronger it is as an oxidising agent.

ⓔ An oxidation potential measures the ease of oxidation of a species. The more positive the oxidation potential is, the more likely it is that the species will be oxidised.

Worked example 1

Use the following data and those in Table 10.7 to predict whether hydrogen peroxide will oxidise chromium(III) hydroxide to chromate(VI) ions in alkaline solution. If so, write the overall equation.

$$H_2O_2 + 2e^- \rightleftharpoons 2OH^- \quad E^{\ominus} = +1.24 \text{ V}$$

Answer

The reduction potential equation of $CrO_4^{2-}/Cr(OH)_3$ must be reversed (and multiplied by 2) and then added to the H_2O_2/OH^- half-equation (multiplied by 3 to get $6e^-$ in both half-equations).

$2Cr(OH)_3 + 10OH^- \rightarrow 2CrO_4^{2-} + 8H_2O + 6e^-$ $E^\ominus = -(-0.13) = +0.13\ V$

$3H_2O_2 + 6e^- \rightleftharpoons 6OH^-$ $E^\ominus = +1.24\ V$

$2Cr(OH)_3 + 3H_2O_2 + 4OH^- \rightleftharpoons 2CrO_4^{2-} + 8H_2O$ $E^\ominus_{cell} = +0.13 + (+1.24) = +1.37\ V$

The value of $E^\ominus_{cell}$ is positive, so the reaction is feasible.

Worked example 2

Use the following data and those in Table 10.7 to predict whether dichromate(VI) ions, $Cr_2O_7^{2-}$, in acid solution, will oxidise hydrogen peroxide to oxygen. If so, write the overall equation.

$O_2 + 2H^+ + 2e^- \rightleftharpoons H_2O_2$ $E^\ominus = +0.68\ V$

Answer

The reduction potential of O_2/H_2O_2 must be reversed (and multiplied by 3) and then added to the $Cr_2O_7^{2-}/Cr^{3+}$ half-equation:

$3H_2O_2 \rightleftharpoons 3O_2 + 6H^+ + 6e^-$ $E^\ominus = -(+0.68) = -0.68\ V$

$Cr_2O_7^{2-} + 14H^+ + 6e^- \rightarrow 2Cr^{3+} + 7H_2O$ $E^\ominus = +1.33\ V$

$3H_2O_2 + Cr_2O_7^{2-} + 8H^+ \rightleftharpoons 3O_2 + 2Cr^{3+} + 7H_2O$ $E^\ominus_{cell} = +1.33 + (-0.68) = +0.65\ V$

The value of $E^\ominus_{cell}$ is positive, so the reaction is feasible. Hydrogen peroxide should be oxidised to oxygen by acidified dichromate(VI) ions.

Whether hydrogen peroxide oxidises Cr^{3+} to chromate(VI) or reduces chromate(VI) to Cr^{3+} depends on the pH of the solution.

Copper(I) ions are not stable in aqueous solution. The reduction potentials in Table 10.7 show that copper(I) ions will disproportionate into copper metal and copper(II) ions as $E^\ominus_{cell}$ for the reaction is positive:

$Cu^+ + e^- \rightleftharpoons Cu$ $E^\ominus = +0.52\ V$

$Cu^+ \rightleftharpoons Cu^{2+} + e^-$ $E^\ominus = -(+0.15)\ V = -0.15\ V$

$2Cu^+ \rightleftharpoons Cu + Cu^{2+}$ $E^\ominus_{cell} = +0.52 + (-0.15) = +0.37\ V$

Insoluble copper(I) compounds and copper(I) complex ions exist.
- Copper(I) oxide, Cu_2O, is the red precipitate formed when an aldehyde reduces Fehling's solution.
- Copper(I) iodide is precipitated when iodide ions reduce copper(II) ions:

$2Cu^{2+} + 4I^- \rightarrow 2CuI + I_2$

The addition of ammonia solution to this precipitate produces a colourless solution of the copper(I) ammonia complex:

$CuI(s) + 2NH_3(aq) \rightarrow [Cu(NH_3)_2]^+(aq) + I^-(aq)$

A blue colour begins to form on the surface of this colourless solution as the copper(I) complex is slowly oxidised by the oxygen in the air to form the copper(II) complex. This blue colour gradually spreads through the whole solution.

e Note that hydrogen peroxide can be either a reducing agent or an oxidising agent because the oxygen is in the –1 oxidation state and can be oxidised to 0 in O_2 or reduced to –2 in H_2O.

10

Vanadium chemistry

Vanadium forms compounds in the +2, +3, +4 and +5 oxidation states. The colour of the ions depends on the oxidation state of vanadium.

Oxidation state	Formula of the ion	Colour
+2	V^{2+}	Lavender
+3	V^{3+}	Green
+4	VO^{2+}	Blue
+5	VO_2^+	Yellow
	VO_3^-	Colourless

Table 10.8 Oxidation states of vanadium and colours of the ions

Solutions of vanadium in the +2, +3, +4 and +5 oxidation states

ANDREW LAMBERT PHOTOGRAPHY/SPL

Ammonium vanadate(v), NH_4VO_3, is a colourless solid, but when added to water, the solution is yellow. This is because of the reaction:

$$VO_3^- + H_2O \rightleftharpoons VO_2^+ + 2OH^-$$

Addition of acid drives the equilibrium to the right and the yellow colour becomes more intense.

This is not a redox reaction because vanadium is in the +5 oxidation state in both VO_3^- and VO_2^+.

The standard reduction potentials for the redox changes of vanadium are shown in Table 10.9.

Reduction half-equation	Change in oxidation state	$E^\ominus$/V
$VO_2^+ + 2H^+ + e^- \rightleftharpoons VO^{2+} + H_2O$	+5 to +4	+1.00
$VO^{2+} + 2H^+ + e^- \rightleftharpoons V^{3+} + H_2O$	+4 to +3	+0.34
$V^{3+} + e^- \rightleftharpoons V^{2+}$	+3 to +2	−0.26

Table 10.9 Standard reduction potentials for vanadium

Reduction of vanadium species

Reduction from +5 to +2

Any substance with an *oxidation* potential in acid solution (pH 0) that is more positive than −0.26 V will reduce vanadium from the +5 state to the +2 state, assuming that the reaction is *kinetically* feasible.

The standard reduction potential of Zn^{2+}/Zn is -0.76 V, so the oxidation potential of Zn is given by:

$$Zn \rightleftharpoons Zn^{2+} + 2e^- \quad E^\circ = -(-0.76) = +0.76 \text{ V}$$

This is more positive than -0.26 V, so it is thermodynamically feasible for zinc metal to reduce vanadium(v) to vanadium(ii).

If a solution of ammonium vanadate(v) is reacted with zinc powder in hydrochloric acid, the colour of the solution changes as the vanadium is reduced in stages from the +5 state to the +2 state:

- The solution is initially yellow, because of the VO_2^+ ions.
- As reduction starts, the solution turns green. This is when some of the yellow VO_2^+ ions have been reduced to blue VO^{2+} ions — yellow plus blue appears green.
- The green colour changes to blue. This is when all the VO_2^+ ions have been reduced to blue hydrated VO^{2+} ions.
- The solution next changes to green. This is when all the VO^{2+} ions have been converted into green hydrated V^{3+} ions.
- After prolonged reduction in the absence of air, the solution finally turns lavender. This is caused by hydrated V^{2+} ions.

The sequence is:

Yellow	$\rightarrow$	Green	$\rightarrow$	Blue	$\rightarrow$	Green	$\rightarrow$	Lavender
VO_2^+	$\rightarrow$	VO_2^+ and VO^{2+}	$\rightarrow$	VO^{2+}	$\rightarrow$	V^{3+}	$\rightarrow$	V^{2+}

Reduction from +5 to +4

A reducing agent must be chosen that has an oxidation potential between -1.00 V and -0.34 V.

> **Worked example**
>
> Show that Fe^{2+} ions will reduce vanadium from the +5 state to the +4 state and no further.
> $$Fe^{3+} + e^- \rightleftharpoons Fe^{2+} \quad E^\circ = +0.77 \text{ V}$$
>
> **Answer**
>
> The oxidation potential for $Fe^{2+} \rightleftharpoons Fe^{3+} + e^- = E^\circ = -(+0.77) = -0.77$ V
>
> E°_{cell} and the overall equation for the reduction of VO_2^+ to VO^{2+} by Fe^{2+} ions are given by:
>
> | | |
> |---|---|
> | $VO_2^+ + 2H^+ + e^- \rightleftharpoons VO^{2+} + H_2O$ | $E^\circ = +1.00$ V |
> | $Fe^{2+} \rightleftharpoons Fe^{3+} + e^-$ | $E^\circ = -0.77$ V |
> | $VO_2^+ + 2H^+ + Fe^{2+} \rightleftharpoons VO^{2+} + H_2O + Fe^{3+}$ | $E^\circ_{cell} = +1.00 + (-0.77) = +0.23$ V |
>
> E°_{cell} is positive, so the reaction is feasible.
>
> The cell potential for the reduction of VO^{2+} to V^{3+} is given by:
>
> | | |
> |---|---|
> | $VO^{2+} + 2H^+ + e^- \rightleftharpoons V^{3+} + H_2O$ | $E^\circ = +0.34$ V |
> | $Fe^{2+} \rightleftharpoons Fe^{3+} + e^-$ | $E^\circ = -0.77$ V |
> | $VO^{2+} + 2H^+ + Fe^{2+} \rightleftharpoons V^{3+} + H_2O + Fe^{3+}$ | $E^\circ_{cell} = +0.34 + (-0.77) = -0.43$ V |
>
> E°_{cell} is negative, so this reaction will not take place. Therefore, iron(ii) ions will reduce vanadium(v) to vanadium(iv) and no further.

e The final stage is best carried out with a Bunsen valve fitted to the apparatus. This allows hydrogen, produced by the zinc and acid, to escape, but does not allow air into the flask.

Reduction from +4 to +3

A reducing agent must be chosen that has an oxidation potential between -0.34 V and $+0.26$ V.

Tin(II) compounds will carry out this reduction. The standard reduction potential for the Sn^{4+}/Sn^{2+} system is $+0.15$ V. The oxidation potential is:

$$Sn^{2+} \rightleftharpoons Sn^{4+} + 2e^- \qquad E^\circ = -0.15 \text{ V}$$

E°_{cell} for the reduction of VO^{2+} to V^{3+} = $+0.34 + (-0.15) = +0.19$ V. This is a positive value, so the reaction is feasible.

Further reduction to V^{2+} would have an $E^\circ_{cell} = -0.26 + (-0.15) = -0.41$ V. This is negative, so further reduction will not take place.

Oxidation of vanadium species

Oxidation from +2 to +3

Any oxidising agent that has a reduction potential that is less negative than -0.26 V will oxidise vanadium(II). However, to oxidise vanadium(II) to vanadium(III) and no further, the reduction potential must be in the range -0.26 V to $+0.34$ V.

Oxidation from +3 to +4

Any oxidising agent that has a reduction potential between $+0.34$ V and $+1.00$ V will oxidise vanadium to the +4 state and no further.

Fe^{3+} ions ($Fe^{3+} + e^- \rightleftharpoons Fe^{2+}$ $E^\circ = +0.77$ V) will do this.

Oxidation from +4 to +5

To oxidise the +4 state to +5 requires a powerful oxidising agent that has a standard reduction potential greater than 1.0 V. A simple example is chlorine gas:

$$\frac{1}{2}Cl_2 + e^- \rightleftharpoons Cl^- \qquad\qquad E^\circ = +1.36 \text{ V}$$
$$\underline{VO^{2+} + H_2O \rightleftharpoons VO_2^+ + 2H^+ + e^- \qquad E^\circ = -1.00 \text{ V}}$$
$$VO^{2+} + H_2O + \tfrac{1}{2}Cl_2 \rightleftharpoons VO_2^+ + 2H^+ + Cl^- \qquad E^\circ_{cell} = +1.36 + (-1.00) = +0.36 \text{ V}$$

The value of E°_{cell} is positive, so the oxidation of vanadium(IV) to vanadium(V) by chlorine is feasible.

Uses of some *d*-block metals and their compounds

Many transition metals or their alloys are used for structural or decorative purposes.

An alloy is a mixture of a metal with at least one other element, usually another metal, but sometimes carbon.

Transition metals are often used as catalysts in industrial processes.

Titanium

Titanium forms a protective oxide layer and does not corrode, even at high temperatures. It also has a significantly high melting point and a good strength-to-weight ratio. It is used as a structural material where weight is an important factor (such as in aeroplanes and racing bicycles) or where high temperatures have to be withstood, such as in jet engines.

It is very difficult to weld, so articles made from titanium are expensive.

Titanium(IV) oxide is used as the main component of domestic paints. It is white but can be mixed with dyes to form coloured paints.

Titanium(IV) chloride is used as a catalyst in the Ziegler–Natta process for polymerisation of alkenes (p. 313).

JAMES KING-HOLMES/SPL

Titanium fan blades for the engines used to power jet aircraft

Chromium

Chromium also forms a protective oxide layer, but does not have as good a strength-to-weight ratio as titanium. It is itself not used as a structural metal, but is found, alloyed with iron and nickel, in stainless steel.

Iron

Iron is the second most abundant metal in the Earth's crust. It is also easily extracted from its ore by reducing iron oxide with carbon monoxide made in the blast furnace from pre-heated air and coke. It is by far the cheapest metal and has many structural uses: from frameworks in industrial buildings to car bodies. It is normally alloyed with a small percentage of carbon, which increases its strength. Cast iron has a higher percentage of carbon (about 2%) and is extremely strong, but brittle. Iron is used as the catalyst in the Haber process for manufacturing ammonia.

The iron bridge at Ironbridge

ONTANET/R. G. PARKES

Copper

Copper is a very good electrical conductor; only silver is better.

Copper can be alloyed with zinc to form brass and with tin to form bronze. Ores containing tin and copper are easily reduced to the metals, so early civilisations were able to manufacture bronze for weapons and artefacts. Higher technological skills are needed to reduce iron ore to iron, so the Iron Age followed the Bronze Age.

Copper(II) compounds are used as fungicides and copper metal is used as a catalyst in the manufacture of hydrogen from methane.

A bronze chariot from the tombs at Xian in China

SUSANNAH HEAD

Questions

1 Give the electron configurations of vanadium and the V^{3+} ion.

$$V \qquad 1s^2 ....$$
$$V^{3+} \qquad 1s^2 ....$$

2 Explain why molybdenum has the electron configuration $[Kr]\ 4d^5\ 5s^1$.

3 Explain why the first ionisation energies of the p-block elements increase considerably from left to right whereas those of the d-block elements hardly alter.

4 Explain why the melting point of titanium is higher than that of calcium.

5 Draw a dot-and-cross diagram, showing the outer electrons only, for:
   a CrO_4^{2-}
   b VO_2^{+}

6 Explain why titanium can form both 2+ and 3+ ions whereas calcium and zinc do not form 3+ ions.

7 Write equations for the reactions, if any, of dilute hydrochloric acid and of aqueous sodium hydroxide with:
a iron(III) oxide, Fe_2O_3
b iron(VI) oxide, FeO_3

8 Draw a diagram of the $[Cr(H_2O)_6]^{3+}$ ion to show its shape. Mark on your diagram the bond angles. Name the types of bond in the ion and say where in the structure these bonds occur.

9 Give the formula of a compound of chromium in the following oxidation states:
a +2
b +3
c +6

10 Give the name and formula of a copper compound in:
a the +1 oxidation state
b the +2 oxidation state

11 Give the formula of:
a a chromium(III) complex ion
b a copper(II) complex ion

12 What colour of light is absorbed by:
a $[Cr(H_2O)_4Cl_2]^+$, which is green?
b $[Fe(H_2O)_5NCS]^{2+}$, which is red?

13 Explain why hydrated Ti^{4+} ions are colourless, but hydrated Ti^{3+} ions are coloured.

14 Explain why, when ammonia is added to copper(II) sulphate solution, the colour changes from turquoise (blue-green) to violet-blue.

15 What factors affect the colours of transition metal ions?

16 Why is anhydrous copper(II) sulphate white?

17 State what you would see, and write the equations for, the reactions of sodium hydroxide and of ammonia solution with:
a a solution of cobalt(II) ions
b a solution of copper(II) ions

18 When sodium hydroxide solution is added to a solution of iron(II) ions, a green precipitate is produced. When hydrogen peroxide solution is then added, the precipitate turns red-brown. Identify the green and red-brown precipitates and explain what is happening in the two reactions.

19 Hydrated chromium(III) ions can be deprotonated. Write equations to show the deprotonation that takes place when:
a the hydrated ions are dissolved in water
b sodium hydroxide is added to the hydrated ions, slowly and then in excess

20 Tartrate ions have the formula $C_4H_4O_6^{2-}$. They can be oxidised by hydrogen peroxide in aqueous solution, but the reaction is very slow, so bubbles of carbon dioxide are released slowly:

$$C_4H_4O_6^{2-} + 5H_2O_2 + 2H^+ \rightarrow 4CO_2 + 8H_2O$$

When some pink cobalt(II) solution is added, vigorous bubbling is seen as carbon dioxide is rapidly produced and the solution turns green.

After the bubbles have ceased, the solution slowly turns back to pink.

a Explain the function of the cobalt(II) ions. Justify your answer.
b Suggest equations for the reactions involving the cobalt(II) ions.

21 A 25.0 cm³ sample of a 0.100 mol dm⁻³ solution of V^{3+} ions was placed in a conical flask and excess dilute sulphuric acid added. Potassium manganate(VII) of concentration 0.0500 mol dm⁻³ was added from a burette until a faint pink colour was seen. The titre was 20.0 cm³.

a Calculate the amount (moles) of potassium manganate(VII) ions in the titre that is reduced from the +7 to the +2 state.
b Calculate the number of moles of electrons that the manganate(VII) has received from the vanadium(III) ions.
c Calculate the amount (moles) of vanadium(III) ions in the sample.
d Calculate the oxidation state of the vanadium after reaction with potassium manganate(VII).

Use the E° values in Table 10.7 on page 200 and Table 9.1 on page 167 for data for the following questions.

22 a Predict whether hydrogen sulphide will reduce VO_2^+ ions to VO^{2+} or V^{3+} ions.
b Write the equation for the reaction that takes place.

23 a Predict the oxidation state of vanadium when oxygen gas is blown through an acidified solution of V^{2+} ions.

b Write the equation for the reaction that takes place.

24 a Predict whether iodine will oxidise V^{3+} ions to VO^{2+} or to VO_2^+ or not react at all.

   b Write the equation for the reaction that takes place.

25 Predict whether chloride and bromide ions will be oxidised by manganese(IV) oxide, MnO_2, in acid solution.

26 The reduction potential for Cr^{2+} ions being reduced to chromium metal is $-0.91\,V$ and that for Cr^{3+} ions being reduced to Cr^{2+} ions is $-0.41\,V$:

$$Cr^{2+} + e^- \rightleftharpoons Cr \quad E^\ominus = -0.91\,V$$

$$Cr^{3+} + e^- \rightleftharpoons Cr^{2+} \quad E^\ominus = -0.41\,V$$

Predict whether Cr^{2+} ions will disproportionate in aqueous solution to Cr metal and Cr^{3+} ions. If so, write the equation for the reaction that takes place.

Reaction kinetics

Chapter 11

Introduction

The rate of a chemical reaction is the rate of change of concentration of a reactant or product with time.

Its units are mol dm^{-3} s^{-1}.

The *average* rate is defined as:

$$\text{rate} = \frac{\Delta \text{concentration}}{\Delta \text{time}}$$

where Δconcentration is the change in concentration of a reactant or product and Δtime is the time over which this change takes place.

This is only a reasonable assumption if the concentration of a reactant has fallen by less than 10% during the time elapsed.

Required AS chemistry

Collision theory

For a reaction to take place, reactant molecules must collide:
- with kinetic energy greater than or equal to the activation energy of the reaction
- with the correct orientation

Maxwell–Boltzmann distribution of energy

The molecules in a gas or liquid and the molecules or ions in a solution move at different speeds. They possess different amounts of kinetic energy. This is shown by the blue line in Figure 11.1. The total number of molecules with energy equal to or greater than a particular energy value is given by the area under the graph to the *right* of that energy. Thus the blue area to the right of the **activation energy**, E_a, is the fraction of molecules that have sufficient energy (at temperature T_1) to react on collision, providing that the orientation of collision is correct.

ℯ The value of Δ[reactant] is negative because its concentration decreases with time. Therefore, a more correct definition of rate is:

$$\text{rate} = \frac{-\Delta[\text{reactant}]}{\Delta \text{time}}$$

or

$$\text{rate} = \frac{+\Delta[\text{product}]}{\Delta \text{time}}$$

This gives a positive value for the rate in both cases.

ℯ The content of Unit 2 is assumed knowledge for Unit 5.

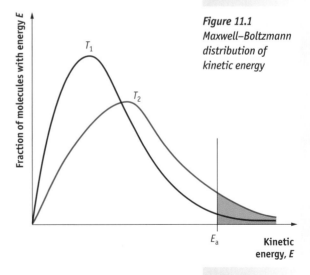

Figure 11.1
Maxwell–Boltzmann distribution of kinetic energy

Effect of temperature on rate

When the temperature is increased, the molecules or ions gain kinetic energy. They have a greater range of energies (greater entropy) and the average energy is increased. This means that the peak of the Maxwell–Boltzmann distribution is lowered and moved to the right. This is shown by the red line (at temperature T_2) in Figure 11.1. The red area to the right of the activation energy is greatly increased because a much greater *proportion* of the colliding molecules have energy greater than or equal to the activation energy. Therefore, a greater proportion of collisions will result in reaction.

A reaction that takes place fairly quickly at room temperature has an activation energy of about 60 kJ mol⁻¹. This means that less than one in a billion collisions will have the necessary energy for a reaction to take place.

An approximate guide is that the rate doubles for a 10 K increase in temperature. The magnitude of the effect of increasing temperature depends on the value of the activation energy. A rise from 298 K to 308 K will cause the rate to increase by a factor of:

$$\frac{e^{(-E_a/308R)}}{e^{(-E_a/298R)}}$$

where R is the gas constant (8.13 J K⁻¹ mol⁻¹) and E_a is the activation energy for the reaction.

If $E_a = 60$ kJ mol⁻¹, the rate increases by a factor of $\dfrac{1.98 \times 10^{-9}}{1.01 \times 10^{-9}} = 1.96 \approx 2$ or 100%.

An increase in temperature also increases the average speed of the molecules and so increases the collision *frequency*. For a 10 K rise from 298 K, this increases the rate by a factor of $\sqrt{308/298} = 1.02$ (2%). This is negligible compared with the increase in rate caused by the increased proportion of collisions that result in reaction.

Effect of pressure on the rate of a gaseous reaction

If the pressure on a gaseous system is increased at constant temperature, the molecules become packed more closely together. There is no change in their speed or energy, but the collision *frequency* increases. The same proportion of the collisions results in reaction. However, because the frequency of collisions increases, the rate of reaction also goes up.

The situation is different if a gas is reacting with a solid, such as a catalyst. The surface area of the solid is usually the limiting factor, so the rate is independent of the pressure of the gas (p. 191).

Experimental methods

The rate of a reaction cannot be measured directly. It can only be determined from concentration and time data. There are a number of methods for 'following' a reaction which enable these data to be measured.

Titration

If the concentration of a reactant or product can be estimated by a titration the reaction can be followed using this technique:

- Measure out samples of the reactants with known concentration.
- Mix them together, start a clock and stir the mixture thoroughly.
- At regular time intervals, withdraw samples using a pipette and quench (stop) the reaction. Quenching can usually be achieved either by adding the solution from the pipette to ice-cold water or to a solution that reacts with one of the reactants, to prevent further reaction from taking place. The time at which half the contents of the pipette have been added to the quenching solution is noted.
- The quenched solution is then titrated against a suitable standard solution.

The titre is proportional to the concentration of the reactant or product being titrated.

This method can be used when an acid, alkali or iodine is a reactant or product. Acids can be titrated with a standard alkali, alkalis with a standard acid and iodine with a standard solution of sodium thiosulphate.

> *e* Care must be taken that the quenching reagent does not react with one of the reagents to give the same product that is being measured. For example, the acid hydrolysis of an ester cannot be quenched by adding alkali because this would react with the ester and increase the amount of product. It is always safer to quench with iced water. Sodium hydrogencarbonate will remove acid without making the solution alkaline.

Worked example

In the presence of an acid catalyst, aqueous solutions of iodine and propanone react according to the equation:
$$CH_3COCH_3 + I_2 \rightarrow CH_2ICOCH_3 + HI$$
Describe a method to find how the concentration of iodine varies with time in this reaction.

Answer

- Place 25 cm^3 of propanone solution in a beaker, followed by 25 cm^3 of dilute sulphuric acid.
- Place 25 cm^3 of iodine solution of known concentration in a second beaker.
- Simultaneously, mix the two solutions and start a clock.
- Stir the mixture thoroughly. After 5 minutes remove 10 cm^3 of the solution in a pipette and run it into a cold sodium hydrogencarbonate solution. Note the time when half the liquid in the pipette has run into the sodium hydrogencarbonate solution.
- Titrate the iodine present with standard sodium thiosulphate solution, adding starch when the iodine colour has faded to a straw colour.
- Stop when the blue-black colour of the starch–iodine complex has vanished. Read the burette volume.
- Repeat the process every 5 minutes until there is no solution left.

The concentration of iodine is proportional to the volume of sodium thiosulphate solution required to decolourise the iodine.

Colorimetry

If a reactant or product is coloured, the concentration of the coloured species can be measured using a spectrophotometer. The amount of light of a particular frequency that is absorbed is proportional to the concentration of the coloured substance.

The reactants are mixed and a clock started. The light absorbed is measured at set time intervals.

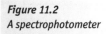

Light source · Reaction vessel · Detector

A suitable example is the reaction between bromine and methanoic acid:

$$Br_2(aq) + HCOOH(aq) \rightarrow 2Br^-(aq) + CO_2(g) + 2H^+(aq)$$

If this reaction is done in a beaker, the colour of bromine can be seen to fade gradually. A spectrophotometer is used to follow the absorption of light by bromine.

The fading colour of bromine as it reacts with methanoic acid

Infrared spectroscopy

Infrared spectroscopy can be used in a similar way to colorimetry. The spectrometer is set at a particular frequency and the amount of infrared radiation absorbed at that frequency is measured at regular time intervals. The oxidation of propan-2-ol to propanone by acidified potassium dichromate(VI) can be followed by setting the spectrometer at 1700 cm^{-1} (the absorption frequency due to the stretching of the C=O bond) and measuring the increase in absorption as the CHOH group is oxidised to the C=O group.

Polarimetry

If a reactant is optically active and the product either has a different optical activity or is a racemic mixture, the reaction can be followed by measuring the extent to which the plane of polarisation of plane-polarised light is rotated.

The reaction mixture is placed in a cell in the polarimeter and the angle of rotation is measured at regular time intervals. The angle of rotation is proportional to the concentration of the optically active substance.

Sodium discharge tube · Fixed polariser · Reaction tube · Rotatable polariser · Eye

If a sample of one of the optical isomers of 2-iodobutane is mixed with aqueous sodium hydroxide solution, hydrolysis occurs. The product is the racemic mixture of butan-2-ol. The angle of rotation of the plane of polarisation of the plane-polarised light gradually decreases as the single chiral isomer of 2-iodobutane is hydrolysed.

The rate of the hydrolysis of sucrose by the enzyme invertase can also be studied using a polarimeter. The products are fructose and glucose. Sucrose is dextrorotatory (rotates the plane clockwise) and the final mixture is laevorotatory (rotates the plane counter clockwise).

$$C_{12}H_{22}O_{11} + H_2O \rightarrow C_6H_{12}O_6 + C_6H_{12}O_6$$
sucrose   glucose   fructose

Volume of gas evolved

If the reaction produces a gas, the volume of gas produced can be measured at regular time intervals. The volume of gas is proportional to the moles of gas and can, therefore, be used to measure the concentration of the product.

The rate of the reaction of an acid with a solid carbonate can be studied this way. The acid is added to the carbonate and the volume of carbon dioxide noted every 30 seconds.

$$CaCO_3(s) + 2H^+(aq) \rightarrow Ca^{2+}(aq) + H_2O(l) + CO_2(g)$$

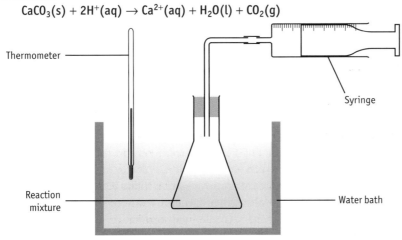

Thermometer

Syringe

Reaction mixture

Water bath

Figure 11.4 Measuring the volume of carbon dioxide produced in a reaction

This method can be modified by measuring the loss of mass as the gas produced escapes from the solution. The reactants are mixed and placed on a top-pan balance. The mass is measured at set times.

The problem with this method is that the changes in mass are very small. 50 cm³ of carbon dioxide weighs less than 0.1 g at room temperature and pressure and 50 cm³ of hydrogen weighs less than 0.005 g. Very sensitive balances are needed to measure the mass change accurately.

'Clock' reactions

In a 'clock' reaction, the reactants are mixed and the time taken to produce a fixed amount of product is measured. The experiment is then repeated several times using different starting concentrations.

The iodine 'clock'

The oxidation of iodide ions by hydrogen peroxide in acid solution can be followed as a 'clock' reaction:

$$H_2O_2(aq) + 2I^-(aq) + 2H^+(aq) \rightarrow I_2(s) + 2H_2O(l)$$

- 25 cm^3 of hydrogen peroxide solution is mixed in a beaker with 25 cm^3 of water and a few drops of starch solution are added.
- 25 cm^3 of potassium iodide solution and 5 cm^3 of a dilute solution of sodium thiosulphate are placed in a second beaker.
- The contents of the two beakers are mixed and the time taken for the solution to go blue is measured.
- The experiment is repeated with 20 cm^3 of hydrogen peroxide and 30 cm^3 of water, and then with other relative amounts of hydrogen peroxide and water, totalling 50 cm^3.

The reaction produces iodine, which reacts with the sodium thiosulphate. When all the sodium thiosulphate has been used up, the next iodine that is produced reacts with the starch to give an intense blue-black colour.

The amount of iodine produced in the measured time is proportional to the volume of sodium thiosulphate solution taken. Therefore, the average rate of reaction for each experiment is proportional to 1/time.

The sulphur 'clock'

Sodium thiosulphate is decomposed by acid, producing a precipitate of sulphur:

$$S_2O_3^{2-}(aq) + 2H^+(aq) \rightarrow S(s) + SO_2(aq) + H_2O(l)$$

- A large X is drawn on a white tile with a marker pen.
- 2 cm^3 of sodium thiosulphate solution is mixed with 25 cm^3 of water in a beaker.
- 25 cm^3 of dilute nitric acid is placed in a second beaker.
- The first beaker is placed on top of the X and the contents of the second one are added
- The mixture is stirred and the time (t) taken for sufficient sulphur to be produced to hide the X when looking down through the beaker is measured.
- The experiment is repeated with different relative amounts of sodium thiosulphate and water, totalling 50 cm^3.

The number of moles of sulphur produced is the same in all experiments. Therefore, the average rate of reaction for each experiment is proportional to $1/t$.

pH measurements

If one of the reactants or one of the products in a reaction is an acid or an alkali and the reaction takes place in aqueous solution, the change in pH with time can be measured.

The problem with this technique is that pH is a logarithmic quantity. If a strong acid is a reactant and the starting concentration is 1.0 mol dm^{-3}, the pH only changes by 1 unit (from 0 to 1) when 90% of the acid has reacted. The pH rises to 2 when 99% of the acid has reacted. This method requires a very accurate, and hence expensive, pH meter to monitor the change in acid concentration. This makes the method unsuitable for school laboratory use.

Rate equations

The purpose of the experimental methods described above is to find the rate equation. Consider the reaction:

   nA + mB → products

The rate equation for this reaction is of the form:

   rate = k[A]^p[B]^q

where n and m are the stoichiometries in the chemical equation and p and q are the powers of the substances in the rate equation.

The quantity k is called the **rate constant** and varies with the nature of the reaction and the temperature.

The *order* of reaction is $p + q$. The order with respect to substance A (also called the partial order) is p. The order with respect to substance B is q.

> The order of a reaction is the sum of the powers to which the *concentrations* of the reactants are raised in the experimentally determined rate equation.

> The partial order of one reactant is the power to which the *concentration* of that reactant is raised in the rate equation.

The values of p and q cannot be predicted from the chemical equation. They depend on both the stoichiometry *and* the mechanism of the reaction. Therefore, they have to be found by experiment.

Deduction of order of reaction

From initial rates

The initial rate of a reaction is the rate at the instant that the chemicals are mixed. This is normally found by measuring the time taken for the concentration of a reactant or product to change by a known amount, which must be less than 10% of the initial concentration of the reactant. The experiment is then repeated, changing the concentration of one of the reactants but keeping the concentration of all the others constant.

Consider a reaction:

   A + B + C → products

The experimental method is as follows:
- The initial rate is measured when all three reactants have the same concentration, for example, 1.0 mol dm^{-3}.
- The experiment is repeated with [A] = 0.50 mol dm^{-3} and [B] and [C] unchanged at 1.0 mol dm^{-3}.
  - If the rate does not alter, the reaction is zero order with respect to substance A.

The rate constant is always represented by a lower-case k. An upper-case K is the symbol for equilibrium constant.

The general formula given for the rate equation is not always correct. Some reversible reactions have much more complex rate equations, often containing fractional partial orders. These are beyond the scope of A-level.

- If the rate doubles (increases by a factor of 2^1), it is first order in A.
- If it increases by a factor of 4 (2^2) it is second order in A.

■ A third experiment is performed with [A] and [C] equal to 1.0 mol dm^{-3} and [B] = 0.50 mol dm^{-3}. This enables the partial order with respect to B to be deduced.

■ A fourth experiment is carried out in which [C] is altered but [A] and [B] are kept the same as in one of the previous experiments. This enables the order with respect to C to be deduced.

The overall order is the *sum* of all the partial orders.

The change in concentration can usually be measured by one of the procedures described earlier in this chapter.

Worked example

The reaction between nitrogen(II) oxide and hydrogen at 1000°C is:

$$2NO(g) + 2H_2(g) \rightarrow N_2(g) + 2H_2O(g)$$

Use the data below to deduce the order of reaction with respect to hydrogen and nitrogen(II) oxide. Calculate the overall order of the reaction. Write the rate equation and calculate the value of the rate constant.

Experiment	[NO]/mol dm^{-3}	[H$_2$]/mol dm^{-3}	Initial rate/mol dm^{-3} s^{-1}
1	4.0×10^{-3}	1.0×10^{-3}	1.2×10^{-5}
2	8.0×10^{-3}	1.0×10^{-3}	4.8×10^{-5}
3	8.0×10^{-3}	4.0×10^{-3}	1.92×10^{-4}

Answer

Consider experiments 1 and 2:
■ [NO] is increased by a factor of 2. [H$_2$] is unchanged.
■ The rate increases by a factor of 2^2. Therefore, the reaction is second order in nitrogen(II) oxide.

Consider experiments 2 and 3:
■ [H$_2$] goes up by a factor of 4. [NO] is unchanged.
■ The rate increases by a factor of 4^1. Therefore, the reaction is first order with respect to hydrogen (even though there are two hydrogen molecules in the chemical equation for the reaction).

overall order $= 2 + 1 = 3$

rate $= k[NO]^2[H_2]^1$

rate constant, $k = \dfrac{\text{rate}}{[NO]^2[H_2]^1}$

Using the data from experiment 1:

$$k = \frac{1.2 \times 10^{-5}}{(4.0 \times 10^{-3})^2 \times (1.0 \times 10^{-3})} = 750 \text{ mol}^{-2} \text{ dm}^6 \text{ s}^{-1}$$

$$\text{units} = \frac{\text{concentration} \times \text{time}^{-1}}{\text{concentration}^2 \times \text{concentration}} = \text{concentration}^{-2} \times \text{time}^{-1}$$

Note that if the reaction were second order in hydrogen, when [H$_2$] was increased by a factor of 4, the rate would increase by a factor of 4^2 or 16 times. This was not the case in this reaction.

e The units of the rate constant, k, vary according to the total order of reaction.

e The symbol for half-life is $t_{\frac{1}{2}}$.

From half-lives

Half-life is the time taken for the concentration of a reactant to halve.

- For a *first*-order reaction, the half-life is constant at a fixed temperature.
This means, for example, that if it takes 25 s for the concentration of any reactant to fall from 8 units to 4 units, then it also takes 25 s for it to fall from 4 units to 2 units or from 6 units to 3 units.

- For a *second*-order reaction, the half-life increases in a regular geometric manner.
This means, for example, that if it takes 25 s for the concentration of any reactant to fall from 8 units to 4 units, then it will take 50 s for it to fall from 4 units to 2 units.

If a graph of the concentration of a reactant is plotted against time and the concentration falls during the experiment to less than 25% of its initial value, two consecutive half-lives can be measured. If the fall is less than this, two half-lives can still be measured, but the fall must be greater than 66% to be certain that the half-lives are accurate within experimental error.

Worked example

Consider the reaction:

$A + B \rightarrow$ products

Use the data below to plot a graph of [A] against time. Measure two half-lives and hence deduce the order of reaction.

$[A]/mol\ dm^{-3}$	Time/s
1.00	0
0.90	5
0.75	12
0.42	38
0.30	52
0.20	70
0.15	82

Answer

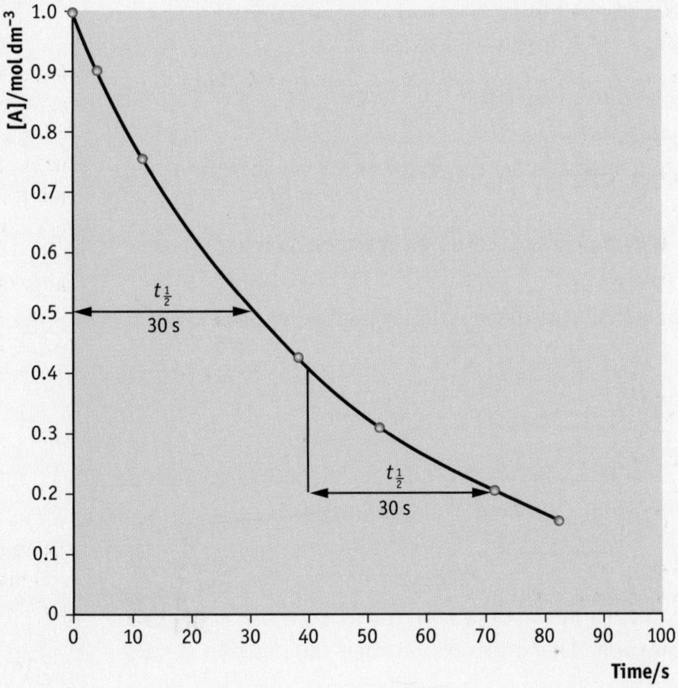

e All kinetic experiments should be carried out at constant temperature and for most reactions the laboratory itself acts as a constant-temperature medium. However, most reactions are exothermic, so the temperature may rise spontaneously. This can cause the half-life to be slightly shorter.

The half-life from $[A] = 1.0 \text{ mol dm}^{-3}$ to $[A] = 0.50 \text{ mol dm}^{-3} = 30 \text{ s}$
The half-life from $[A] = 0.40 \text{ mol dm}^{-3}$ to $[A] = 0.20 \text{ mol dm}^{-3} = 30 \text{ s}$
The half-life is constant, so the reaction is first order.

Extension for students studying A-level mathematics

For a reaction $A + 2B \rightarrow C + 3D$, the expression:

$$\text{rate} = \frac{-\Delta[A]}{\Delta t}$$

is an approximation that measures the average rate during this period. The instantaneous rate is the differential of this:

$$\text{rate} = -d[A]/dt \quad (\text{or} -\tfrac{1}{2}d[B]/dt \text{ or } +d[C]/dt \text{ or } +\tfrac{1}{3}d[D]/dt)$$

For a first order reaction this becomes:

$$\text{rate} = -d[A]/dt = k[A]$$
$$\int k \, dt = -\int [A]^{-1} d[A]$$
$$kt = \ln[A]_0 - \ln[A]_t = \ln\{[A]_0/[A]_t\}$$

where $[A]_0$ is the initial concentration of A and $[A]_t$ is its concentration at time t.
After one half-life the initial concentration of A has halved:

$$[A]_{t_{\frac{1}{2}}} = \tfrac{1}{2}[A]_0$$

Therefore:

$$kt_{\frac{1}{2}} = \ln\{[A]_0/\tfrac{1}{2}[A]_0\} = \ln 2$$
$$t_{\frac{1}{2}} = \frac{\ln 2}{k} \quad \text{or} \quad k = \frac{\ln 2}{t_{\frac{1}{2}}}$$

This proves that the half-life of a first-order reaction is constant at a given temperature and that its value can be used to calculate the rate constant, k.
In the worked example above, the half-life is 30 s, so $k = \dfrac{\ln 2}{30} = 0.023 \text{ s}^{-1}$

From the slope of a concentration–time graph

Form of the graph

When a graph of $[A]$ is plotted against time, the shape of the graph depends on the order of reaction.

The slope of the graph at any value of $[A]$ is the rate of reaction at that concentration.

■ If it is a horizontal line, it means that the reaction is not taking place (rate of reaction = 0).

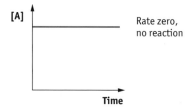

■ If a straight line sloping downwards is obtained, the slope is constant. This means that the rate is constant. This only occurs when the reaction is zero order.

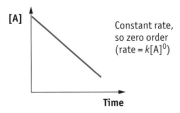

Constant rate,
so zero order
(rate = $k[A]^0$)

Time

Figure 11.5
Determining reaction order from concentration–time curves

■ If a downward curve is obtained, with decreasing slope, the rate is decreasing as [A] falls. Therefore, the reaction is first order or greater.

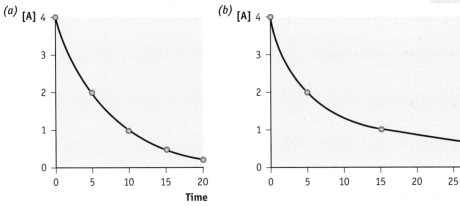

Drawing tangents

The rate at any particular concentration can be calculated by drawing a tangent to the curve at that point and measuring the slope of the tangent.

For a plot of concentration of reactant against time, the rate of reaction is equal to minus the slope of the graph.

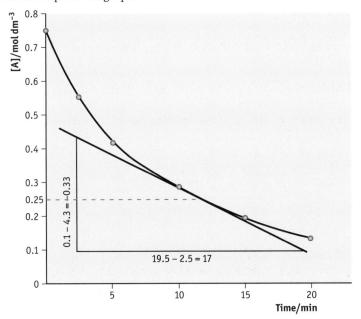

The half-lives on the graph in Figure 11.5(a) are constant. Therefore, this reaction is first order.

The half-lives on the graph in Figure 11.5(b) increase rapidly (they double as the concentration is halved). Therefore, this reaction is second order.

Figure 11.6
Calculating the rate of a second-order reaction by drawing a tangent

It is difficult to draw a tangent accurately. Also, the tangential line must be long enough for the coordinates at the top and the bottom of the line to be read from the graph without a large error.

By drawing tangents at two points, or by comparing the initial rate with the rate measured by the tangent, the order of reaction can be deduced.

> **Worked example**
>
> The reaction $A + 2B \rightarrow C + D$ was studied and the graph of $[A]$ as a function of time was drawn, as in Figure 11.6.
>
> Draw the tangent at $[A] = 0.25$ mol dm^{-3} and measure its slope.
>
> The initial rate, when $[A]$ was 0.75 mol dm^{-3}, was 0.17 mol dm^{-3} min^{-1}. Deduce the order of the reaction and suggest rate equations that fit the order.
>
> **Answer**
>
> $$\text{gradient of the slope} = \frac{(0.1 - 0.43)}{(19.5 - 2.5)} = \frac{-0.33}{17} = -0.019 \text{ mol dm}^{-3} \text{ s}^{-1}$$
>
> rate of reaction when $[A] = 0.25$ mol dm^{-3} = +0.019 mol dm^{-3} s^{-1}
>
> initial rate when $[A] = 0.75$ mol dm^{-3} = 0.17 mol dm^{-3} min^{-1}
>
> The concentration of $[A]$ was decreased by a factor of 3 and the rate decreased by a factor of $0.17/0.019 = 8.9 \approx 9$ (3^2), so the reaction is second order. Possible rate equations are:
>
> rate $= k[A]^2$
>
> rate $= k[B]^2$
>
> rate $= k[A][B]$

e Following the concentration of one of the reactants gives the *overall* order of reaction, not the partial order with respect to the substance whose concentration is being measured. Thus, if $[B]$ as a function of time were measured, the order would still be 2, regardless of which of the three possible rate equations is correct.

Units of rate constants

For a first-order reaction, the rate equation is rate $= k[A]^1$. Therefore, $k = \text{rate}/[A]$. The units of the rate constant are:

$$\frac{\text{concentration} \times \text{time}^{-1}}{\text{concentration}} = \text{time}^{-1} \text{ (e.g. s}^{-1} \text{ or min}^{-1})$$

For a second-order reaction, rate $= k[A]^2$ or rate $= k[A][B]$

$$k = \text{rate}/[A]^2 \text{ or } k = \text{rate}/[A][B]$$

The units of the rate constant are

$$\frac{\text{concentration} \times \text{time}^{-1}}{\text{concentration}^2}$$

$$= \text{concentration}^{-1} \text{ time}^{-1} \text{ (e.g. mol}^{-1} \text{ dm}^3 \text{ s}^{-1})$$

The units of the rate constant for other orders can be worked out in a similar way.

Effect of temperature on the rate constant

The value of the rate constant depends on:

- the complexity of the geometry of the molecules. This is also called the orientation factor. If only 1 in 10 collisions occurs with the correct orientation, the orientation factor equals 0.1. This factor is a constant for a particular reaction.
- the activation energy of the reaction
- the temperature

The second and third factors cause the rate constant to be proportional to:

$$e^{(-E_a/RT)}$$

where E_a is the activation energy, R is the gas constant and T is the temperature in kelvin.

A large E_a results in a large negative exponent and, therefore, a small value for the rate constant. A catalyst effectively lowers the activation energy (by providing a different route for the reaction). Therefore, the exponent becomes less negative and k gets larger.

A rise in temperature increases the denominator of the exponential term and makes its value less negative, increasing the value of k. This means that a greater proportion of collisions result in reaction.

The relationship between the rate constant and temperature is described by the Arrhenius equation:

$$\ln k = \ln A - E_a/RT$$

where A is a constant.

If the value of the rate constant is measured at different temperatures, a graph can be plotted of $\ln k$ against $1/T$. The graph is a straight line of slope $-E_a/R$, allowing the activation energies to be determined.

> **(e)** Remember that reactions that have a high activation energy have a small value for the rate constant and are, therefore, slow at room temperature. An increase in temperature increases the value of the rate constant and so the reaction is faster.

Worked example

The second-order rate constant for the reaction of 1-bromopropane with aqueous hydroxide ions was measured as a function of temperature.

$$CH_3CH_2CH_2Br(aq) + OH^-(aq) \rightarrow CH_3CH_2CH_2OH(aq) + Br^-(aq)$$

The results are shown in the table below.

Temperature/°C	Temperature/K	$1/T$	$k/mol^{-1}\,dm^3\,s^{-1}$	$\ln k$
25	298	0.00336	1.4×10^{-4}	−8.9
35	308	0.00325	3.0×10^{-4}	−8.1
45	318	0.00314	6.8×10^{-4}	−7.3
55	328	0.00306	1.4×10^{-3}	−6.6

Plot a graph of $\ln k$ against $1/T$. Measure the slope of the line and hence calculate the activation energy of the reaction.

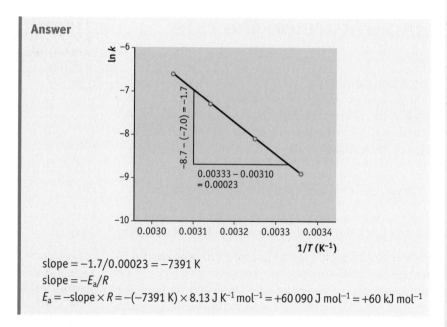

slope $= -1.7/0.00023 = -7391$ K

slope $= -E_a/R$

$E_a = -\text{slope} \times R = -(-7391\text{ K}) \times 8.13\text{ J K}^{-1}\text{mol}^{-1} = +60\,090\text{ J mol}^{-1} = +60\text{ kJ mol}^{-1}$

ⓔ The activation energy is always positive because it is the energy that the colliding molecules must have for a reaction to take place.

Mechanisms and the rate-determining step

Single-step reactions

Some reactions take place in a single step. For example, the reaction between aqueous hydroxide ions and a primary halogenoalkane is a one-step reaction that is thought to involve a collision between the two species. During the collision, the C–halogen bond begins to break and a new O–C bond forms. At this halfway point, the system is said to have reached a position of maximum potential energy. This is the **transition state** between the reactants and the products — for example, with CH_3I:

The reaction energy profile for a single-step reaction is shown in Figure 11.7.

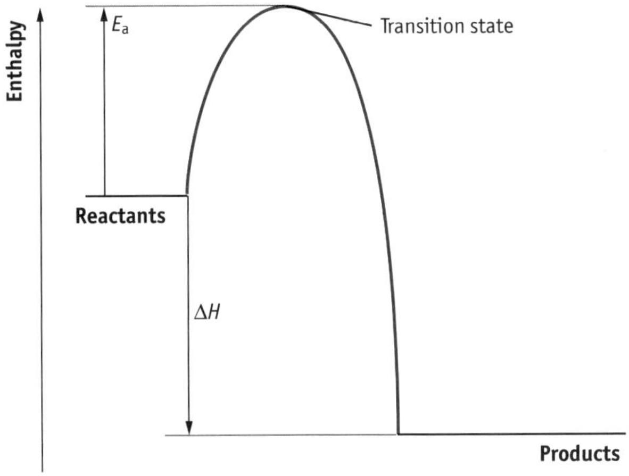

Figure 11.7 Reaction profile for a single-step reaction

As this is a single-step reaction between two species, the reaction is second order and the rate equation is:

rate = $k[A][B]$

In this example,

rate = $k[OH^-][CH_3I]$

> **e** The powers to which the concentrations are raised in the rate equation for a *single*-step reaction are the same as the stoichiometry.

Multi-step reactions

Many reactions take place in more than one step, via intermediate compounds, ions or radicals.

The hydrolysis of a tertiary halogenoalkane, for example 2-chloro-2-methylpropane, with aqueous hydroxide ions is an example of a two-step reaction.

Step 1: the C–Cl bond breaks heterolytically, forming a carbocation and a chloride anion:

$(CH_3)_3CCl \rightarrow (CH_3)_3C^+ + Cl^-$

The rate equation for step 1 is:

rate = $k_1[(CH_3)_3CCl]$

Step 2: the lone pair of electrons on the oxygen of the OH$^-$ ion forms a new bond with the positive carbon atom:

$(CH_3)_3C^+ + OH^- \rightarrow (CH_3)_3COH$

The rate equation for step 2 is

rate = $k_2[(CH_3)_3C^+][OH^-]$

The overall rate is controlled by the rate of the slowest step in the mechanism. This step is called the **rate-determining step**.

> The rate-determining step is the slowest step in a multi-step mechanism.

For the hydrolysis of 2-chloro-2-methylpropane, the first step is the slower step and is therefore rate-determining. Hence, the rate equation for this reaction is:

rate = $k_1[(CH_3)_3CCl]$

Using a rate equation to suggest a mechanism

First step is rate-determining

If the rate-determining step is the first step, then the rate equation for the overall reaction is the same as that for the rate-determining step.

For the hydrolysis of 2-chloro-2-methylpropane, the rate equation is:

$$\text{rate} = k[(CH_3)_3CCl]$$

Second or subsequent step is rate-determining

If the second (or a subsequent) step is rate-determining, the derivation of the overall rate equation is more complex.

Consider the reaction:

$$A + 2B + C \rightarrow D + E$$

Step 1 is a rapid step that is reversible:

$$A + B \rightleftharpoons Int$$

where Int is an intermediate.

Step 2 is the slowest step and hence is rate-determining:

$$Int + B \rightarrow X$$

Step 3 is faster than step 2:

$$C + X \rightarrow D + E$$

The overall rate is determined by the rate of the slowest step 2:

$$\text{overall rate} = \text{rate of step 2} = k_2[B][Int]$$

The value of [Int] can be found by treating step 1 as an equilibrium reaction:

$$K_1 = \frac{[Int]}{[A][B]}$$

$$[Int] = K_1 \times [A][B]$$

Substituting [Int] into the rate equation for step 2:

$$\text{overall rate} = \text{rate step 2} = k_2 K_1[A][B]^2$$

The reaction is third order and $k_2 K_1$ equals the rate constant.

A rate-determining step that does not involve the reactant

If a substance enters the mechanism *after* the rate-determining step, its partial order is zero.

The iodination of propanone in alkaline solution takes place in several steps. The overall equation is:

$$CH_3COCH_3 + I_2 + OH^- \rightarrow CH_2ICOCH_3 + H_2O + I^-$$

The reaction is found to be second order overall and zero order with respect to iodine.

The rate equation is:

$$\text{rate} = k[CH_3COCH_3][OH^-]$$

> **e** The powers to which the concentrations are raised in the rate equation for an individual step in a multi-step reaction are the same as the stoichiometry for that step.

A suggested mechanism is:

Step 1: the base removes an H^+ from a $-CH_3$ group:

$$CH_3COCH_3 + OH^- \rightarrow CH_3COCH_2^- + H_2O$$

Step 2: the lone pair of electrons on the C^- of the carbanion forms a bond with an iodine atom in I_2 and the I_2 bond breaks:

$$CH_3COCH_2^- + I_2 \rightarrow CH_3COCH_2I + I^-$$

As the reaction is first order in propanone and OH^- ions and zero order in I_2, step 1 must be the rate-determining step.

Further evidence for this is that the rate is exactly the same whether iodine, bromine or chlorine is the reactant.

Reaction-profile diagrams for multi-step reactions

In a multi-step reaction, the reactants go via a transition state to an intermediate, which then reacts via a further transition state to form the products. The intermediate is usually at a lower energy level than the reactants.

e If the partial order of a reactant is zero, that reactant enters the mechanism *after* the rate-determining step.

Figure 11.8 Energy profile diagrams for two different reactions

(a)

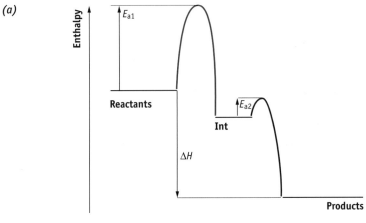

(b)

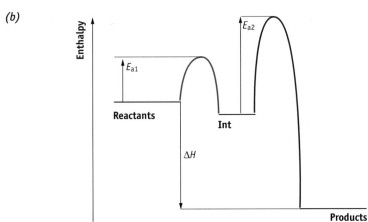

In Figure 11.8(a), the activation energy for the production of the intermediate is greater than the activation energy for the intermediate going to the products.

This means that the first step is the rate-limiting step.

In Figure 11.8(b), the second activation energy is greater, so the second step is the rate-determining step.

Pseudo-zero-partial-order reactions

The classic examples of pseudo-zero-partial-order reactions are the enzyme-catalysed reactions in living organisms.

The rate of reaction depends on the concentration of the enzyme and not on the concentration of the substrate.

A simplified explanation of enzyme activity is that the enzyme rapidly adsorbs the reactant and slowly converts it to a product that is then rapidly released by the enzyme. As long as there is enough reactant (the substrate) to saturate the enzyme, the reaction rate is not be increased by increasing the concentration of reactant. Therefore, the reaction has an apparent zero partial order, even though the substrate enters the mechanism before the rate-determining step.

If the concentration of the substrate drops too far, the enzyme ceases to be saturated and the reaction becomes dependent on the concentration of the substrate.

A similar mechanism occurs in almost all metal-catalysed gaseous reactions. The catalyst has active sites on its surface that rapidly become saturated by reactants, which are then slowly converted into products. These leave the metal surface, thus allowing more of the reactant to be adsorbed. This means that the rate of a reaction is not altered by an increase in pressure of the gaseous reactants. This is true of:

- the Haber process, in which the reaction between nitrogen and hydrogen is catalysed by iron
- the manufacture of hydrogen from steam and methane, which is catalysed by nickel
- the oxidation of ammonia by air, which is catalysed by platinum

These reactions are all zero order with respect to both reactant gases, unless the pressure is very low, when the partial orders of the gases are greater than zero.

Altering the order by the method of excess reagent

Consider a reaction:

$$A + 2B \rightarrow C + D$$

The rate equation is of the form:

$$\text{rate} = k[A]^p[B]^q$$

However, if the initial concentration of B is made at least ten times that of A, the change in [B] during the reaction will be negligible. This means that [B] is constant within experimental error, and so the rate equation becomes:

$$\text{rate} = \text{constant} \times [A]^p$$

where the constant $= k \times$ the approximately constant value of $[B]^q$.

The value of p (the order with respect to substance A) can be found by the usual methods of initial rate or half-life.

If the experiment is repeated with the same initial concentration of A but 20 times as much B (doubling the concentration of B from the first experiment) the way in which the initial rate alters will depend on the order with respect to B. If the rate doubles, the reaction is first order with respect to B. If the rate quadruples, the reaction is second order in B.

e This method works only if one reagent is in *considerable* excess, so that its concentration does not effectively alter during the reaction.

Questions

1 Hydrogen peroxide slowly oxidises ethanol in acid solution. In an experiment, after 45 s the amount of hydrogen peroxide in $50\,cm^3$ of solution had fallen from 1.46×10^{-3} moles to 1.32×10^{-3} moles. Calculate the rate of the reaction.

2 a Draw the distribution of energies of a mixture of hydrogen and iodine at a temperature T_1 and at a lower temperature, T_2.
  b Explain, in terms of energy and frequency of collisions, why the reaction between hydrogen and iodine is slower at the lower temperature.
  c Which of energy and frequency of collisions is more important in causing the rate to decrease?
  d What effect would an increase in pressure have on the frequency and energy of collisions and hence on the rate of the reaction?

3 Potassium manganate(VII) reacts slowly with a solution of ethanedioic acid in dilute sulphuric acid at room temperature. The equation is:

$2MnO_4^-(aq) + 6H^+(aq) + 5(COOH)_2(aq) \rightarrow$
$2Mn^{2+}(aq) + 8H_2O(l) + 10CO_2(g)$

  a Describe a *chemical* method by which the progress of this reaction could be followed.
  b Describe a *physical* method by which the progress of this reaction could be followed.
  c If this reaction is carried out at a constant higher temperature, the rate at first increases and then slows down. Suggest an explanation for this and suggest an experiment to confirm your hypothesis for the initial increase in rate.

4 Consider the reaction:

$A + 2B + 3C \rightarrow$ products

It was found to be first order in A and B and second order in C. Write the rate equation for this reaction.

5 Consider the reaction:

$2A + B \rightarrow$ products

It was found to be second order. Write two rate equations that fit these data.

6 The kinetics of the reaction:

$C_2H_5I + KOH \rightarrow C_2H_5OH + KI$

was studied at a temperature T. The following initial rate data were obtained:

Experiment	$[C_2H_5I]/$ mol dm^{-3}	$[KOH]/$ mol dm^{-3}	Initial rate/ mol dm^{-3} s^{-1}
1	0.20	0.10	2.2×10^{-5}
2	0.40	0.10	4.4×10^{-5}
3	0.20	0.20	4.4×10^{-5}

  a Deduce the partial orders of reaction with respect to iodoethane, C_2H_5I, and potassium hydroxide.
  b Write the rate equation for the reaction.
  c Calculate the value of the rate constant at this temperature and give its units.

7 The reaction between three reactants, A, B and C, was studied. The initial rates of reaction at different concentrations of the three reactants were measured and are given in the table.

Experiment	$[A]/$ mol dm^{-3}	$[B]/$ mol dm^{-3}	$[C]/$ mol dm^{-3}	Initial rate/ mol dm^{-3} s^{-1}
1	1.0	1.0	1.0	2.3×10^{-3}
2	1.0	3.0	1.0	6.9×10^{-3}
3	2.0	3.0	1.0	1.4×10^{-2}
4	2.0	1.0	2.0	4.6×10^{-3}

  a Deduce the partial orders of reaction of A, B and C.
  b State the overall order of this reaction.
  c Write the rate equation.
  d Calculate the value of the rate constant, giving its units.

8 The reaction between persulphate ions, $S_2O_8^{2-}$, and iodide ions was studied by an iodine clock method.

$$S_2O_8^{2-}(aq) + 2I^-(aq) \rightarrow 2SO_4^{2-}(aq) + I_2(aq)$$

a Describe the iodine clock method.

b The initial rates of reaction were measured at different concentrations. The results are shown below.

Experiment	$[S_2O_8^{2-}]/$ mol dm^{-3}	$[I^-]/$ mol dm^{-3}	Initial rate/ mol dm^{-3} s^{-1}
1	0.038	0.050	1.2×10^{-5}
2	0.076	0.050	2.4×10^{-5}
3	0.152	0.100	9.6×10^{-5}

Deduce the overall order of reaction.

c Write the rate equation and calculate the value of the rate constant.

9 The reaction between 2-bromopropane and an aqueous solution of sodium hydroxide is as follows:

$$CH_3CHBrCH_3 + NaOH \rightarrow CH_3CH(OH)CH_3 + NaBr$$

In an experiment, the initial concentration of both reagents was 0.10 mol dm^{-3}. The concentration of hydroxide ions was measured at set time intervals, the graph of [OH$^-$] against time was plotted and the rate of reaction found by drawing tangents to the graph at two different values of [OH$^-$]:

- [OH$^-$] = 0.10 mol dm^{-3}; slope of tangent = 1.6×10^{-3}
- [OH$^-$] = 0.05 mol dm^{-3}; slope of tangent = 0.8×10^{-3}

a What is the order of reaction?

b In a separate experiment, [2-bromopropane] was measured at intervals of time. The starting concentration of each reactant was 0.10 mol dm^{-3}. What would be the relative values of the slopes of tangents drawn to a graph of [2-bromopropane] against time at the points where [2-bromopropane] were 0.10 mol dm^{-3} and 0.050 mol dm^{-3}?

c How would you modify the experiment to find out the partial orders of the two reagents?

10 Cyclopropane can be converted into its isomer, propene by heating to 500°C:

[Cyclopropane]/mol dm^{-3}	Time/min
0.080	0
0.062	5
0.048	10
0.038	15
0.023	25
0.014	35
0.0065	50

a Use the data in the table to plot a graph of concentration (y-axis) against time (x-axis).

b Measure three consecutive half-lives and hence deduce the order of the reaction.

c Calculate the value of the rate constant, stating its units.

11 The half-lives of two different reactions were measured. The results are shown in the table.

Reaction I [Reactant]/ mol dm^{-3}	Half-life/min	Reaction II [Reactant]/ mol dm^{-3}	Half-life/min
0.8	20.0	0.8	2.2
0.4	19.7	0.4	4.3
0.2	19.9	0.2	8.5
0.1	20.4	0.1	17.0

Deduce the order of both reactions.

12 The data in the table refer to a reaction between A and B.

[A]/mol dm^{-3}	Time/s
0.20	0
0.16	10
0.13	20
0.11	30
0.07	50
0.04	80

a Plot a graph of [A] against time.

b Draw tangents at [A] = 0.16 mol dm^{-3} and at [A] = 0.08 mol dm^{-3}. Measure the slope of both tangents.

c Use your answers from b to estimate the order of the reaction.

13 Consider a reaction that has a two-step mechanism in which both steps are exothermic. Step 2 is the rate-determining step.

Step 1: A + B → Intermediate + C

Step 2: A + Intermediate → D

a Write the overall equation for the reaction.
b Draw the reaction-profile diagram for the overall reaction.
c Predict the rate equation for the reaction.
d How would the rate equation differ if step 1 were the rate-determining step?

14 The Arrhenius equation is:

$\ln k = \ln A - E_a/RT$

where k is the rate constant, A (the Arrhenius constant) is specific to the reaction, E_a is the activation energy, R the universal gas constant and T is the temperature in kelvin.

The acid hydrolysis of sucrose has an activation energy of $1.1 \times 10^5 \, J \, mol^{-1}$. The Arrhenius constant, A, for this reaction is $1.2 \times 10^{15} \, mol^{-1} \, dm^3 \, s^{-1}$.

(The gas constant, R, $= 8.31 \, J \, K^{-1} \, mol^{-1}$)
Calculate the value of the rate constant at a temperature of 303 K.

15 The values of the rate constant, k, at different temperatures for the cracking of ethane into ethene and hydrogen are given in the table.

Temperature/K	660	680	720	760
Rate constant/s^{-1}	0.00037	0.0011	0.0082	0.055

The Arrhenius equation is:

$\ln k = \ln A - E_a/RT$

a Draw a graph of $\ln k$ against $1/T$.
b Measure the slope of the line and hence calculate the value of the activation energy of this reaction.
c Use the graph to calculate the value of the rate constant at a temperature of 700 K.

Aromatic chemistry

Introduction

Organic chemistry can be divided into three categories:

- **Aliphatic chemistry**: this is the study of simple compounds that have straight or branched carbon chains or rings of carbon atoms. Alkenes, ethanol, propanone, ethylamine, cyclohexane and cyclohexene are examples of aliphatic compounds.

Cyclohexane   Cyclohexene

- **Aromatic compounds**: these all contain a benzene ring. This is a ring of six carbon atoms in which each forms two σ-bonds with its neighbouring carbon atoms and has one *p*-electron in a π-bond. The fourth valence electron is in a σ-bond with an atom that is joined to the ring.
- **Natural products**: these compounds are complex organic substances found in nature. They include colouring matter, poisons, flavourings, proteins, hormones and compounds with specific odours that may be used to attract pollinating insects or are pheromones.

The benzene ring

Benzene has the formula C_6H_6. There was doubt about its structure until the German chemist Kekulé suggested that the carbon atoms were arranged in a ring with alternate single and double bonds.

There are two were major problems with the Kekulé structure:

- A C=C is shorter than a C–C bond, but all the bonds between the carbon atoms in benzene are the same length. This is clearly shown by the electron-density diagram of benzene:

August Kekulé, 1829–96

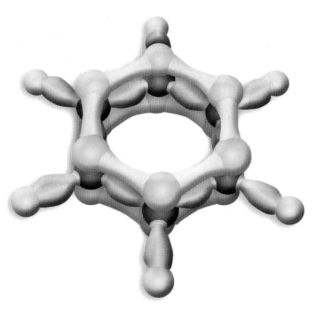

- Benzene does not show the typical addition reactions of unsaturated compounds such as ethene and cyclohexene. For example, it reacts with bromine by substitution rather than by addition.

One solution to the problem was to apply the concept of a **resonance structure**. This was first used to account for the identical bond lengths in ozone, $O=O\rightarrow O$. In theory, the double bond should be shorter than the dative bond. However, both bonds are the same length. The reason is that the molecule of ozone is a unique structure that appears to resonate between $O=O\rightarrow O$ and $O\leftarrow O=O$. The idea of resonance is that the actual molecule is a definite structure that is a hybrid of two theoretical structures. An ozone molecule is neither $O\leftarrow O=O$ nor $O=O\rightarrow O$ and it does not oscillate between the two. Resonance can be shown as a double-headed arrow between the two theoretical structures, both of which must obey the normal rules of bonding.

Ozone can be written as:

$O=O\rightarrow O \quad \leftrightarrow \quad O\leftarrow O=O$

Benzene can be written as:

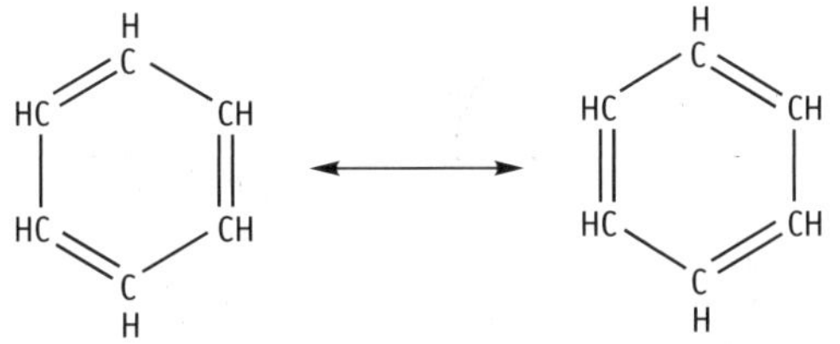

It is usual to write the formula of benzene without showing either the carbon atoms or the hydrogen atoms. Thus, a hexagon with alternate double and single bonds can be used to represent benzene, although it would be better to show that it is a resonance structure, as in Figure 12.1.

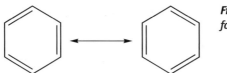

Figure 12.1 The Kekulé formulae of benzene

A double bond is a σ-bond (an overlap of atomic orbitals between two atoms) and a π-bond (an overlap of *p*-orbitals above and below the σ-bond).

The best representation of a benzene molecule is six carbon atoms in a hexagonal plane bonded to each other and each bonded to a hydrogen atom by σ-bonds. The fourth valence electron on each carbon atom is in a p_z-orbital at right angles to the plane of the six carbon atoms. The p_z-orbital of one carbon atom overlaps equally with the p_z-orbitals of *both* adjacent carbon atoms, forming a continuous π-bond above and below the ring of carbon atoms. These six p_z-electrons are **delocalised** over the ring. This gives the molecule greater stability compared with a theoretical molecule in which the π-electrons are localised between individual atoms.

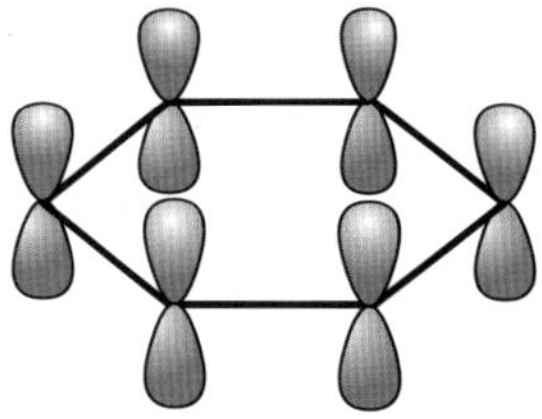

Figure 12.2 Overlap of p_z-orbitals in benzene

This gain in stability is called the **resonance stabilisation energy**. In benzene, its value is 150 kJ mol^{-1} less than that of the theoretical molecule that has three single and three localised double bonds (p. 236).

The way in which a delocalised π-system is written in a formula is to draw a continuous curve round the atoms that are part of that system — for benzene, a circle is drawn within the hexagon representing the six carbon atoms (Figure 12.3).

The formula of cyclohexane, which has no π-electrons, is drawn as in Figure 12.4.

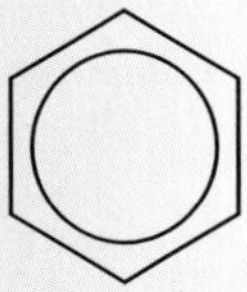

C_6H_6

Figure 12.3 The standard formula for benzene

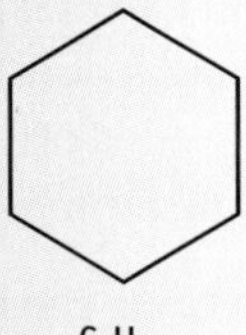

C_6H_{12}

Figure 12.4 The standard formula for cyclohexane

> ℮ Remember that there is a hydrogen atom attached to each carbon atom in benzene. When benzene reacts by substitution, a hydrogen atom is replaced by another group. Therefore, one of the products is a simple molecule such as HBr, HCl or H$_2$O.

Nomenclature of aromatic compounds

Single substituents

If a single atom or group replaces one hydrogen atom in the ring, the name of the compound has the stem –benzene with a prefix of the group or atom entering, thus:

- C_6H_5Cl is called chlorobenzene.
- $C_6H_5CH_3$ is called methylbenzene.
- $C_6H_5NO_2$ is called nitrobenzene.
- $C_6H_5NH_2$ is called aminobenzene.

◀ Methylbenzene used to be called toluene because it was first isolated from the resin of the South American tree *Tolu balsam*.

An additional naming system is based on the **phenyl group**, –C_6H_5 group, thus:

- C_6H_5OH is called phenol.
- $CH_3CH(C_6H_5)CH_3$ is called 2-phenylpropane.
- $C_6H_5COCH_3$ has a carbon chain of two atoms (ethan-) and is a ketone (-one) with a phenyl group substituted into it, so it is called phenylethanone.

Two or more substituents

If there are two or more groups in a benzene ring, positional isomerism occurs. For example, there are three isomers of $C_6H_4Cl_2$. The relative positions of the two chlorine atoms are shown by numbers. One substituent is always named as being in the 1-position and the second substituent by the lower of the possible numbers.

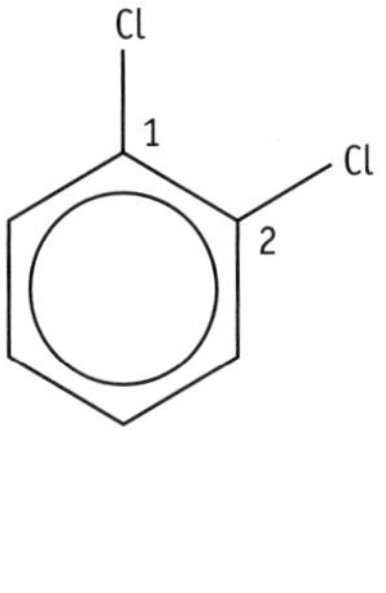

- Structure A is 1,2-dichlorobenzene (not 1,6-dichlorobenzene).
- Structure B is 1,3-dichlorobenzene (not 1,5-dichlorobenzene).
- Structure C is 1,4-dichlorbenzene.

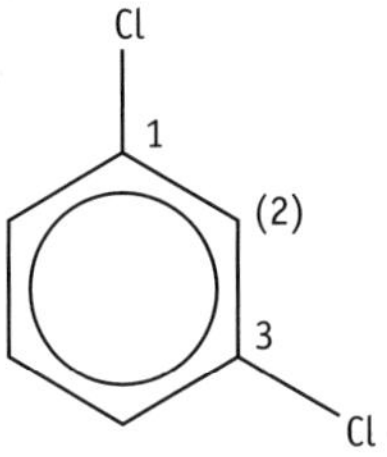

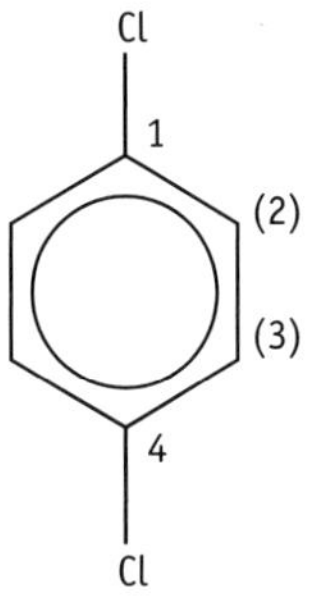

The compound 2,4,6-tribromophenol has the formula:

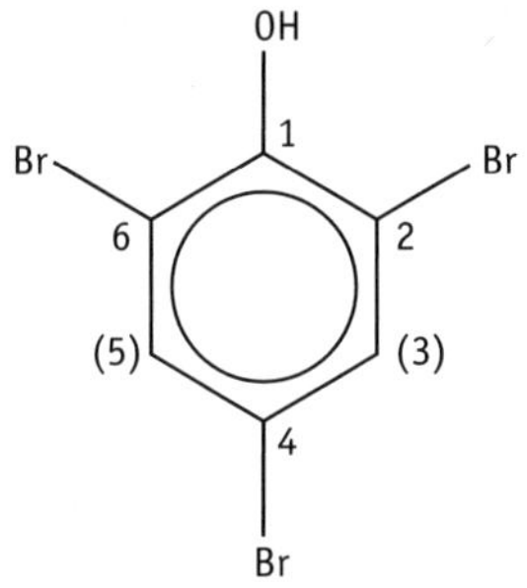

TNT is 2,4,6-trinitrotoluene and has the formula:

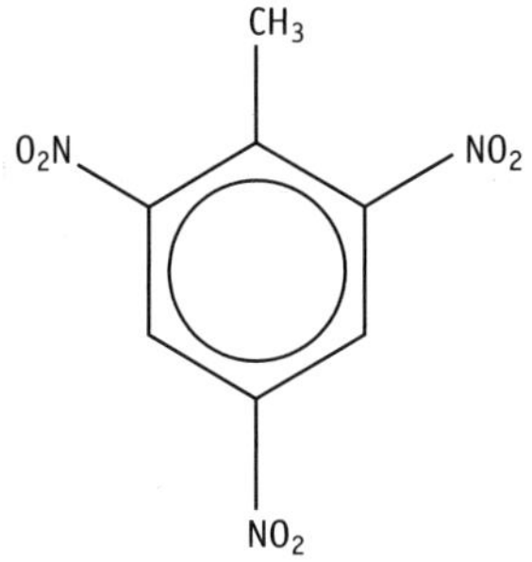

Aminobenzene is also called phenylamine. Its common name is aniline.

The old name for A was *ortho*-dichlorobenzene, the prefix *ortho*- indicating that the two substituents are on adjacent carbon atoms; B was *meta*-dichlorobenzene (the substituents being one carbon apart); C was *para*-dichloro-benzene (the substituents being opposite each other).

An exception to the rules for naming aromatic compounds is C_6H_5COOH, which is called benzoic acid, rather than the cumbersome phenylmethanoic acid.

Many aromatic substances are still known by their old names, which that were derived from the source of the chemical. For example, the compound with the formula

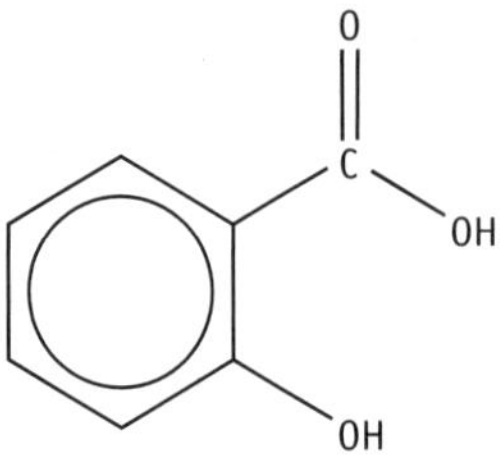

is commonly referred to as salicylic acid, rather than 2-hydroxybenzoic acid.

◀ Salicylic acid is derived from *salix*, the Latin name for a willow tree.

Benzene, C_6H_6

Physical properties

Benzene and many compounds that contain a substituted benzene ring have a characteristic smell — hence the name aromatic. The modern name for compounds that contain a benzene ring is **arene.**

◀ Arene is derived from *aromatic* and *–ene*, representing a carbon–carbon double bond.

Benzene is a non-polar liquid at room temperature. The main forces between molecules are instantaneous induced dipole (dispersion) forces and as the molecule has 42 electrons, these forces are strong enough for benzene to be a liquid. It cannot form hydrogen bonds with water and so it is immiscible.

The physical properties of benzene are:
- melting temperature, 5.5°C
- boiling temperature, 80.1°C
- density, 0.878 g cm^{-3}

◀ Benzene and some other compounds that contain a benzene ring are carcinogenic.

Chemical reactions

Benzene, like all organic compounds, burns in air. It also undergoes addition and substitution reactions.

Combustion

In excess air, benzene burns to form carbon dioxide and water:

$$C_6H_6(l) + 7\tfrac{1}{2}O_2(g) \rightarrow 6CO_2(g) + 3H_2O(l) \quad \Delta H_c^\circ = -3273 \text{ kJ mol}^{-1}$$

In a limited amount of air, it burns with a smoky flame since carbon is formed, rather than carbon dioxide:

$$C_6H_6(l) + 1\tfrac{1}{2}O_2(g) \rightarrow 6C(s) + 3H_2O(g)$$

The smoky flame can be used as a test to suggest the presence of a benzene ring in an organic compound.

Free-radical addition

Reaction with chlorine

When chlorine is bubbled into boiling benzene in the presence of ultraviolet light, addition takes place and 1,2,3,4,5,6-hexachlorocyclohexane is produced:

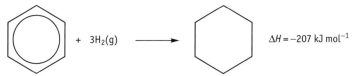

◀ A mixture of the geometric isomers of $C_6H_6Cl_6$ is obtained with different *cis* and *trans* arrangements on adjacent carbon atoms, only one of which is shown in this formula.

The mechanism is that ultraviolet light splits a chlorine molecule into two radicals:

$$Cl_2 + \text{light energy} \rightarrow 2Cl\bullet$$

The chlorine radicals add on, one at a time, to the benzene ring until all the π-bonds have been broken.

Bromine reacts in a similar way.

Reaction with hydrogen

When benzene vapour and hydrogen are passed over a heated nickel catalyst, three moles of hydrogen per mole of benzene add on and cyclohexane is formed.

Hydrogen is adsorbed as atoms at the active sites on the surface of the catalyst. These hydrogen radicals add on, one at a time, breaking the π-bonds until a saturated cycloalkane is formed:

$$+ \ 3H_2(g) \longrightarrow \qquad \Delta H = -207 \text{ kJ mol}^{-1}$$

The reaction is similar to the addition of hydrogen to cyclohexene, which has one localised π-bond:

$$+ \ H_2(g) \longrightarrow \qquad \Delta H = -119 \text{ kJ mol}^{-1}$$

If benzene had three *localised* π-bonds, the enthalpy change for the addition of 3 mol of hydrogen would be $3 \times -119 = -357$ kJ mol^{-1}. The difference between this value and the actual enthalpy change for the addition of 3 mol of hydrogen to benzene is 150 kJ mol^{-1}. This is the value by which the benzene molecule is stabilised because of the delocalisation of the π-electrons (resonance stabilisation energy).

The theoretical molecule with three localised double bonds is called 'cyclohexatriene'. The energy levels of this molecule and the actual molecules of benzene and cyclohexane are shown in Figure 12.5.

Figure 12.5
*Stabilisation energy
of benzene*

Benzene is at an energy level 150 kJ mol^{-1} lower than that of 'cyclohexatriene'. Therefore, the resonance stabilisation energy is 150 kJ mol^{-1}.

Electrophilic substitution reactions

Electrophiles attack the high-electron density in the delocalised π-ring of the benzene molecule.

- The first step is the addition of the electrophile to form an intermediate that is positively charged and in which the full delocalisation has been partially broken.
- The second step is the elimination of an H$^+$ ion. The fully delocalised ring and stabilisation energy are thus regained.

The reaction is:

addition + elimination = substitution

The delocalised π-system is stable compared with the localised π-bond in alkenes, so the activation energy required to break it is fairly high. Therefore, the electrophilic substitution reactions of benzene always require a catalyst.

Reaction with nitric acid

When concentrated nitric acid, benzene and a catalyst of concentrated sulphuric acid are warmed together at a temperature of 60°C in a flask fitted with a reflux condenser, nitrobenzene and water are formed:

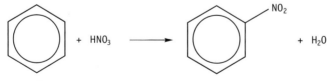

Below 55°C the reaction is too slow; above 65°C a second –NO$_2$ group is substituted into the ring.

The reaction proceeds in three steps.

Step 1: concentrated sulphuric acid protonates a nitric acid molecule, forming H$_2$NO$_3$$^+$. This loses water, forming NO$_2$$^+$, which is a powerful electrophile.

$$H_2SO_4 + HNO_3 \rightarrow H_2NO_3^+ + HSO_4^-$$
$$H_2NO_3^+ \rightarrow NO_2^+ + H_2O$$

The H$_2$O is then protonated by another H$_2$SO$_4$ molecule.

Step 2: the NO$_2$$^+$ ion draws a pair of electrons from the π-system and forms a covalent bond:

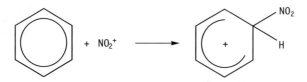

Step 3: the intermediate loses an H$^+$ ion to a HSO$_4$$^-$ ion. The stability of the benzene ring is regained and the H$_2$SO$_4$ catalyst is regenerated.

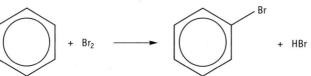

If the temperature is too high, a second –NO$_2$ group is substituted in the 3-position.

The products are 1,3-dinitrobenzene and water.

Reaction with halogens

Under certain conditions, chlorine and bromine react rapidly with benzene. A catalyst of anhydrous iron(III) halide (or aluminium halide) must be used and all the reagents must be dry. For the bromination of benzene, the catalyst is made *in situ* by adding iron filings to a mixture of benzene and liquid bromine. Clouds of hydrogen bromide fumes are given off in this exothermic reaction:

◀ *In situ* means in the same apparatus.

Step 1: if iron filings are added (rather than iron(III) bromide), they react to form the catalyst:

$$2Fe + 3Br_2 \rightarrow 2FeBr_3$$

This then reacts with more bromine to form the electrophile, Br$^+$:

$$FeBr_3 + Br_2 \rightarrow Br^+ + FeBr_4^-$$

Step 2: the Br$^+$ electrophile attacks the benzene ring:

Step 3: H^+ is lost, HBr is formed and the catalyst, $FeBr_3$, is regenerated:

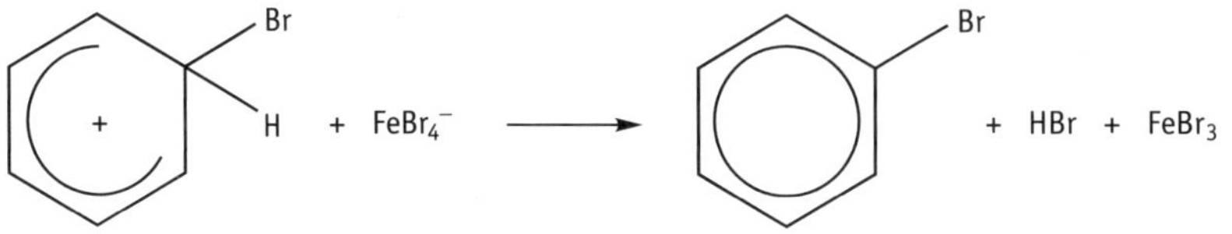

e Alkenes, such as ethene, react with bromine water. There is no reaction between bromine water and benzene.

Friedel–Crafts reactions

The French chemist Charles Friedel and the American James Crafts discovered the reaction of benzene with organic halogen compounds.

- The reaction can be represented by the equation:

    $C_6H_6 + RCl \rightarrow C_6H_5R + HCl$

- The catalyst has to be a covalent anhydrous metal chloride, for example aluminium chloride, $AlCl_3$, or iron(III) chloride, $FeCl_3$. All water must be excluded from the reaction.
- The reaction can be:
    - alkylation, with a halogenoalkane
    - acylation, with an acid chloride

In **alkylation reactions**, benzene reacts with a halogenoalkane in the presence of a catalyst of anhydrous aluminium chloride, under dry conditions, to form a hydrocarbon and gaseous hydrogen halide. For example, benzene and chloroethane react to form ethylbenzene and hydrogen chloride:

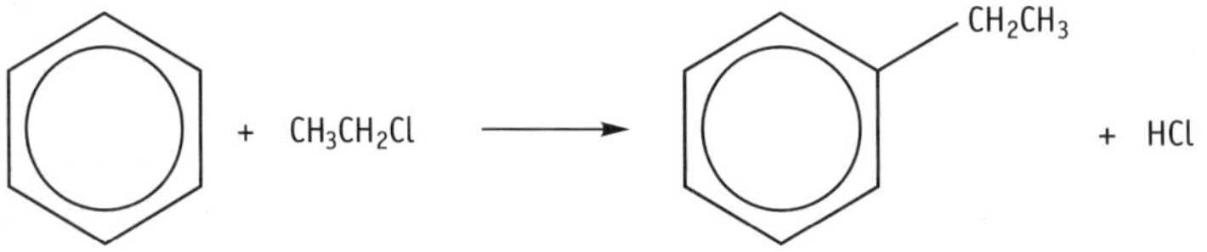

It is difficult to stop the reaction at this stage, as further alkylation to 1,2- and 1,4-diethylbenzene takes place.

Step 1: the catalyst reacts with the halogenoalkane to form $CH_3CH_2^+$, which is the electrophile:

$CH_3CH_2Cl + AlCl_3 \rightarrow CH_3CH_2^+AlCl_4^-$

Step 2: the electrophile accepts a pair of π-electrons from the ring, forming a covalent bond:

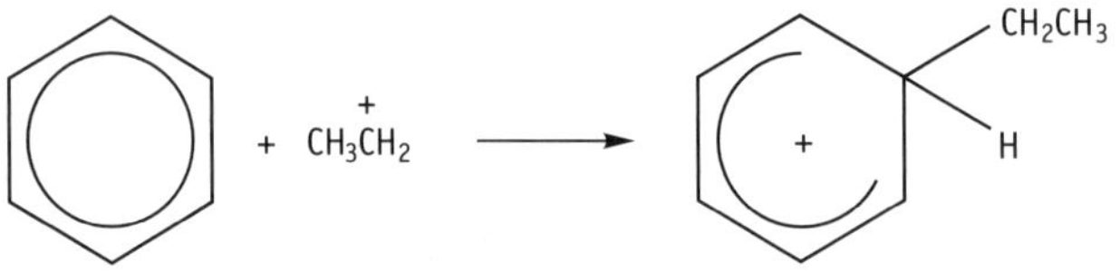

Step 3: the intermediate loses an H^+ ion. The stability of the benzene ring is regained and the catalyst is regenerated:

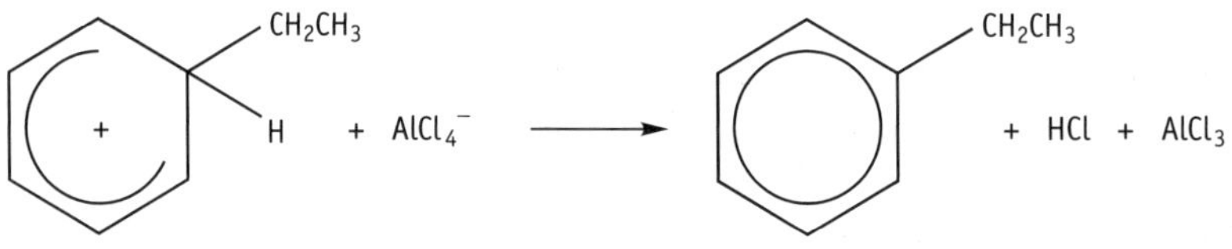

e When drawing this mechanism, make sure that the ethyl group is bonded to the benzene ring by the CH_2 carbon and not by the carbon of the CH_3.

Friedel–Crafts **acylation reactions** are carried out using an acid chloride such as ethanoyl chloride, CH_3COCl. The catalyst is anhydrous aluminium chloride, which produces the electrophile $CH_3-C^+=O$:

The remainder of the mechanism is similar to that of Friedel–Crafts alkylation reactions.

The overall reaction is:

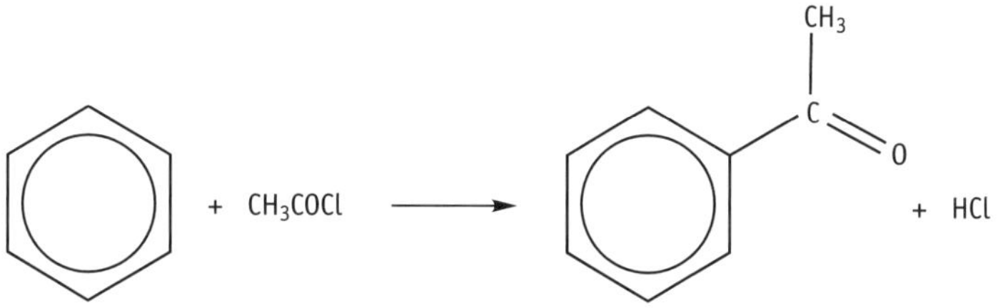

The products are the ketone (phenylethanone) and hydrogen chloride.

Further substitution does not take place, because the $COCH_3$ group deactivates the benzene ring.

Other substitution reactions of benzene

Benzene will also react with sulphuric acid and with alkenes:

- The **sulphonation** of benzene requires gentle heating with sulphuric acid that contains some dissolved sulphur trioxide (fuming sulphuric acid or oleum). The products are benzenesulphonic acid and water:

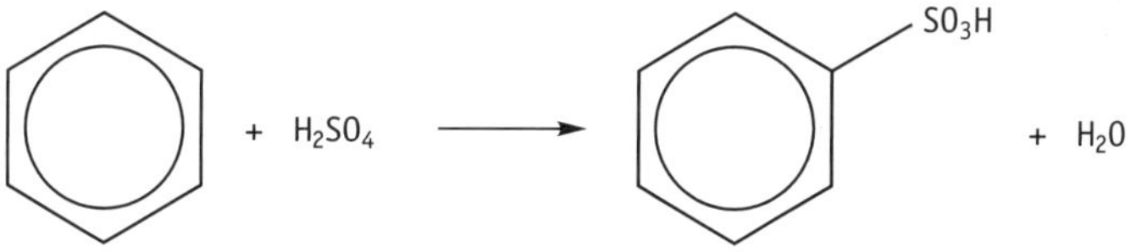

- Benzene adds on to alkenes under Friedel–Crafts conditions. The reaction can also be thought of as substitution into a benzene ring. The product with alkenes (other than ethene) is a branched-chain alkane substituted into the benzene ring, for example:

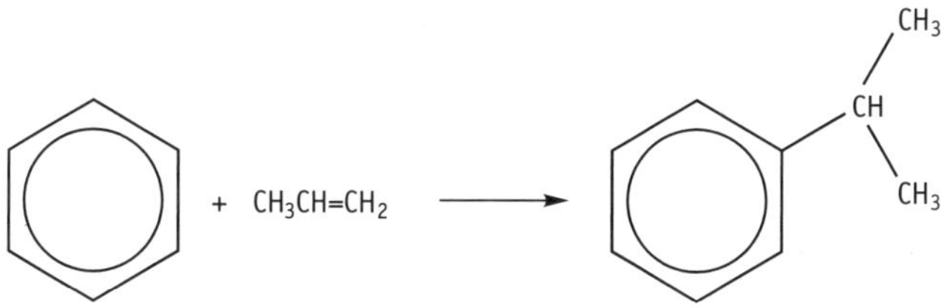

These two reactions are important in the manufacture of detergents. A long-chain alkene (C_{10} or greater) is reacted with benzene and the product is sulphonated. This product is then neutralised. It is an excellent detergent because its calcium salt is soluble, so no scum is formed in hard water.

e All substitution reactions of benzene must be carried out in dry conditions with a catalyst that produces a powerful electrophile.

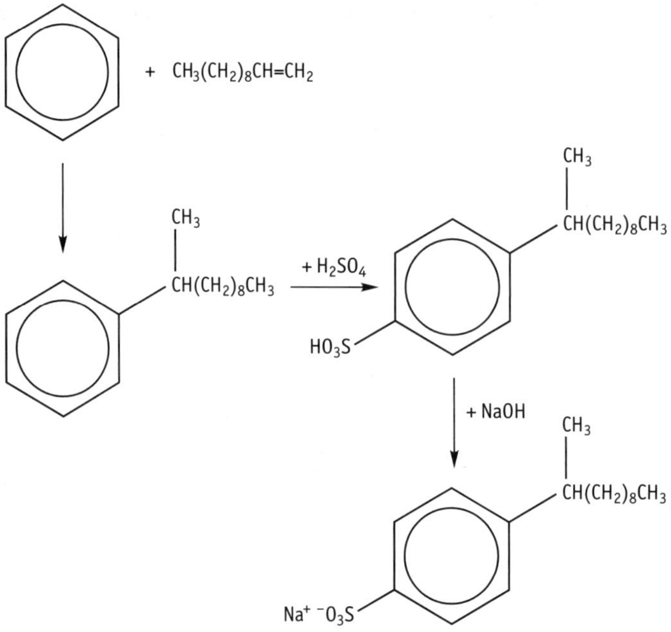

Aromatic compounds with a carbon side chain

If a group is attached via a carbon atom to the benzene ring, the compound has all the properties of an aliphatic compound with that group, as well as the reactions due to the benzene ring.

Alkane side chain

Methylbenzene, $C_6H_5CH_3$, reacts similarly to both alkanes and benzene.

Reaction with chlorine

When chlorine gas is bubbled into methylbenzene in the presence of UV light, the hydrogen atoms of the $-CH_3$ group are replaced one at a time:

$$C_6H_5CH_3 + Cl_2 \rightarrow C_6H_5CH_2Cl + HCl$$
$$C_6H_5CH_2Cl + Cl_2 \rightarrow C_6H_5CHCl_2 + HCl \quad \text{etc.}$$

Reaction with concentrated nitric acid

If methylbenzene and concentrated nitric acid are warmed to 50°C in the presence of concentrated sulphuric acid, a mixture of 2- and 4-nitromethylbenzene and water is produced:

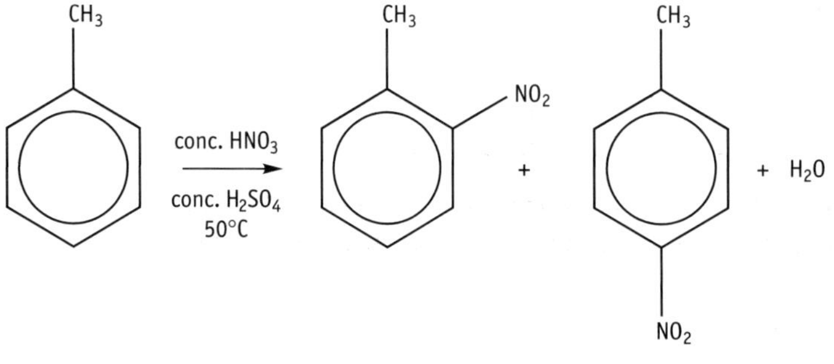

If methylbenzene is heated under reflux with the nitrating mixture, 2,4,6-tri-nitrotoluene (TNT) is produced.

The old name for methylbenzene is toluene.

Ketone side chain

Phenylethanone, $C_6H_5COCH_3$, has similar reactions to propanone, including the iodoform reaction.

Reaction with 2,4-dinitrophenylhydrazine

Phenylethanone reacts with 2,4-dinitrophenylhydrazine to produce a 2,4-di-nitrophenylhydrazone:

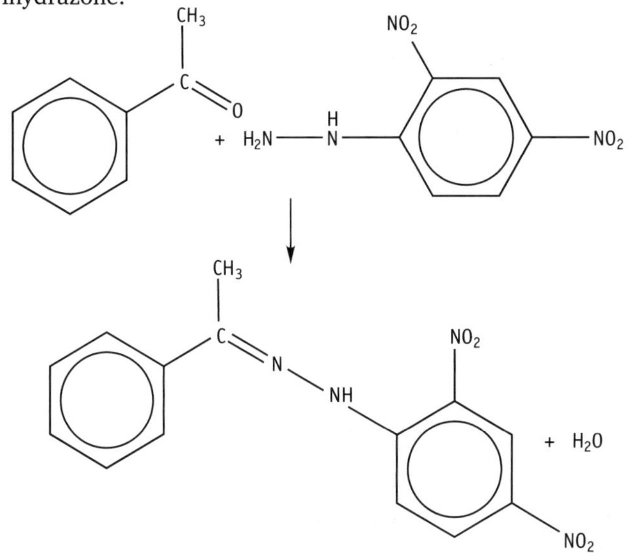

Reaction with HCN

In the presence of a trace of base, hydrogen cyanide adds on to the C=O group of phenylethanone:

$$C_6H_5COCH_3 + HCN \rightarrow C_6H_5C(OH)(CN)CH_3$$

Reaction with LiAlH$_4$

Phenylethanone is reduced by lithium tetrahydridoaluminate(III) in dry ether, followed by the addition of dilute acid. The product is a secondary alcohol, 1-phenylethanol:

$$C_6H_5COCH_3 + 2[H] \rightarrow C_6H_5CH(OH)CH_3$$

Reaction with iodine and sodium hydroxide

This is the iodoform reaction.

$$C_6H_5COCH_3 + 3I_2 + 4NaOH \rightarrow CHI_3 + 3NaI + C_6H_5COONa + 3H_2O$$

Oxidation of the side chain

If the side chain is joined to the benzene ring via a carbon atom, it can be oxidised by heating under reflux with an *alkaline* solution of potassium manganate(VII).

The side chain, whatever the number of carbon atoms that it contains, is oxidised to a COO$^-$ group, water and, if the side chain contains two or more carbon atoms, carbon dioxide:

$$C_6H_5CH_3 + 3[O] + OH^- \rightarrow C_6H_5COO^- + 2H_2O$$

Chapter 12: Aromatic chemistry   241

$$C_6H_5CH_2CH_3 + 6[O] + OH^- \rightarrow C_6H_5COO^- + 3H_2O + CO_2$$
$$C_6H_5COCH_3 + 4[O] + OH^- \rightarrow C_6H_5COO^- + 2H_2O + CO_2$$

The salt of benzoic acid is produced in all these reactions. If benzoic acid is required, the product is acidified with dilute sulphuric acid and cooled. Crystals of benzoic acid are precipitated:

$$C_6H_5COO^-(aq) + H^+(aq) \rightarrow C_6H_5COOH(s)$$

Phenol, C_6H_5OH

Phenol is an aromatic alcohol. It contains an –OH group bonded directly to a carbon atom in a benzene ring:

The lone pair of electrons in the p_z-orbital on the oxygen atom interacts with the delocalised π-electrons in the ring (Figure 12.6). This increases the electron density inside the ring, making it easier for phenol to be attacked by an electrophile. It also decreases the δ^- charge on the oxygen atom, making it less reactive as an alcohol. The hydrogen atom is much more easily lost from phenol than it is from aliphatic alcohols, so phenol has stronger acid properties than ethanol.

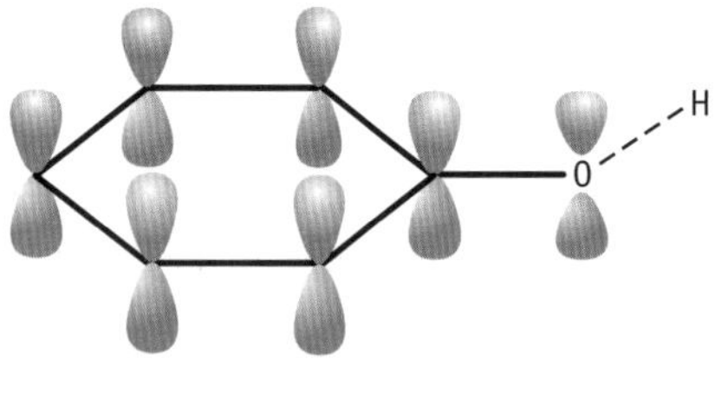

Figure 12.6
Interaction of the oxygen electrons with the aromatic ring

Physical properties

Phenol is a white solid that absorbs water from damp air.

Melting temperature

Phenol is a polar molecule with a δ^- oxygen atom and a δ^+ hydrogen atom. It can, therefore, form hydrogen bonds with other phenol molecules (intermolecular hydrogen bonding):

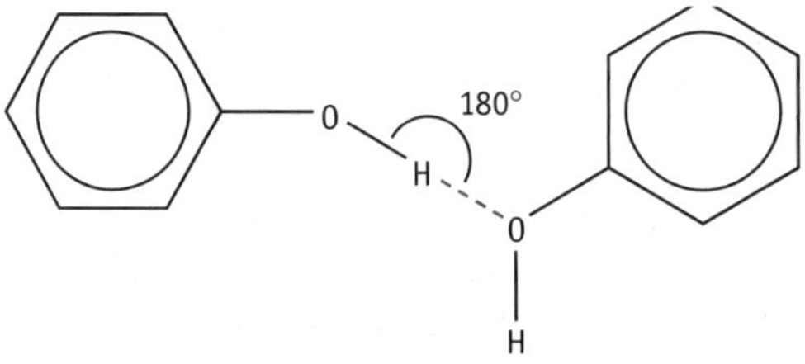

This is why phenol melts at a higher temperature than benzene and methylbenzene, which have only weaker dispersion forces between their molecules.

Pure phenol melts at 41°C and boils at 182°C.

Solubility

When phenol is added to water at room temperature, two liquid layers are formed. One is a solution of phenol in water and the other is a solution of water in phenol. If the temperature is raised to above 66°C, a single layer is formed because phenol and water are totally miscible above this temperature.

Phenol dissolves in water because hydrogen bonds are formed between phenol molecules and water molecules:

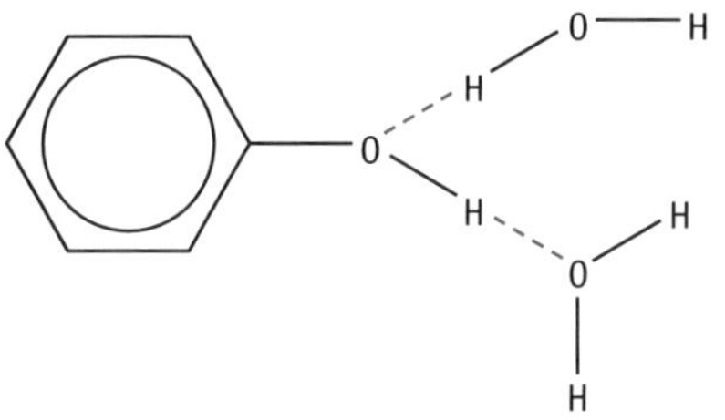

It is not very soluble in water (unlike ethanol, which is totally miscible) because of the large hydrophobic benzene ring.

Phenol is soluble in a variety of organic solvents because of the existence of dispersion (van der Waals) forces between its molecules and those of the solvent.

Chemical reactions

Phenol undergoes some of the reactions of aromatic compounds and some of the reactions of alcohols.

■ The presence in phenol of the oxygen atom attached to the ring increases the electron density of the π-system and so makes electrophilic substitution easier. However, as the p_z-electrons are slightly drawn into the ring, the oxygen atom becomes less δ^-. Therefore, it is less effective in alcohol-type reactions. It does not react with oxidising agents to give a carbonyl compound, so it can be regarded as a tertiary alcohol.

Another result of drawing the lone pair of electrons into the ring is to make the hydrogen atom more δ^+ than it is in alcohols. This makes phenol a much stronger acid than ethanol. However, it is still much weaker than a carboxylic acid.

Electrophilic aromatic substitution reactions

The electron density of the delocalised π-system is greater in phenol than in benzene. This makes phenol more reactive towards electrophiles. The substituents go into the 2- and/or 4-positions.

The substitution reactions of benzene require anhydrous conditions and a catalyst. Phenol reacts in aqueous conditions and no catalyst is needed. This is best explained by looking at the Kekulé resonance structures of phenol:

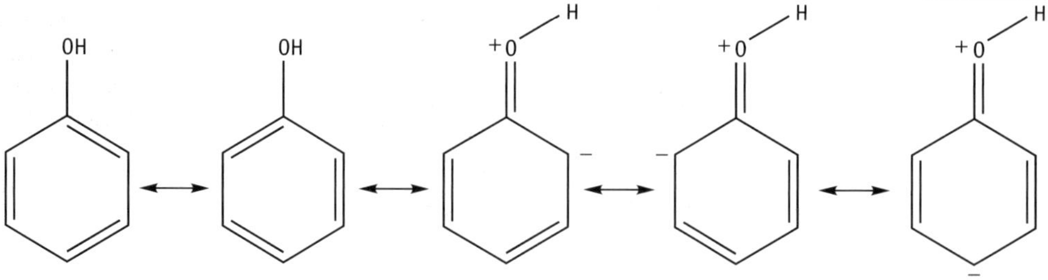

there the two benzene-type resonance structures, there are three others that have a negative charge on the 2-, 4- or 6-positions. Although the contribution of these structures is less than that of the two benzene-type structures, it is enough to make the incoming electrophile more likely to attack these electron-rich positions instead of the 3- and 5-positions.

Reaction with bromine

The conditions for the substitution of bromine into benzene are liquid bromine and a catalyst of iron(III) bromide (usually made *in situ* by adding iron filings to the bromine and benzene mixture).

The conditions for the bromination of phenol are quite different. When bromine *water* is added to a mixture of phenol and water, the red-brown bromine colour disappears and a white antiseptic-smelling precipitate of 2,4,6-tribromophenol in a solution of hydrogen bromide is immediately formed. The molecular equation for this reaction is:

$$C_6H_5OH(aq) + 3Br_2(aq) \rightarrow C_6H_2Br_3(OH)(s) + 3HBr(aq)$$

The equation showing structural formulae is:

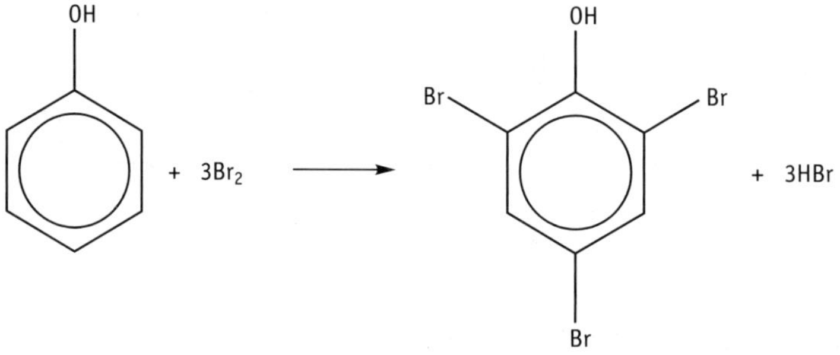

The electrophile is the δ^+ bromine atom in an HOBr molecule, made by the reaction of bromine and water:

$$Br_2 + H_2O \rightleftharpoons HOBr + HBr$$

2,4,6-tribromophenol, like many halogenated phenols, is an antiseptic. Dettol is 2,4-dichloro-3,5-dimethylphenol and TCP is 2,4,6-trichlorophenol. Phenol itself is also an antiseptic and was used in the nineteenth century by the surgeon Lister to reduce deaths from infection after major surgery.

Nitration

Phenol reacts with dilute nitric acid to form a mixture of 2-nitrophenol and 4-nitrophenol plus water.

e Do not forget that these are substitution reactions, so there must be two products on the right-hand side of the equation. The second product is a simple molecule, such as HBr or H_2O.

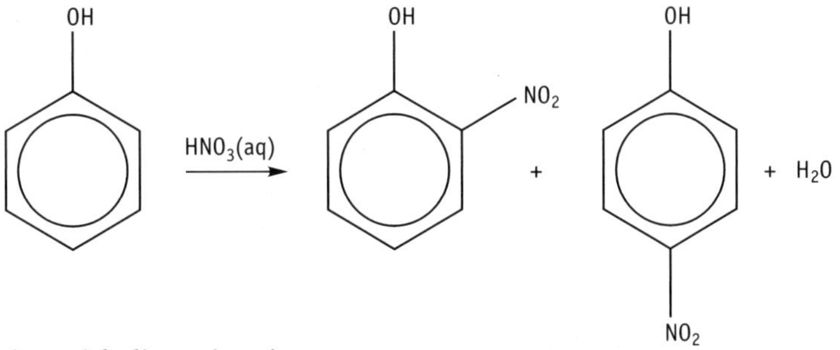

Remember that nitration of benzene requires concentrated nitric acid with a catalyst of concentrated sulphuric acid.

Reaction with diazonium ions

In alkaline solution, phenol is substituted by diazonium ions (p. 252).

Friedel–Craft reactions

Phenol reacts with acid chlorides, but not in a Friedel–Crafts reaction. Instead the oxygen atom in phenol acts as a nucleophile and attacks the δ^+ carbon atom in the acid chloride, forming an ester (p. 246).

Phenol as an acid

The p_z-lone pair on the oxygen atom is partially drawn into the ring and this makes the hydrogen atom much more δ^+ than in alcohols. Thus, phenol reacts with water to form an acidic solution and with alkalis to form a salt.

Reaction with water

$$C_6H_5OH + H_2O \rightleftharpoons H_3O^+ + C_6H_5O^- \quad K_a = 1.3 \times 10^{-10} \, mol \, dm^{-3}$$

The pH of a 0.10 mol dm^{-3} solution of phenol is 5.44.

The phenate ion formed is stabilised by resonance:

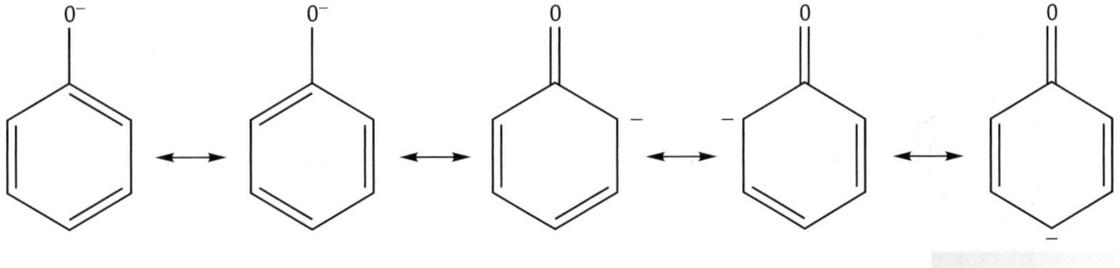

@ In all reactions involving the –OH group, the simplest way to write the formula of phenol is C_6H_5OH. The benzene ring needs to be drawn in full only for aromatic (electrophilic substitution) reactions.

Reaction with sodium hydroxide

Aqueous hydroxide ions are a strong enough base to deprotonate phenol to form the salt sodium phenate and water:

$$C_6H_5OH + NaOH \rightarrow C_6H_5ONa + H_2O$$

The ionic equation is:

$$C_6H_5OH(s) + OH^-(aq) \rightarrow C_6H_5O^-(aq) + H_2O(l)$$

Solid phenol 'dissolves' in aqueous sodium hydroxide.

The word 'dissolves' is often used in this context. A more correct description would be that solid phenol *reacts* to form a solution.

Reaction with sodium

Phenol is a strong enough acid to react with metallic sodium to form hydrogen:

$$C_6H_5OH + Na \rightarrow C_6H_5ONa + \tfrac{1}{2}H_2$$

Reaction with sodium hydrogencarbonate and sodium carbonate

Phenol is a weaker acid than carbonic acid, which has $K_a = 3.4 \times 10^{-7}$ mol dm^{-3}. Therefore, it will not liberate carbon dioxide from either sodium hydrogencarbonate or sodium carbonate. This is one way to distinguish phenol from a carboxylic acid.

e Water, alcohols and carboxylic acids all give hydrogen gas with sodium metal.

	Add blue litmus	Add sodium hydroxide	Add sodium carbonate	Add sodium
Alcohols	Stays blue	No reaction	No reaction	H_2 evolved
Phenol	Goes red	Salt formed	No reaction	H_2 evolved
Carboxylic acids	Goes red	Salt formed	CO_2 evolved	H_2 evolved

Table 12.1. Acidity of alcohols, phenol and carboxylic acids

Phenol as an alcohol

Phenol does not react as an alcohol as readily as aliphatic alcohols, for example ethanol and propan-2-ol.

Reaction with acid chlorides

Phenol reacts slowly with aliphatic acid chlorides, for example ethanoyl chloride, to form an ester and fumes of hydrogen chloride.

$$C_6H_5OH + CH_3COCl \rightarrow CH_3COOC_6H_5 + HCl$$

The structural formula of the ester phenylethanoate is:

The oxygen atom in phenol acts as a nucleophile and attacks the δ^+ carbon atom in the acid chloride.

Aromatic acid chlorides, such as benzoyl chloride, C_6H_5COCl, are less reactive. Sodium hydroxide has to be added to create $C_6H_5O^-$ ions, which are a stronger nucleophile than phenol molecules. The ester, phenyl benzoate, is formed along with chloride ions:

$$C_6H_5O^- + C_6H_5COCl \rightarrow C_6H_5COOC_6H_5 + Cl^-$$

e Remember that aliphatic alcohols, such as ethanol, react rapidly with both aliphatic and aromatic acid chlorides.

Reaction with carboxylic acids

Phenol does not form esters with carboxylic acids, unlike aliphatic alcohols which react reversibly.

Reaction with phosphorus halides

Phenol reacts slowly with PCl$_5$ to give a very poor yield of chlorobenzene:

$$C_6H_5OH + PCl_5 \rightarrow C_6H_5Cl + POCl_3 + HCl$$

Phenol does not react with PBr$_3$, or with a mixture of 50% sulphuric acid and potassium bromide or with a mixture of moist red phosphorus and iodine.

e Remember that aliphatic alcohols undergo all these reactions with phosphorus halides.

Benzoic acid, C₆H₅COOH

The structural formula of benzoic acid is

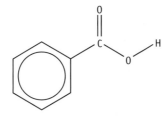

- It is a solid with a melting temperature of 122°C.
- It is almost insoluble in cold water.
- The dissolving of benzoic acid is endothermic, so the position of the equilibrium:

$$C_6H_5COOH(s) + aq \rightleftharpoons C_6H_5COOH(aq)$$

is driven to the right by an increase in temperature. Benzoic acid is soluble in hot water and so can be purified by recrystallisation using hot water (p. 298).
- Benzoic acid has the typical reactions of a carboxylic acid. It is slightly stronger than ethanoic acid:
  - K_a of benzoic acid = 6.31×10^{-5} mol dm^{-3};
    pH of 0.10 mol dm^{-3} solution = 2.60
  - K_a of ethanoic acid = 1.74×10^{-5} mol dm^{-3};
    pH of 0.10 mol dm^{-3} solution = 2.88
- On warming with a mixture of concentrated nitric and sulphuric acids, 3-nitrobenzoic acid and water are formed:

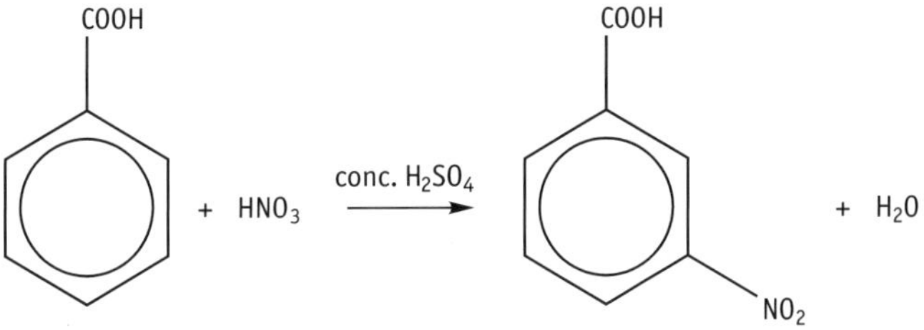

COOH $\quad$ + $\quad$ HNO₃ $\quad \xrightarrow{\text{conc. H}_2\text{SO}_4}\quad$ COOH ... NO₂ $\quad$ + $\quad$ H₂O

e The rules that determine the position of an aromatic substitution are as follows:
- If the atom that is bonded by a σ-bond to the benzene ring also has a π-bond, the ring is less easily substituted and the substituent goes into the 3- (or 5-) position. Nitration of benzoic acid forms 3-nitrobenzoic acid; nitration of nitrobenzene forms 1,3-dinitrobenzene.
- If the atom which is bonded to the benzene ring does not have any π-bonding, the ring is activated to substitution and the incoming substituent goes into the 2-, 4- and/or 6- positions. Methylbenzene and phenylethanone both give a mixture of 2- and 4- nitro compounds on nitration. Phenol gives 2,4,6-tribromophenol with bromine water.

Nitrobenzene, C₆H₅NO₂

Nitrobenzene is an oily liquid that smells of almonds. It boils at 211°C and has a density of 1.14 g cm^{-3}.

Preparation and purification

Nitrobenzene can be prepared from benzene and nitric acid:

$$C_6H_6 + HNO_3 \rightarrow C_6H_5NO_2 + H_2O$$

The procedure is as follows:

- The nitrating mixture, which consists of equal amounts of concentrated nitric and sulphuric acids, is mixed with benzene and the mixture is heated in a water bath maintained at 60°C. The temperature must not rise above this or a significant amount of 1,3-dinitrobenzene will be formed. If the temperature is allowed to fall below 60°C, the reaction becomes very slow.
- After refluxing, the mixture is cooled and water is added to dilute the acids. The mixture is then poured into a separating funnel and the bottom layer, which contains the nitrobenzene, is run off. The top layer is discarded.
- The impure nitrobenzene is washed with sodium carbonate solution, to remove residual acid, and then with water, to remove residual sodium carbonate. This is also carried out in the separating funnel.
- The oily liquid nitrobenzene is dried by adding lumps of anhydrous calcium chloride and leaving for several hours.
- It is then decanted into a flask and distilled. The fraction that boils between 210°C and 212°C is collected. This is pure nitrobenzene.

> ⓔ Benzene is carcinogenic, so this preparation should not be carried out in a school laboratory. Methylbenzene is not carcinogenic and can be used in place of benzene. The mixture is heated in a water bath maintained at 50°C rather than 60°C. This is because methylbenzene is more reactive than benzene. The 2-nitromethylbenzene (boiling temperature 220°C) can be separated from the 4-nitromethylbenzene (boiling temperature 238°C) by distillation.

Chemical reactions

The nitro group is joined to the benzene ring by a nitrogen atom that is π-bonded to an oxygen atom. This makes the ring less susceptible to electrophilic attack.

Electrophilic substitution reactions

Nitration

Nitrobenzene can be nitrated by heating it with concentrated nitric and sulphuric acids in a water bath, with the temperature maintained at 90°C. The products are 1,3-dinitrobenzene and water:

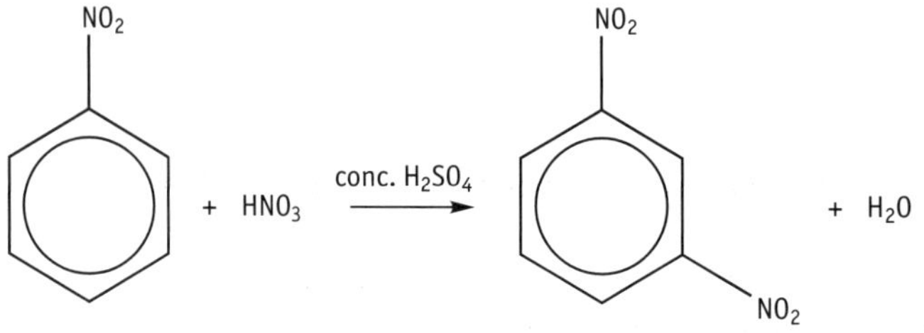

Bromination

When liquid bromine and nitrobenzene are warmed in the presence of iron filings or anhydrous iron(III) bromide, a bromine atom substitutes into the benzene ring in the 3-position:

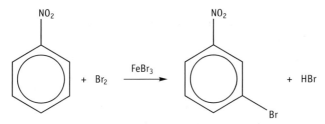

Reduction of the –NO₂ group

The –NO₂ group can be reduced to –NH₂ by the action of tin and concentrated hydrochloric acid. The tin reacts with the acid to form Sn^{2+} ions, which reduce the –NO₂ group and become oxidised to Sn^{4+} ions.

The product of the reaction is a mixture of the salt of phenylamine and tin(II) and tin(IV) chlorides. The phenylamine is liberated by the addition of sodium hydroxide. The overall process can be represented by:

$$C_6H_5NO_2 + 6[H] \rightarrow C_6H_5NH_2 + 2H_2O$$

Phenylamine, $C_6H_5NH_2$

The structural formula of phenylamine is:

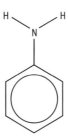

The lone pair of electrons on the nitrogen atom is in the same plane as the delocalised π-electrons of the ring and so, to some extent, becomes part of the delocalised system. This pulling of the electrons into the ring and away from the nitrogen atom has two effects — the ring becomes more susceptible to electrophilic attack and the nitrogen atom becomes less δ^- and so less effective as a base.

Physical properties

- Phenylamine is a liquid at room temperature. It boils at 184°C and is slightly denser than water.
- The nitrogen atom is δ^- and the hydrogen atoms attached to the nitrogen are δ^+. Therefore, phenylamine can form intermolecular hydrogen bonds as well

Phenylamine used to be called aniline.

as strong dispersion (van der Waals) forces between molecules. It is slightly soluble in water because it forms hydrogen bonds with water molecules. However, the benzene ring inhibits solubility.

- It dissolves readily in many organic solvents such as ether (ethoxyethane) and ethanol.
- It is a toxic substance that can be absorbed through the skin.

Laboratory preparation

The procedure for the laboratory preparation of phenylamine is as follows:

- Nitrobenzene and tin are mixed in a round-bottomed flask fitted with a reflux condenser. Concentrated hydrochloric acid is carefully added and, after the rapid evolution of hydrogen has ceased, the mixture is heated to 100°C in a bath of boiling water for 30 minutes.
- The reaction mixture is cooled to room temperature, the condenser removed and an *excess* of sodium hydroxide is carefully added with cooling.
- The mixture is steam distilled to remove the phenylamine from the sludge of tin hydroxides. This is carried out by blowing steam into the mixture and condensing the phenylamine and steam mixture that comes off.
- The distillate is placed in a separating funnel and some solid sodium chloride is added to reduce the solubility of phenylamine. The phenylamine layer is run off into a flask and some anhydrous potassium carbonate added to remove any traces of water.
- The phenylamine is decanted off from the solid potassium carbonate and distilled, using an air condenser. The fraction that boils between 180°C and 185°C is collected.

The equation for the process can be represented by:

$$C_6H_5NO_2 + 6[H] \rightarrow C_6H_5NH_2 + 2H_2O$$

Chemical reactions

Phenylamine reacts as both an aromatic compound and as a primary amine. It also reacts with nitric(III) acid (nitrous acid).

Electrophilic substitution reactions

In neutral or weakly acidic solutions the benzene ring is activated by the lone pair of electrons on the nitrogen atom. In strongly acidic conditions, the $-NH_2$ group is protonated to form an NH_3^+ group, which withdraws electrons from the ring and deactivates it.

This is similar to the reaction between phenol and bromine water to form a white precipitate of 2,4,6-tribromophenol.

Bromination

Phenylamine reacts with bromine water to form a white precipitate of 2,4,6-tribromophenylamine and hydrogen bromide. The molecular equation is:

$$C_6H_5NH_2 + 3Br_2 \rightarrow C_6H_2Br_3NH_2 + 3HBr$$

Nitration

Concentrated nitric and sulphuric acids protonate the $-NH_2$ group in phenylamine, which deactivates the benzene ring. Electrophilic substitution does not occur. Phenylamine is oxidised to a black solid of indeterminate structure.

Friedel–Crafts reaction

The $-NH_2$ group reacts preferentially with acid chlorides and halogenoalkanes, so phenylamine does not undergo Friedel–Crafts reactions.

Reactions of the NH_2 group

The pulling of the lone pair of electrons from the nitrogen atom by the benzene ring makes the nitrogen atom less δ^- and, therefore, less effective as a base and as a nucleophile.

Phenylamine as a base

Phenylamine is a weak base, so it reacts reversibly with water:

$$C_6H_5NH_2 + H_2O \rightleftharpoons C_6H_5NH_3^+ + OH^-$$

> **e** If you draw the *full* structural formula or the displayed formula of the phenylammonium ion (showing the three hydrogen atoms separately attached to the nitrogen) make sure that you put the positive charge on the nitrogen atom and not on a hydrogen atom. For the ordinary structural formula, writing the group as NH_3^+ is acceptable.

It reacts with strong acids to form phenylammonium salts. For example, the molecular equation for the reaction of phenylamine with hydrochloric acid to form phenylammonium chloride is:

$$C_6H_5NH_2 + HCl \rightarrow C_6H_5NH_3Cl$$

The ionic equation is:

$$C_6H_5NH_2(l) + H^+(aq) \rightarrow C_6H_5NH_3^+(aq)$$

Liquid phenylamine dissolves in aqueous acids because it forms an ionic salt.

Phenylamine is a weaker base than ammonia, because of the electron-withdrawing effect of the benzene ring.

> These reactions are similar to those of ammonia:
>
> $NH_3 + H_2O \rightleftharpoons NH_4^+ + OH^-$
>
> $NH_3 + HCl \rightarrow NH_4Cl$
> or
> $NH_3(aq) + H^+(aq) \rightarrow NH_4^+(aq)$

Phenylamine as a nucleophile

Phenylamine, like an aliphatic primary amine, reacts with an acid chloride to form a secondary amide:

$$C_6H_5NH_2 + CH_3COCl \rightarrow C_6H_5NHCOCH_3 + HCl$$

Reaction with nitric(III) acid, HNO_2

Nitric(III) acid is unstable and has to be made *in situ* by mixing a solution of sodium nitrite, $NaNO_2$, with excess dilute hydrochloric acid. If this mixture is maintained between 5°C and 10°C and added to phenylamine, benzenediazonium chloride is formed.

$$C_6H_5NH_2 + HNO_2 + HCl \rightarrow C_6H_5N_2Cl + 2H_2O$$

> The old name for nitric(III) acid is nitrous acid.

> This reaction is called diazotisation.

Benzenediazonium compounds

Benzenediazonium compounds contain the $C_6H_5N_2^+$ ion. The structure of this ion is:

These compounds are very unstable. If the temperature is allowed to rise above 10°C, or if the solution becomes too concentrated, they decompose giving off nitrogen gas.

Laboratory preparation

The procedure for the preparation of benzenediazonium compounds is as follows:

- Phenylamine and concentrated hydrochloric acid are mixed and the mixture is cooled to 5°C in an ice bath.
- A solution of sodium nitrite (cooled to 5°C) is slowly added, making sure that the temperature neither rises above 10°C nor falls below 5°C.
- The solution is kept at 5°C and used as necessary.

> **e** If the temperature rises above 5°C, the benzenediazonium ions decompose. If the temperature falls below 5°C, the reaction does not take place.

Coupling reactions of diazonium ions

One nitrogen atom in the diazonium ion is positively charged and, as nitrogen is a very electronegative element, it is a powerful electrophile. It will substitute into a benzene ring if the ring is activated by an –OH or –NH$_2$ group. The resulting compound can form hydrogen bonds with groups in cotton and wool and so binds strongly to the fabrics. This makes diazonium compounds useful as dyes.

The organic products of these coupling reactions have two benzene rings joined by a –N=N– group.

Reaction with phenol

When phenol is mixed with sodium hydroxide, the phenate ion C$_6$H$_5$O$^-$ is produced. A diazonium ion attacks this species by an electrophilic substitution reaction. A yellow precipitate of 4-hydroxyazobenzene is obtained:

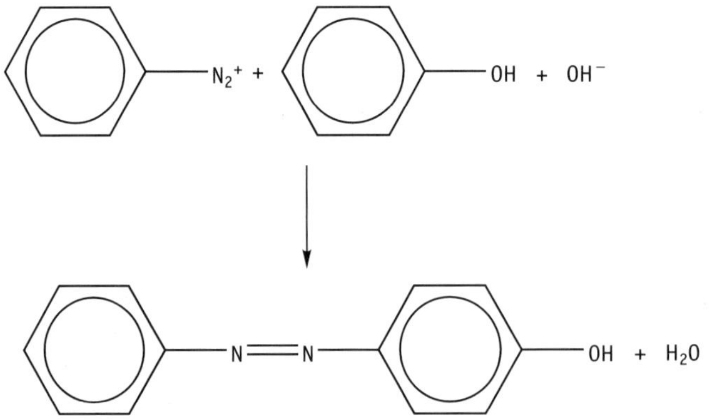

Reaction with 2-naphthol

Naphthols are compounds with two fused benzene rings and an –OH group on one of the rings. 2-naphthol couples with diazonium ions to form a red precipitate that can be used as a Turkey-red dye:

e If you draw the full structural formula of a diazonium ion (with the nitrogen atoms shown separately) make sure that you put the positive charge on the nitrogen atom that is attached to the benzene ring.

The term azo refers to compounds in which two nitrogen atoms are covalently bonded together. It is derived from the French for nitrogen, which is *azote*.

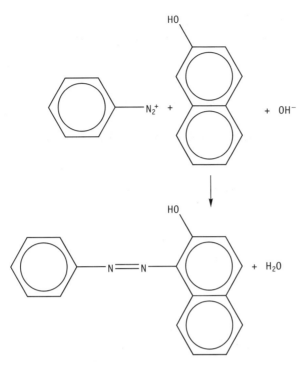

Reaction with phenylamine

If a solution of diazonium ions is added to phenylamine, a yellow precipitate of 4-aminoazobenzene is formed.

Questions

1 Some enthalpy data are given below.

ΔH_a of carbon = +715 kJ mol^{-1}

ΔH_a of hydrogen = +218 kJ mol^{-1}

ΔH_f of benzene(g) = +83 kJ mol^{-1}

Average bond enthalpy	ΔH/kJ mol^{-1}
C–C	+348
C=C	+612
C–H	+412

Use the data to calculate:

a the enthalpy of formation of the theoretical gaseous molecule, cyclohexatriene

b the resonance stabilisation energy of benzene

c Hence, draw a labelled energy-level diagram showing both the formation of cyclohexatriene and benzene from solid carbon and hydrogen gas and the resonance stabilisation energy.

2 Draw the resonance structures of the ethanoate, CH_3COO^-, ion.

3 Draw and name all the aromatic isomers of $C_6H_4ClNO_2$.

4 Draw and name all the aromatic isomers of $C_6H_3Br_2OH$.

5 State the conditions for the conversion of nitrobenzene, $C_6H_5NO_2$, to:
   a $C_6H_5Br_6NO_2$
   b $C_6H_4BrNO_2$

6 Write equations for the production of the electrophiles for the following reactions of aromatic compounds:
   a nitration
   b bromination
   c alkylation

7 Write equations for both steps in the mechanism of the reaction of benzene with the electrophile, CH_3C^+O, in the acylation reaction of benzene with ethanoyl chloride.

8 Write equations and state the conditions for the reactions of methylbenzene with:
   a ethanoyl chloride
   b bromine
   c nitric acid

9 Outline how you could convert 1-chloro-2-phenylethane, $C_6H_5CH_2CH_2Cl$, into benzoic acid, C_6H_5COOH.

10 Explain why phenol:
   a is a stronger acid than ethanol
   b has a higher boiling temperature than ethanol
   c is less soluble in water than ethanol

11 Write the structural formulae of the organic products, if any, of attempting to react phenol with:
   a aqueous potassium hydroxide
   b sodium hydrogencarbonate
   c chlorine water
   d benzoyl chloride, C_6H_5COCl, in alkaline solution

12 Calculate the pH of a 0.20 mol dm^{-3} solution of phenol, $K_a = 1.3 \times 10^{-10}$ mol dm^{-3}.

13 Calculate:
   a the mass of bromine that would react with 1.23 g of phenol
   b the percentage yield, if 4.25 g of 2,4,6-tribromophenol were produced

14 Give an example of phenol reacting as a nucleophile.

15 Draw a diagram to show how two molecules of benzoic acid are hydrogen bonded. Mark in the bond angles around the hydrogen bond.

16 Explain the importance of the conditions in:
   a the nitration of benzene
   b the diazotisation of phenylamine

17 Write equations, using [H] and [O] where necessary, for:
   a the oxidation of 1,4-dimethylbenzene with alkaline potassium manganate(VII)
   b the reduction of 3-chloronitrobenzene with tin and concentrated hydrochloric acid
   c the reaction of phenylamine with sodium nitrite, $NaNO_2$, and hydrochloric acid at 5 °C

18 Write:
   a the structural formula of the $C_6H_5N_2^+$ ion
   b the equation for its reaction with phenol in alkaline solution

19 Phenylamine and chlorobenzene are equally polar molecules, but phenylamine boils at 184 °C whereas chlorobenzene boils at 132 °C. Phenylamine is slightly soluble in water and forms a clear solution when dilute hydrochloric acid is added. Chlorobenzene is immiscible with both water and dilute hydrochloric acid.

   Explain:
   a the difference in boiling temperatures of the two substances
   b why phenylamine is more soluble in hydrochloric acid than in water
   c why chlorobenzene is insoluble both in water and in hydrochloric acid

20 Write equations to show why an aqueous solution of:
   a phenol is acidic
   b phenylamine is alkaline
   c phenylammonium chloride is acidic
   d sodium benzoate is alkaline

21 Search the internet and write a brief account of the discovery in the nineteenth century of phenol and its use as an antiseptic by the surgeon Lister.

Mechanisms

Introduction

The mechanism of an organic reaction shows the pathway from the reactants, via the transition state or any intermediates, to the products. It also shows the movement of electrons during the reaction by the use of arrows.

A **half-headed** or **fishhook arrow** ( ) represents the movement of a *single* electron.

A half-headed arrow can:
- start from a covalent bond. In this case, it goes either to an atom (thus forming a radical) or to another radical (thus forming a covalent bond).
- start from the single electron in a free radical. In this case, it goes either to an atom or to a radical to form a covalent bond.

A free radical is represented by a single dot beside the symbol of the atom. For example, $Cl\bullet$ represents a chlorine radical.

The standard or full **curly arrow** ( ) represents the movement of a *pair* of electrons.

The full curly arrow can:
- start from a covalent σ-bond or a π-bond in a molecule. The bond is broken as the electrons move.
- start from a lone pair of electrons on an atom. The lone pair of electrons is represented by two dots. This movement causes a bond to be formed.

The arrow either goes towards an atom (forming a new covalent bond) or on to an atom (forming a negative ion).

Attacking reagents

The attacking reagents are classified according to their nature.

Free radical

A free radical is an unstable species with an unpaired electron.

$Cl\bullet$ and $CH_3\bullet$ are free radicals.

Free radicals rapidly accept an electron to form a covalent bond.

Nucleophile

A nucleophile is a species with a lone pair of electrons, which is used to form a new covalent bond.

A nucleophile can be a molecule such as $H_2O:$ or $:NH_3$ or an anion such as $:Cl^-$, $:OH^-$ and $:CN^-$. A nucleophile will attack δ^+ sites in a molecule.

The lone pair of electrons is shown in the formula of the nucleophile only when drawing the mechanism of a reaction.

Electrophile

> An electrophile is a species that accepts a pair of electrons from another species and forms a covalent bond.

An electrophile can be a polar molecule such as HBr, a non-polar (but polarisable) molecule such as Br_2 or a cation such as H^+, NO_2^+ or Br^+. In a polar molecule, the electrophile is the δ^+ atom in the molecule.

An electrophile will attack an electron-rich area, such as a π-bond, or a δ^- atom in a molecule.

Classification of reactions

Addition

In an addition reaction, two molecules join to form a single molecule. An example is the addition of hydrogen to ethene:

$$CH_2{=}CH_2 + H_2 \rightarrow CH_3CH_3$$

Substitution

In a substitution reaction, one atom, ion or group of atoms replaces another atom or group in a second molecule. There are always two reactants and two different products. An example is the substitution reaction between OH^- ions and a halogenoalkane:

$$OH^- + CH_3CHClCH_3 \rightarrow CH_3CH(OH)CH_3 + Cl^-$$

Elimination

In an elimination reaction, two atoms or an atom and a simple group are removed from adjacent carbon atoms, forming a new π-bond and a simple inorganic product molecule. Examples are the elimination of water from alcohols to form an alkene and the elimination of HBr from a halogenoalkane, also to form an alkene:

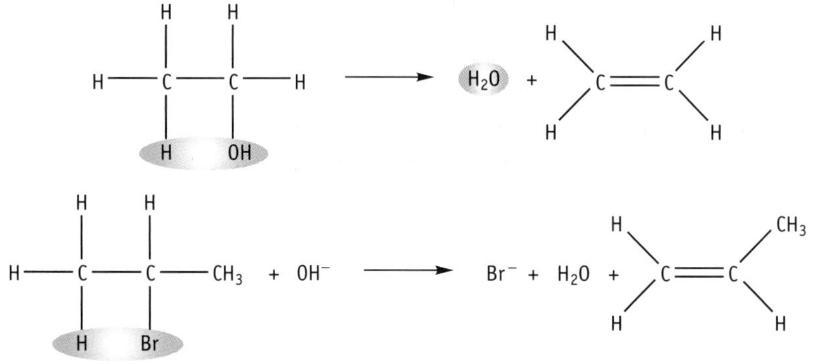

Condensation

Condensation is the loss of a simple molecule such as water, hydrogen chloride or methanol from two organic molecules so that the two organic residues join together. An example is the formation of polyesters or polyamides, such as Terylene®:

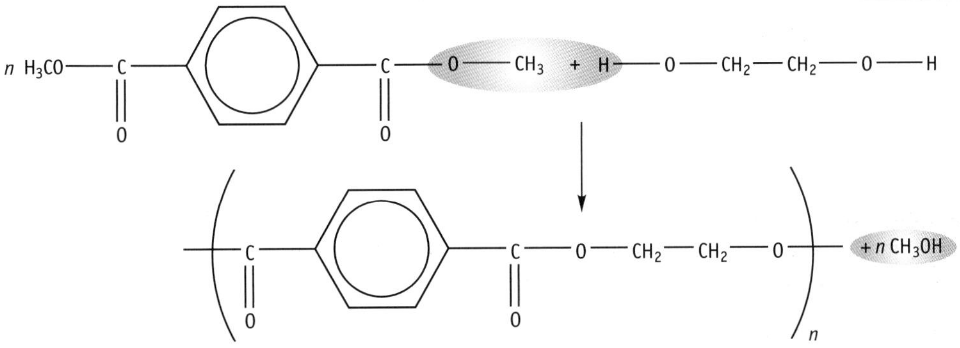

Another example is the reaction between a carbonyl compound and 2,4-dinitrophenylhydrazine:

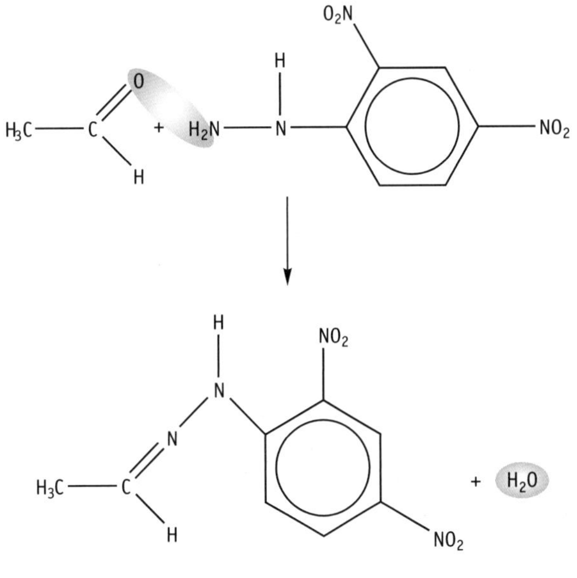

Addition–elimination

In an addition–elimination reaction, one species (usually an ion) adds on to an atom in a π-bond. This is then followed by the loss of an atom or ion, with the π-bond being reformed. The result is substitution. An example is the electrophilic substitution of benzene (p. 236).

Free-radical substitution

An example of a **free-radical substitution** is the reaction between an alkane and chlorine or bromine. The reaction does not occur at room temperature unless the gaseous mixture is exposed to visible or UV light. The simplest reaction of this type is that between chlorine and methane.

Reaction between chlorine and methane

Three distinct processes take place: initiation, propagation and termination.

Initiation

Light energy splits a chlorine molecule into chlorine radicals.

The light must be of a high enough frequency to cause the σ-bond to break. It does so homolytically with one of the bonding electrons going to each chlorine atom:

$$Cl\!\!-\!\!Cl \xrightarrow{\text{UV}} Cl\bullet + Cl\bullet$$

This process is called photolysis, because the bond is broken (-*lysis*) by light (*photo*-).

e Remember that the fishhook arrows show that one electron goes to each atom as the bond breaks.

Propagation

Chlorine radicals are very reactive. When a chlorine radical collides with a methane molecule with sufficient energy, a hydrogen atom is removed to form a methyl radical, $\bullet CH_3$, and a molecule of hydrogen chloride:

$$CH_4 + Cl\bullet \rightarrow \bullet CH_3 + HCl$$

Methyl radicals are also very reactive and will remove a chlorine atom from a chlorine molecule, forming a chloromethane molecule and another chlorine radical:

$$CH_3 + Cl_2 \rightarrow CH_3Cl + Cl\bullet$$

The chlorine radical then removes a hydrogen atom from another methane molecule and so on. This type of reaction is called a **chain reaction** as a small amount of UV light results in many propagation reactions. It has been estimated that, in the reaction of methane with chlorine, a single photon of light causes 10^6 propagation steps.

The chlorine radical cannot bond to the carbon atom until a hydrogen atom has been removed, so the propagation step is *not* $CH_4 + Cl\bullet \rightarrow CH_3Cl + H\bullet$. Also, the energetics of this reaction are much less favourable than for the reaction in which a chlorine radical removes a hydrogen atom.

> **e** The H–Br bond is weaker than the H–Cl bond, so less energy is given out in its formation. This makes the first propagation step endothermic ($\Delta H = +46$ kJ mol^{-1}) for bromine, whereas it is exothermic ($\Delta H = -19$ kJ mol^{-1}) for chlorine. The result is that bromination is much slower than chlorination.

As the concentration of CH_3Cl builds up, an alternative propagation step becomes increasingly likely — a chlorine radical collides with a CH_3Cl molecule and removes a hydrogen radical from it:

$$CH_3Cl + Cl\bullet \rightarrow \bullet CH_2Cl + HCl$$

The $\bullet CH_2Cl$ radical then removes a chlorine atom from a chlorine molecule, thus continuing the chain reaction:

$$\bullet CH_2Cl + Cl_2 \rightarrow CH_2Cl_2 + Cl\bullet$$

Termination (chain breaking)

The chain reaction can be broken when two radicals collide. As their concentration is low, the chance of this happening is slight. The second propagation step has the highest activation energy, so the $\bullet CH_3$ radicals have the longest life and are the most likely to be involved in chain breaking. Examples of chain-breaking reactions are:

$$\bullet CH_3 + \bullet CH_3 \rightarrow CH_3CH_3 \text{ (ethane)}$$
$$\bullet CH_3 + Cl\bullet \rightarrow CH_3Cl$$
$$Cl\bullet + Cl\bullet \rightarrow Cl_2$$

Any of these reactions breaks the chain and slows down the reaction.

When there are no radicals left, the reaction stops.

Products of the reaction

The reaction between methane and chlorine in the presence of UV light produces a mixture of mono- and poly-substituted chloromethanes, hydrogen chloride and some ethane.

It is the presence of the ethane that provides conclusive evidence for the mechanism given above. The absence of any H_2 molecules in the product is evidence that no hydrogen radicals are formed in the propagation steps.

e In a chain reaction, a radical reacts with a molecule and produces another radical, which then continues the process.

Thinning of the ozone layer

CFCs, such as CF_2Cl_2, break down when exposed to UV light in the stratosphere:

$$CF_2Cl_2 \xrightarrow{h\nu} \bullet CF_2Cl + Cl\bullet$$

The chlorine radicals produced react with ozone:

$$Cl\bullet + O_3 \rightarrow \bullet ClO + O_2$$

The UV light also causes oxygen molecules to split homolytically:

$$O_2 \xrightarrow{h\nu} 2O\bullet$$

The $\bullet ClO$ radicals react with oxygen radicals in a fast reaction:

$$\bullet ClO + \bullet O \rightarrow O_2 + Cl\bullet$$

There are few chain-breaking reactions in the thin atmosphere at this altitude. Therefore, one chlorine radical will cause the destruction of thousands of ozone molecules.

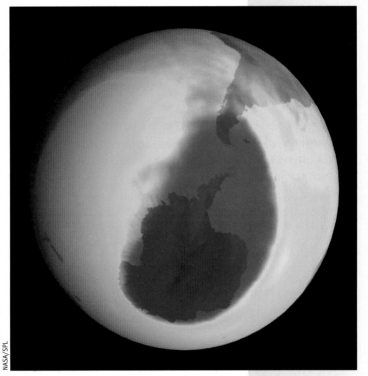

NASA/SPL

Mapping the hole in the ozone layer in Antarctica (22 September, 2004)

Free-radical addition

When a peroxide, such as benzoyl peroxide, is added to compounds with a C=C group, such as phenylethene (styrene), $C_6H_5CH=CH_2$, rapid polymerisation takes place.

Ethene can be polymerised by a peroxide that is formed when it is heated under high pressure with a trace of oxygen.

These reactions are initiated by radicals from the peroxides, which have the general formula R–O–O–R.

- In the **initiation reaction**, the peroxides act as a source of radicals:

$$R\!-\!O\!-\!O\!-\!R \longrightarrow R\!-\!O\bullet + \bullet O\!-\!R$$

- During **propagation,** the radical breaks the π-bond in the alkene and adds on to one carbon atom and the other carbon atom becomes a radical. This new radical can attack another alkene molecule, eventually producing a chain that is thousands of carbon atoms in length.

$$RO\bullet + H_2C\!=\!CH_2 \longrightarrow ROCH_2\!-\!\overset{\bullet}{C}H_2$$

$$ROCH_2\!-\!\overset{\bullet}{C}H_2 + H_2C\!=\!CH_2 \longrightarrow ROCH_2\!-\!CH_2\!-\!CH_2\!-\!\overset{\bullet}{C}H_2$$

- **Termination** of the chain occurs if two radicals collide:

$$RO(CH_2\!-\!CH_2)_n CH_2\overset{\bullet}{C}H_2 + RO\bullet \longrightarrow RO(CH_2\!-\!CH_2)_n CH_2CH_2OR$$

UV light can cause the addition of chlorine to benzene. The mechanism involves radicals and the initiation step involves light energy splitting a chlorine molecule into two chlorine radicals.

When hydrogen bromide is added to propene dissolved in a non-polar solvent in the presence of a peroxide, **anti-Markovnikoff addition** takes place. This means that the hydrogen goes to the carbon with the fewest hydrogen atoms already attached (unlike the normal addition of HBr to propene). The peroxides produce bromine radicals that break the π-bond, preferentially forming a secondary radical, which is more stable than the primary radical.

$$Br\bullet + CH_3CH\!=\!CH_2 \rightarrow CH_3\overset{\bullet}{C}HCH_2Br$$

This radical then removes a hydrogen atom from an HBr molecule, reforming a bromine radical and continuing the chain reaction:

$$CH_3\overset{\bullet}{C}HCH_2Br + HBr \rightarrow CH_3CH_2CH_2Br + Br\bullet \text{ etc.}$$

Electrophilic addition

Alkenes react with reagents such as halogens and hydrogen halides by **electrophilic addition.**

The π-bond between the carbon atoms is an area of high electron density. The first step in electrophilic addition is the movement of these π-electrons towards the electrophile to make a new covalent σ-bond.

In the examples below, the alkene is represented by the formula $RCH\!=\!CH_2$, where R can be a hydrogen atom (ethene) or a group, for example $-CH_3$ (propene). R can also represent much more complex groups in, for example complex natural products such as limonene (Question 6 in Chapter 5).

Addition of hydrogen bromide

Addition of hydrogen bromide across a double bond is a two-step reaction.

The HBr molecule is polar with the hydrogen atom δ^+ and the more electronegative bromine, δ^-. The δ^+ hydrogen is the electrophile. It adds on to one of the carbon atoms by attracting the π-electrons from the double bond and forming a covalent bond. As this happens, the Br–Br σ-bond breaks and the two electrons both go to the bromine atom, forming a Br$^-$ ion. This uneven breaking of the H–Br bond is called **heterolytic fission**.

Step 1:

e Do not forget to include the positive charge on the carbon atom in the intermediate.

The red curly arrow shows the movement of the π-electrons and the blue curly arrow shows the movement of the H–Br σ-electrons.

Step 2: The Br$^-$ ion then adds on to the positive carbon atom.

The red curly arrow shows the movement of the lone pair of electrons on the Br$^-$ ion as it forms a covalent bond with the carbon atom.

Hydrogen chloride, HCl, and hydrogen iodide, HI, also undergo addition reactions with this type of mechanism.

Addition to asymmetrical alkenes: Markovnikoff's rule

If the alkene is asymmetrical, such as propene, two addition products are possible. For example, the reaction between propene, $CH_3CH=CH_2$, and hydrogen bromide can give:

- $CH_3CHBrCH_3$, 2-bromopropane
- $CH_3CH_2CH_2Br$, 1-bromopropane

The *major* product is 2-bromopropane. This is predicted, but *not* explained, by Markovnikoff's rule:

> When HX adds to an asymmetrical alkene, the hydrogen atom goes to the carbon which already has most hydrogen atoms directly attached.

The explanation for this is that a secondary carbocation, $CH_3C^+HCH_3$ is formed preferentially to a primary carbocation, $CH_3CH_2C^+H_2$.

e A carbocation is an organic ion that has a positive charge on a carbon atom.

The secondary carbocation is stabilised by the electron-pushing effect of the $-CH_3$ groups, whereas the primary carbocation is less stabilised.

$$CH_3 \longrightarrow \overset{+}{CH} \longleftarrow CH_3$$

The arrowhead on a σ-covalent bond represents a movement of the bonding electrons in the direction the arrowhead is pointing. In the above example, it is pointing towards the positively charged carbon atom, reducing its charge and hence stabilising the cation. A $-CH_2$ group does not do this to the same extent as a $-CH_3$ group.

This also explains the anti-Markovnikoff addition under peroxide conditions, where the secondary radical is stabilised by the pushing effect of a $-CH_3$ group.

> **e** When working out the structure of the alcohol produced from the reaction of a Grignard reagent with a carbonyl compound, it is important to realise that the alkyl group of the Grignard reagent adds on to the carbonyl carbon atom, forming a new C–C bond.

Addition of bromine (bromination)

Addition of bromine across a double bond is a two-step reaction.

The Br_2 molecule is non-polar. However, on its approach to the high electron density of the π-bond, a δ^+ charge is induced in the nearer bromine. This atom is the electrophile. It attracts the π-electrons and forms a covalent bond with one of the carbon atoms. At the same time, the Br–Br σ-bond breaks heterolytically and a Br^- ion is formed.

Step 1:

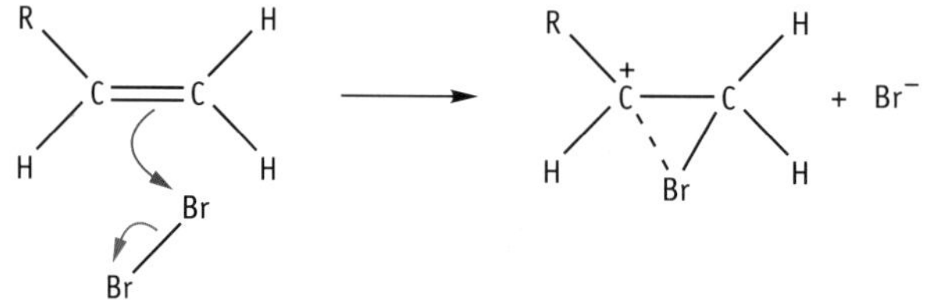

The red curly arrow shows the movement of the π-electrons and the blue curly arrow shows the movement of the Br–Br σ-electrons.

Step 2:

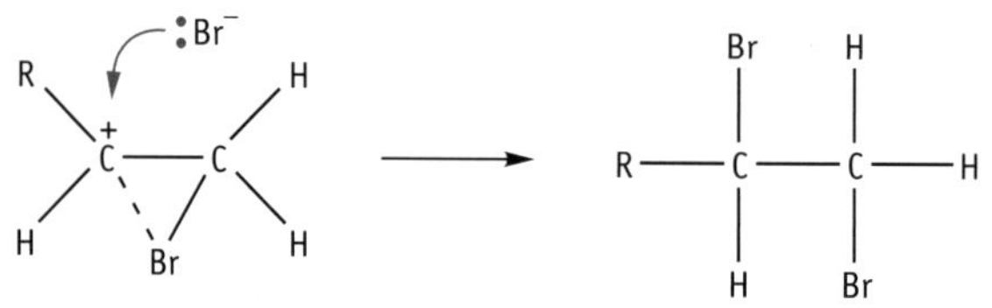

The red curly arrow shows the movement of the lone pair of electrons on the Br^- ion as it forms a covalent bond with the positively charged carbon atom.

There is a partial bond between the bromine atom that has added on and the other carbon atom. This is represented in the intermediate by a dotted line.

The Br^- ion attacks from the side away from the bromine atom. This has stereo-chemical implications for alkenes such as RCH=CHR because stereoisomers are possible in the product. It also means that the *trans*-isomer is formed when a halogen adds to a cyclohexane.

The same mechanism occurs when an alkene reacts with chlorine.

Iodine is not a strong enough electrophile to undergo this reaction, unless the C=C group is activated by an oxygen atom on one of the carbon atoms. The mechanism of the iodoform reaction is the rapid addition of an iodine atom to the CH_2=C(OH)R intermediate formed from the ketone.

The reaction between RCH=CH_2 and bromine water produces $RCH(OH)CH_2Br$ as the major product, rather than $RCHBrCH_2Br$. This is because the intermediate, RC^+HCH_2Br is more likely to collide and react with a water molecule than with a Br^- ion.

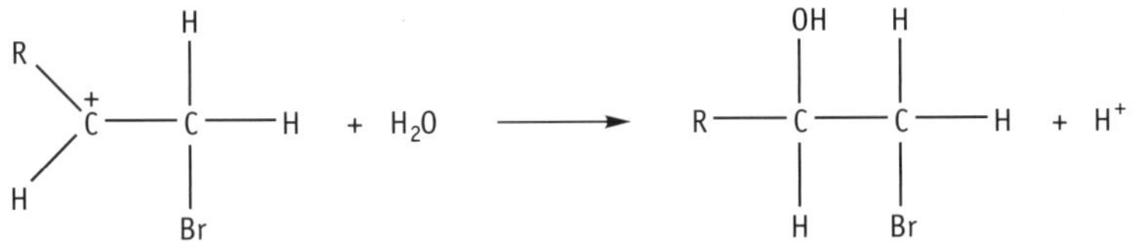

Nucleophilic addition

Carbonyl compounds react with nucleophiles in addition reactions.

The carbonyl carbon atom is δ^+, because it is much less electronegative than the oxygen atom. The reaction proceeds in two steps:

- The nucleophile attacks the δ^+ carbon atom. This is the rate-determining step.
- The intermediate reacts with a hydrogen atom in a molecule HX or a hydrogen ion from a strong acid.

Reaction with hydrogen cyanide

The nucleophile is the CN^- ion. Hydrogen cyanide alone does not react with carbonyl compounds. It is a very weak acid, $K_a = 4 \times 10^{-10}$ mol dm^{-3}, so the concentration of cyanide ions is extremely small. However, if a trace of base is added, or if the reaction mixture is buffered at pH 8, the concentration of CN^- ions rises sufficiently for there to be enough nucleophile to cause the reaction to proceed at a steady rate.

The mechanism of the reaction of ethanal and hydrogen cyanide is shown below.

Step 1:

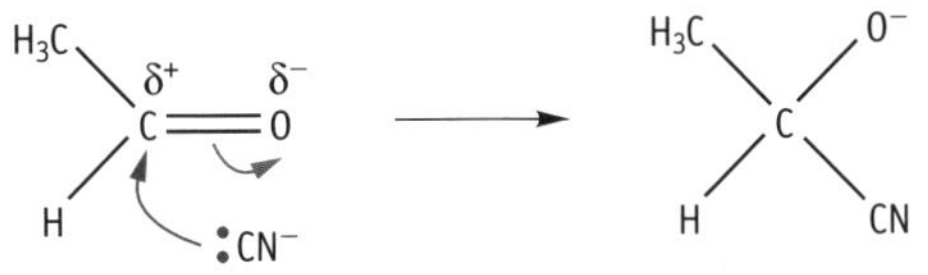

The lone pair of electrons on the carbon atom of the CN^- ion forms a bond with the δ^+ carbon atom. This is shown by the red curly arrow. At the same time, the π-electrons in the C=O group move to the oxygen. This is shown by the blue curly arrow.

Step 2:

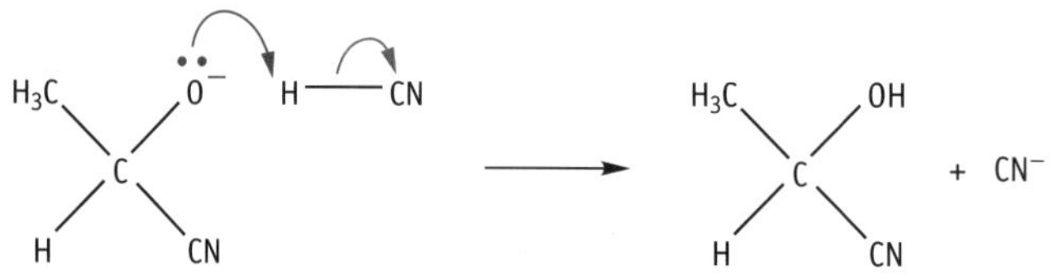

The $-O^-$ group in the intermediate donates a lone pair of electrons to the hydrogen in a HCN molecule (red arrow) as the σ-bond between the H and the CN breaks (blue arrow). This regenerates CN^- ions, which are the catalyst for the reaction.

The conditions for this reaction are very important. If the pH is too low (acidic), there are not enough CN^- ions for step 1 to be observable; if the pH is too high (alkaline) there are not enough HCN molecules for step 2.

The overall equation is:

$$CH_3CHO + HCN \rightarrow CH_3CH(OH)CN$$

Reaction with lithium tetrahydridoaluminate(III)

The reduction of an aldehyde or ketone in dry ether followed by hydrolysis of the intermediate with dilute acid is another example of nucleophilic addition. The nucleophile is an H^- ion derived from AlH_4^-:

$$AlH_4^- \rightarrow AlH_3 + H^-$$

Step 1:

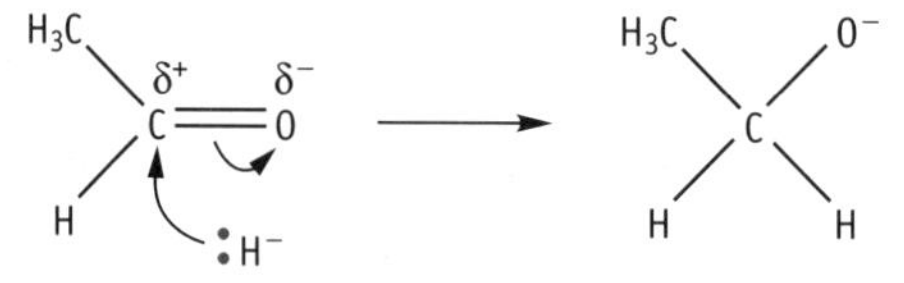

The intermediate is stabilised by the AlH_3 molecule.

Step 2: the intermediate is hydrolysed:

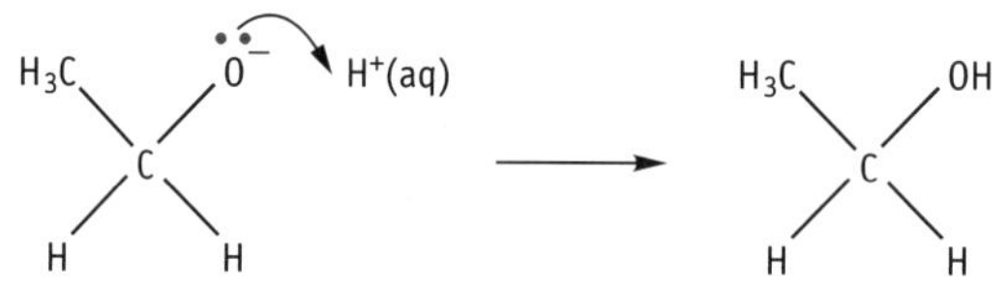

Reaction with a Grignard reagent

In a Grignard reagent, a carbon atom is bonded to a magnesium atom. This makes the carbon δ⁻. Since carbon is not normally electronegative, this is a powerful nucleophile. The δ⁻ carbon atom in the Grignard reagent attacks the δ⁺ carbon atom in an aldehyde or ketone (or in carbon dioxide) forming an intermediate that is stabilised by the magnesium ion. On addition of dilute acid, H^+ ions add on to the $-O^-$ in the intermediate and an alcohol is formed.

Step 1:

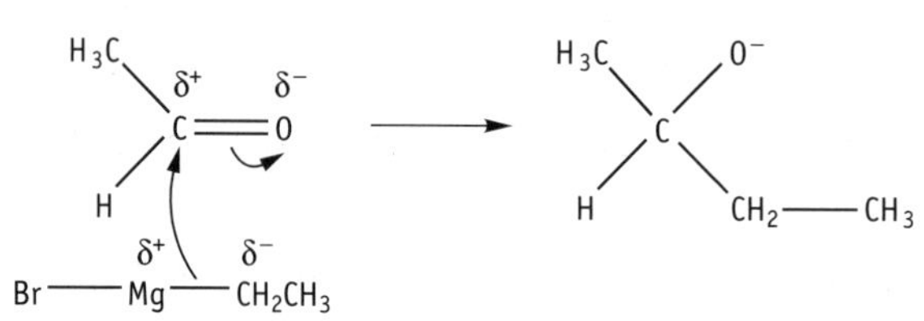

Step 2:

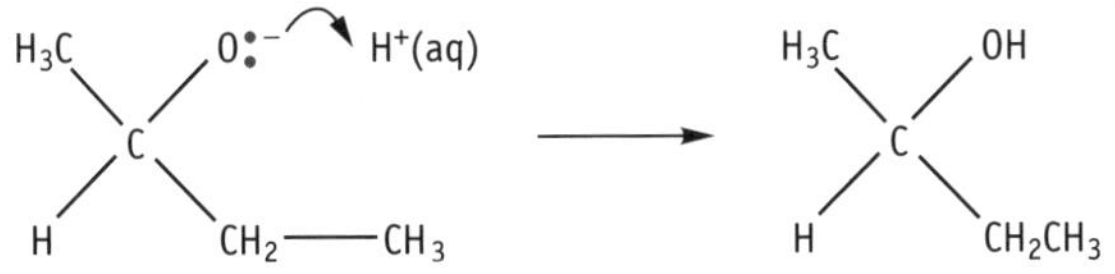

Nucleophilic substitution

Halogenoalkanes react with nucleophiles such as OH^-, H_2O, NH_3 and CN^- in substitution reactions. This is because the carbon atom joined to the halogen is slightly δ^+ and is, therefore, attacked by nucleophiles.

There are two distinct mechanisms by which halogenoalkanes react. Which mechanism is followed depends on whether they are primary, secondary or tertiary halogenoalkanes.

Primary halogenoalkanes

These react in an S_N2 **reaction**. The reaction is second order and the rate equation is:

rate = k[halogenoalkane][nucleophile]

The mechanism is a single step that goes through a **transition state.**

An example of an S_N2 mechanism involving a transition state is the reaction between hydroxide ions and bromoethane:

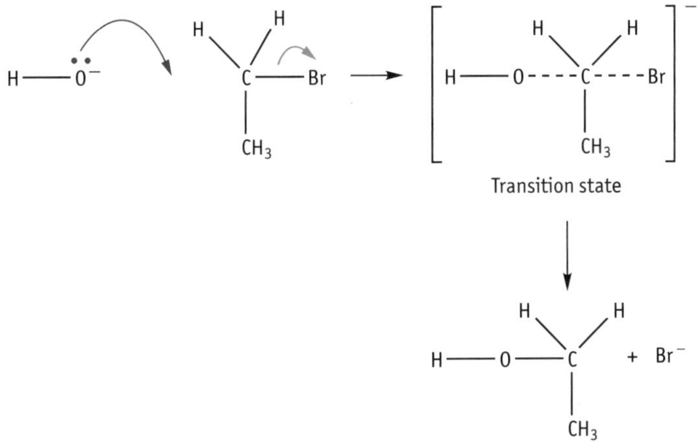

Transition state

The red curly arrow shows the movement of a lone pair of electrons from the oxygen to the carbon as a covalent bond forms. The green arrow represents the electrons in the C–Br σ-bond moving to the bromine atom as the bond breaks.

The transition state occurs when the new O–C bond is half-formed and the C–Br bond is half-broken.

The reaction profile diagram for this type of reaction is shown in Figure 13.1.

> **e** A transition state is not a species that can be isolated. It changes immediately into the product.

> **e** Do not forget to include the negative charge on the transition state.

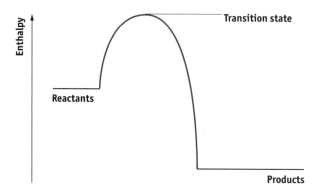

Figure 13.1 Reaction profile for an S_N2 reaction involving a transition state

The energy released in the formation of the O–C bond is enough to provide the energy to break the C–halogen bond. The weaker the C–halogen bond, the faster the rate of the reaction. Therefore, since the C–Cl bond is the strongest and the C–I bond is the weakest, the rate order is:

C–I > C–Br > C–Cl

As the incoming nucleophile enters from the side away from the halogen, a single optically active halogenoalkane gives a single optically active isomer when the mechanism is S_N2 — for example the reaction between OH⁻ and 1-chloro-1-fluoroethane:

Tertiary halogenoalkanes

Tertiary halogenoalkanes react by **S_N1** mechanisms. The reaction is first order and is independent of the concentration of the nucleophile. The rate equation is:

rate = k[halogenoalkane]

This type of reaction takes place in two steps.

Step 1: the carbon–halogen bond breaks, a carbocation is formed and a halide ion is released. This is the slow rate-determining step.

Step 2: the carbocation is attacked by the nucleophile in a fast reaction.

As the nucleophile enters the mechanism *after* the rate-determining step, its partial order of reaction is zero. Step 1 is rate-determining and so its activation energy is less than that of step 2. This is shown in Figure 13.2.

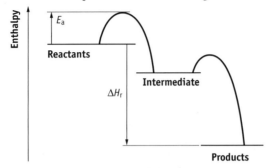

Figure 13.2 Reaction profile for an S_N1 reaction involving an intermediate

The intermediate formed in step 1 is planar as there are three pairs of electrons around the carbon atom. The incoming nucleophile can attack from above or below the plane. Therefore, when the mechanism is S_N1, a racemic mixture is always obtained from a single optically active isomer of a halogenoalkane. An example is the reaction between hydroxide ions and 2-chlorobutane:

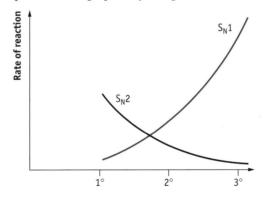

Secondary halogenoalkanes

- The rate of reactions with S_N2 mechanisms decreases in the order primary > secondary > tertiary halogenoalkane.
- The rate of reactions with S_N1 mechanisms increases in the order primary < secondary < tertiary halogenoalkane.

These relationships are shown graphically in Figure 13.3.

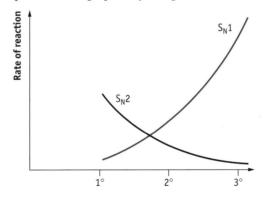

Figure 13.3 Different rates of S_N1 and S_N2 reactions

Figure 13.3 shows that primary halogenoalkanes react almost entirely by an S_N2 mechanism and that tertiary halogenoalkanes react by an S_N1 mechanism.

Secondary halogenoalkanes react by both mechanisms. However, S_N1 is faster and is, therefore, the dominant mechanism.

The overall rate is fastest with a tertiary halogenoalkane and slowest with a primary. For example, 2-chloro-2-methylpropane, $(CH_3)_3CCl$, produces an instant precipitate of silver chloride with aqueous silver nitrate, whereas 1-chloropropane gives a precipitate only after heating for a long period.

Nucleophilic addition–elimination reactions

Overall, these are nucleophilic substitution reactions. When ethanoyl chloride, CH_3COCl, reacts with a nucleophile such as H_2O, C_2H_5OH, NH_3, CH_3NH_2, OH^- or H^-, the nucleophile first bonds onto the δ^+ carbonyl carbon atom and the C=O π-bond breaks. This is followed by the loss of HCl and reformation of the carbon–oxygen π-bond.

Step 1:

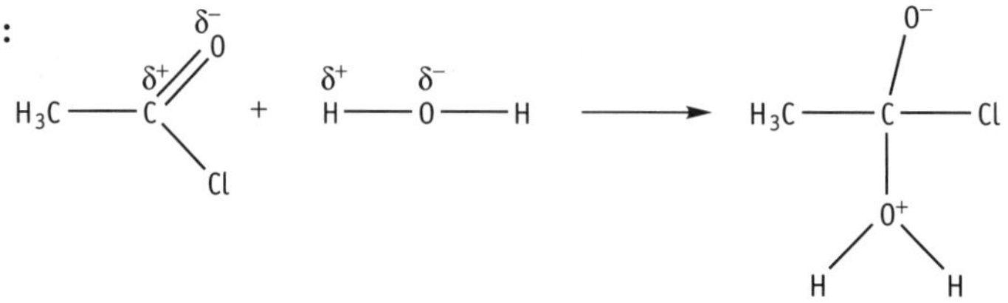

Step 2:

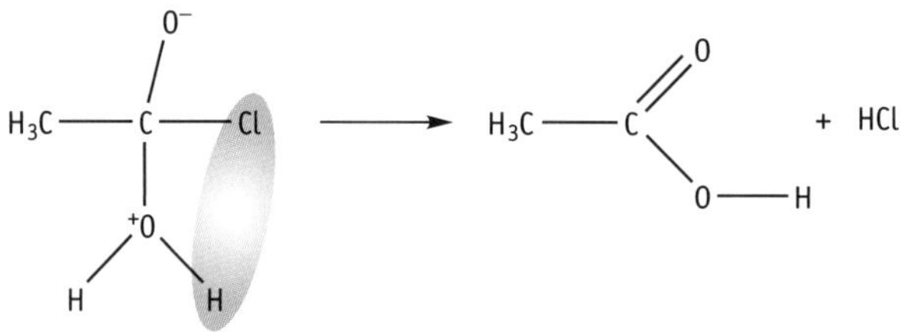

Electrophilic substitution

Benzene undergoes substitution. However, the reaction is not as simple a substitution as in the nucleophilic substitution reactions of halogenoalkanes. The mechanism is that an electrophile, E^+, adds on to a carbon atom in the benzene ring:

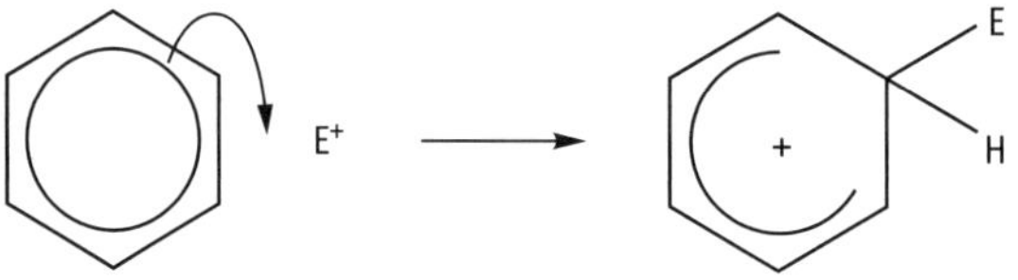

This step is identical to the addition of an electrophile to an alkene.

However, a fully delocalised ring of π-electrons stabilises the benzene ring. Therefore, rather than the second step being the subsequent addition of an anion (as with alkenes), it is loss of an H^+.

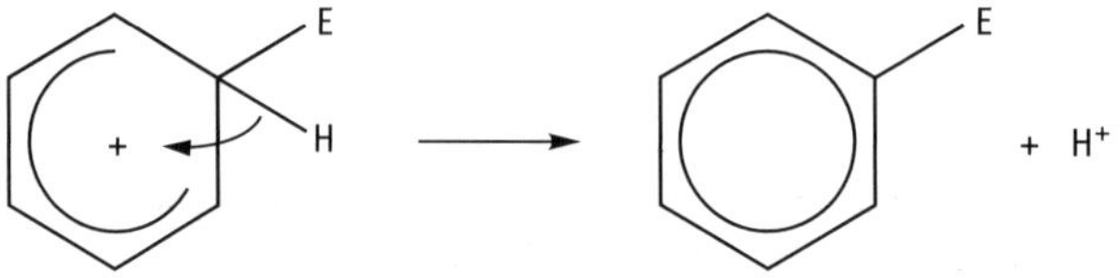

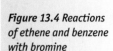

The result is an electrophilic addition–elimination reaction.

With ethene, the second step is the addition of a negative ion to the intermediate. The reactions of benzene and ethene with bromine that do, and do not, occur are shown in Figure 13.4.

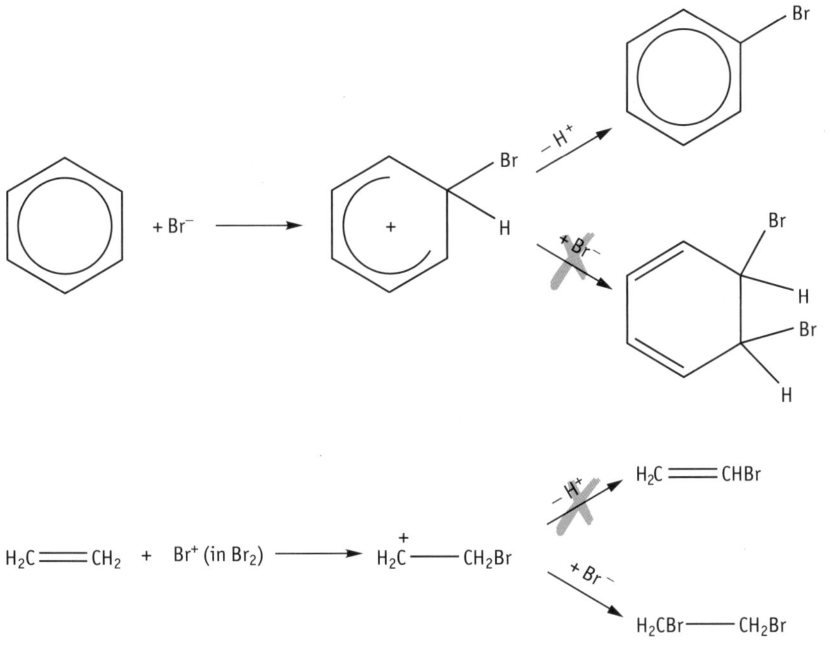

Figure 13.4 Reactions of ethene and benzene with bromine

e Benzene + bromine = electrophilic substitution; ethene + bromine = electrophilic addition

The delocalised π-system is so stable compared with the localised π-bond in alkenes that ordinary electrophiles, such as a bromine atom in Br_2 or the δ^+ hydrogen in HBr are not powerful enough to overcome the stability of the ring. Much more powerful electrophiles, such as Br^+, NO_2^+ or a positively charged carbon atom are needed. These electrophiles are produced by the action of a catalyst, which is always required in this type of reaction of benzene. The individual steps (without the movement of electrons) are shown on pages 237 and 282.

Nitration

The overall reaction is:

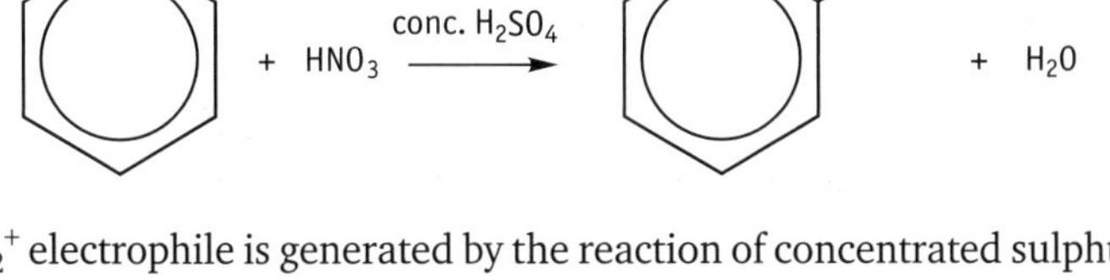

The NO_2^+ electrophile is generated by the reaction of concentrated sulphuric acid on concentrated nitric acid:

$$2H_2SO_4 + HNO_3 \rightarrow NO_2^+ + 2HSO_4^- + H_3O^+$$

Step 1: the electrophile attacks the benzene ring. Two of the delocalised electrons form a covalent bond with the nitrogen atom of the NO_2^+ ion:

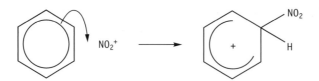

Step 2: the HSO_4^- ion removes an H^+ from the intermediate, regenerating the catalyst and causing the stability of the ring to be regained:

Bromination

The electrophile is made by the action of bromine on a catalyst of anhydrous $FeBr_3$ or aluminium halide. The $FeBr_3$ is usually made *in situ* by having a slight excess of bromine and adding a few iron filings:

$$2Fe + 3Br_2 \rightarrow 2FeBr_3$$

This reacts with more bromine to form the electrophile, Br^+:

$$Br_2 + FeBr_3 \rightarrow Br^+ + FeBr_4^-$$

Step 1: the Br^+ ion attacks the benzene ring:

Step 2: the $FeBr_4^-$ removes H^+ from the intermediate and the catalyst is reformed:

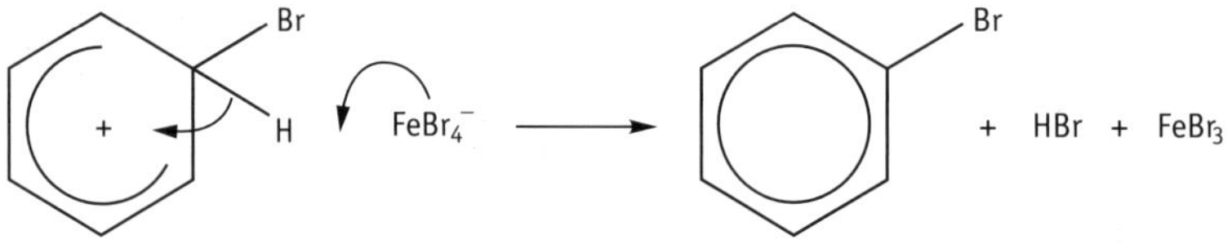

The overall reaction is:

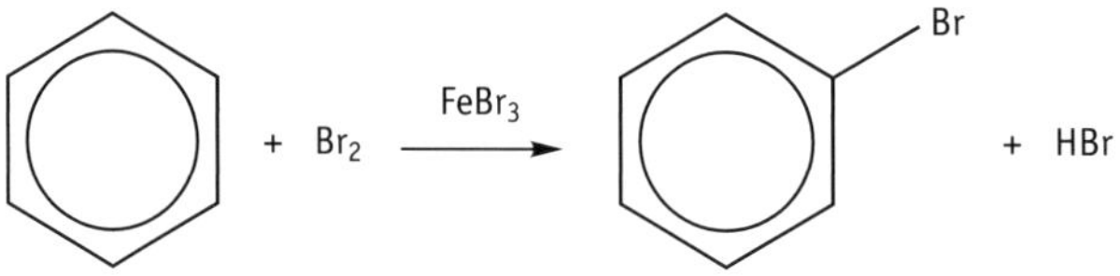

Friedel–Crafts

The electrophile is a positive carbon atom formed by the reaction of a halogenoalkane or an acid chloride with the catalyst anhydrous aluminium chloride — for example:

$$CH_3CH_2Cl + AlCl_3 \rightarrow CH_3CH_2^+ + AlCl_4^-$$

e Do not forget to put the positive charge in the ring in the formula of the intermediate. Also, make sure that the delocalised circle goes round five carbon atoms but not the one to which the NO_2 group is attached.

Step 1: the electrophile bonds with a pair of electrons from the benzene ring:

Step 2: the intermediate loses an H^+ to the $AlCl_4^-$ and the $AlCl_3$ catalyst is regenerated ready for another cycle:

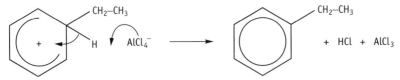

The mechanism is similar with an acid chloride, in which case the electrophile is:

$$CH_3 \overset{+}{-} C \!\!=\!\! O$$

Reaction profile

The reaction profile for the two-step substitution reactions of benzene is shown in Figure 13.5.

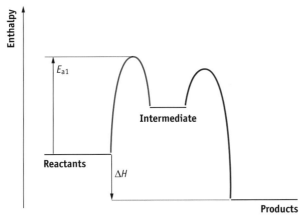

Figure 13.5 Reaction profile for the substitution reactions of benzene

◀ The intermediate is at a higher energy level than the reactants due to the loss of stability of the delocalised π-system.

Step 1 has the higher activation energy and so is rate-determining.

Elimination reactions

Dehydration

When concentrated sulphuric acid or 50% phosphoric acid is used to dehydrate an alcohol to an alkene, the first step is the protonation of the OH group.

ⓔ Detailed mechanisms for these reactions are not required at A-level.

$$H\!-\!\underset{\underset{H}{|}}{\overset{\overset{H}{|}}{C}}\!-\!\underset{\underset{H}{|}}{\overset{\overset{H}{|}}{C}}\!-\!OH \ + \ H_2SO_4 \longrightarrow H\!-\!\underset{\underset{H}{|}}{\overset{\overset{H}{|}}{C}}\!-\!\underset{\underset{H}{|}}{\overset{\overset{H}{|}}{C}}\!-\!\overset{+}{O}\!\!\overset{H}{\underset{H}{\diagdown}} \ + \ HSO_4^-$$

The intermediate then loses water:

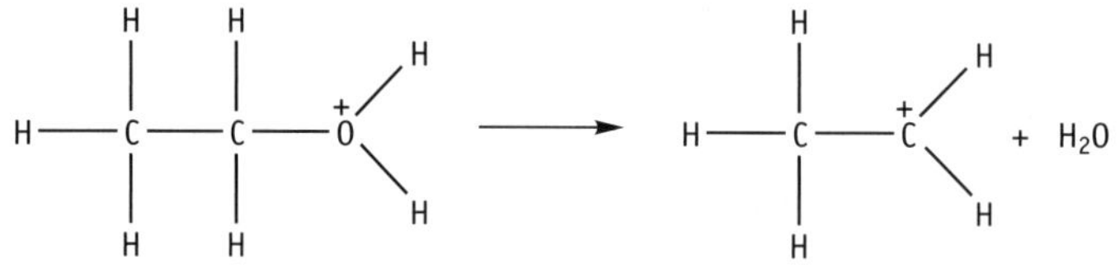

$$H-\underset{\underset{H}{|}}{\overset{\overset{H}{|}}{C}}-\underset{\underset{H}{|}}{\overset{\overset{H}{|}}{C}}-\overset{+}{O}\diagup^{H}_{\diagdown H} \longrightarrow H-\underset{\underset{H}{|}}{\overset{\overset{H}{|}}{C}}-\overset{+}{C}\diagup^{H}_{\diagdown H} + H_2O$$

An HSO_4^- ion then removes an H^+ from the adjacent carbon atom and a π-bond forms between the two carbon atoms.

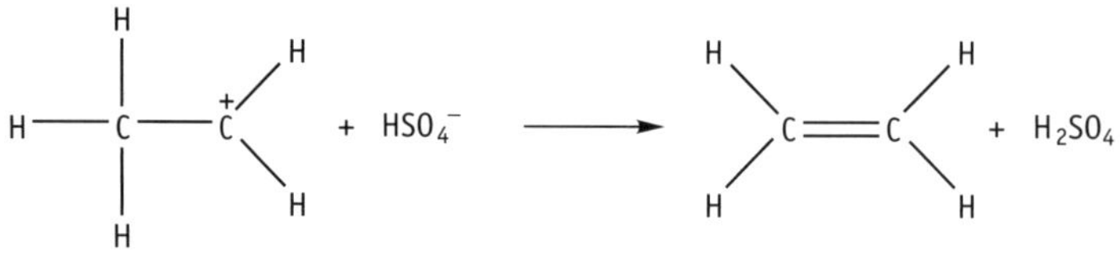

$$H-\underset{\underset{H}{|}}{\overset{\overset{H}{|}}{C}}-\overset{+}{C}\diagup^{H}_{\diagdown H} + HSO_4^- \longrightarrow _H^H{>}C{=}C{<}_H^H + H_2SO_4$$

Removal of a hydrogen halide

When a concentrated solution of potassium hydroxide in ethanol is warmed with a secondary or tertiary halogenoalkane, the first step is the loss of a halide ion — for example:

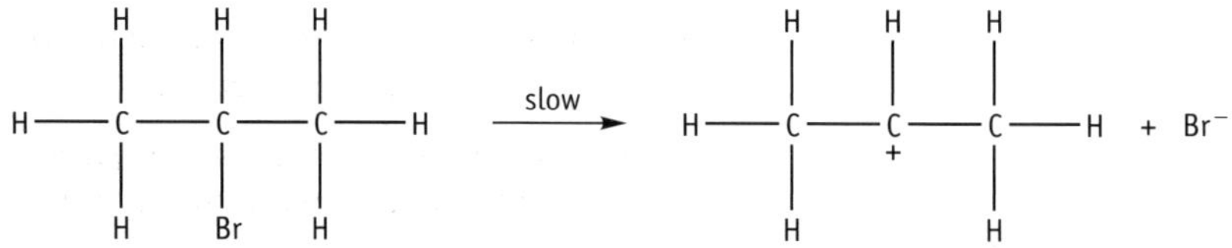

$$H-\underset{\underset{H}{|}}{\overset{\overset{H}{|}}{C}}-\underset{\underset{Br}{|}}{\overset{\overset{H}{|}}{C}}-\underset{\underset{H}{|}}{\overset{\overset{H}{|}}{C}}-H \xrightarrow{\text{slow}} H-\underset{\underset{H}{|}}{\overset{\overset{H}{|}}{C}}-\overset{+}{\underset{}{C}}-\underset{\underset{H}{|}}{\overset{\overset{H}{|}}{C}}-H + Br^-$$

This is identical to the first step in the S_N1 mechanism of substitution.

A π-bond is then formed as an H^+ ion is removed by the base:

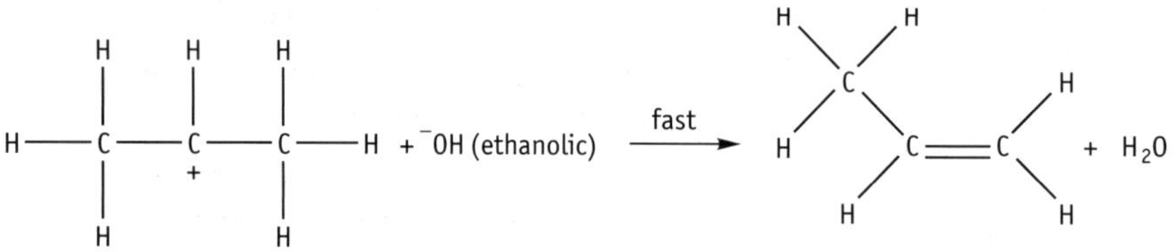

$$H-\underset{\underset{H}{|}}{\overset{\overset{H}{|}}{C}}-\overset{+}{\underset{}{C}}-\underset{\underset{H}{|}}{\overset{\overset{H}{|}}{C}}-H + {}^-OH \text{ (ethanolic)} \xrightarrow{\text{fast}} \text{(alkene)} + H_2O$$

Summary of mechanisms

The mechanisms that you should know in detail are:

- **Free-radical substitution:** alkanes with Cl_2 or Br_2 (UV light needed)
- **Free-radical addition:** polymerisation of alkenes and substituted alkenes
- **Electrophilic addition:**

Alkenes +
- HCl / HBr / HI
- Cl_2 / Br_2

- **Nucleophilic addition:**

Aldehydes and ketones +
- HCN (pH = 8)
- H^- (in $LiAlH_4$)
- Grignard reagents

■ Nucleophilic substitution:

Halogenoalkanes +
- OH^-(aq)
- CN^-
- NH_3

■ Electrophilic substitution:

Benzene +
- Br_2
- HNO_3
- RCl
- $RCOCl$

where R is an alkyl group, such as $-CH_3$ or $-C_2H_5$.

Questions

1 Define the terms:
   a nucleophile
   b electrophile
   c free radical

2 Give the mechanism of the polymerisation of propene using a peroxide catalyst, R—O—O—R, to produce radicals. Your answer should include one equation that uses appropriate mechanistic arrows.

3 Give the mechanism of the light-catalysed reaction of bromine with ethane. Explain why this reaction is much slower than the reaction of ethane and chlorine under the same conditions.

4 Give the mechanism of the reaction between cis-but-2-ene and hydrogen chloride.

5 Predict the major product when but-1-ene reacts with hydrogen iodide. Explain why this, rather than its positional isomer, is the major product.

6 Write the mechanism for the addition of hydrogen cyanide to propanone. Name the substance that would be formed if the product of this reaction were hydrolysed by aqueous sodium hydroxide.

7 Explain why the reaction of ethanal with a Grignard reagent is classified as a nucleophilic addition reaction.

8 Give the mechanism for the reaction between 2-chloro-2-methylpropane and sodium cyanide.

9 Give the mechanism for the reaction between 1-chloropropane and sodium cyanide.

10 The reaction between sodium hydroxide and 2-chloropropan-1-ol has the rate equation:

   rate = k[NaOH][$CH_3CHClCH_2OH$]

   Give the mechanism for this reaction.

11 Explain the difference between a transition state and an intermediate.

12 Explain why iodoethane reacts faster than bromoethane with aqueous ammonia.

13 Write the equations for the individual steps in the reaction of ethanoyl chloride with
   a ethanol
   b ethylamine

14 Explain why benzene reacts with bromine in a substitution reaction whereas ethene reacts with bromine in an addition reaction.

15 State how the conditions differ in the reactions of a halogenoalkane with sodium hydroxide in:
   a a substitution reaction
   b an elimination reaction

16 By considering the mechanism, predict the product of the addition reaction between propene and bromine(I) chloride, BrCl.

Spectroscopy

Chapter 14

Introduction

Electromagnetic radiation consists of an oscillating electric and magnetic field of a wide range of frequencies (Table 14.1). In a vacuum, light travels at a speed of 3.00×10^8 m s^{-1} (670 000 000 miles per hour).

Frequency is measured in hertz, Hz (1 Hz = 1 s^{-1}). The frequency determines the colour and the energy of the light, which is calculated by the expression formulated by Max Planck:

$$E = h\nu$$

where h is Planck's constant and ν is the frequency.

The speed of light, its frequency and the wavelength are combined in the equation:

$$c = \lambda\nu$$

where c is speed of light and λ is the wavelength.

The frequency can also be expressed as a wavenumber:

$$\text{wavenumber} = 1/\lambda$$

where the units of λ are cm.

Type of radiation	Frequency/MHz	Wavenumber/cm^{-1}	Energy/J per photon
Xrays	$> 10^{11}$	$> 3 \times 10^6$	$> 7 \times 10^{-17}$
Ultraviolet	1×10^9	3×10^4	7×10^{-19}
Visible — blue	6×10^8	2.1×10^4	4.2×10^{-19}
Visible — yellow	5×10^8	1.6×10^4	3.2×10^{-19}
Visible — red	4×10^8	1.4×10^4	2.8×10^{-19}
Infrared	$< 3 \times 10^8$	$< 10\,000$	$< 2 \times 10^{-19}$
Microwaves	$< 3 \times 10^4$	< 1	$< 2 \times 10^{-22}$
Radiowaves	< 100	$< 3 \times 10^{-3}$	$< 7 \times 10^{-26}$

Table 14.1 Frequency, wavenumber and energy of different types of electromagnetic radiation

When electromagnetic radiation is passed through a diffraction grating, it is split up into a spectrum according to the frequency of the radiation. Visible light is split by passing it through a prism. Blue light is refracted (bent) more than red light.

A rainbow is caused by droplets of rain splitting up white light into its component colours.

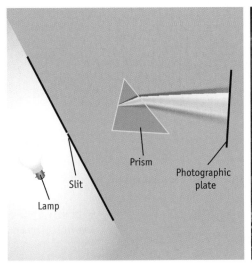

Figure 14.1 *Splitting of visible light by a prism*

A rainbow

Emission spectra

When some inorganic compounds are heated in a Bunsen flame, heat energy is converted into light energy. The heat from the Bunsen flame promotes an electron in a metal to a higher energy level. This is an unstable state. The electron spontaneously drops back to a lower level and radiation is given off. This radiation is in the form of ultraviolet or visible light.

The electron can be promoted to a number of higher levels of different energy, so the light given off is usually of several different frequencies. If this light is observed by eye, the colour is due to all these frequencies. If the light is observed in a spectrometer, bright lines are seen at different frequencies.

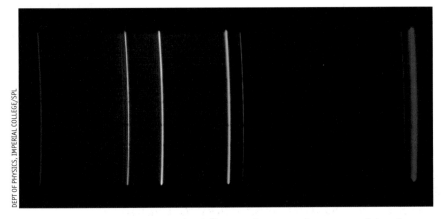

Spectral lines of cadmium

The energy of a spectral line is the difference between the energy of the electron in the higher state, E_2, and that in the lower state, E_1.

$$\Delta E = E_2 - E_1 = h\nu$$

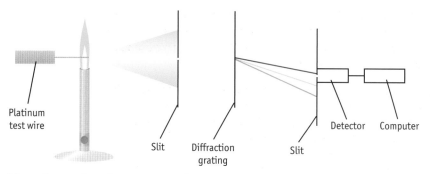

Figure 14.2
Representation of
a flame emission
spectrometer

Platinum
test wire

Slit   Diffraction   Slit
              grating

Detector   Computer

The colours given by group 1 and group 2 cations can be used to show their presence in a compound.

Group 1	Flame colour	Group 2	Flame colour
Lithium	Magenta	Calcium	Brick-red
Sodium	Yellow	Strontium	Crimson
Potassium	Lilac	Barium	Pale green
Rubidium	Red		

Table 14.2 Flame colours of group 1 and group 2 cations

Absorption spectra

When electromagnetic radiation is passed through a substance, some of the radiation is absorbed.

X-rays

X-rays are strongly absorbed by atoms with a high atomic number. Bones contain calcium ions and absorb some X-rays, but soft tissue is mainly carbon, oxygen and hydrogen and does not absorb X-rays. Use is made of this by taking an X ray picture of a suspected fracture.

Barium has a large atomic number and is opaque to X-rays. Taking X-ray pictures of the human gut after the patient has eaten a meal of insoluble barium sulphate can show up blockages in the digestive system.

The state of the arteries around the heart can be analysed in a procedure known as an angiogram. A solution of a compound containing several iodine atoms is injected into the blood around the heart via a catheter introduced into an artery in the patient's groin. The heart area is then X-rayed and any narrowing of the arteries can be detected.

Visible and ultraviolet radiation

Complexes of transition metal ions absorb light in the visible region of the spectrum. The light energy of a particular band of frequencies is absorbed and an

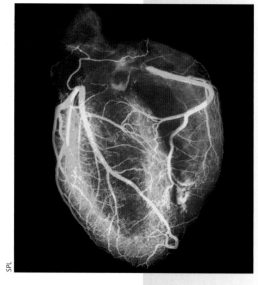

A heart angiogram

SPL

electron is moved from the lower level of the split *d*-orbitals to the upper level. The colour of the ion is the complementary colour to that absorbed. On collision with another molecule, the energy is released as heat. The electron returns to its lower level and is then able to absorb more light energy.

Organic molecules that have a delocalised π-electron system next to a particular group, called a **chromophore**, absorb light in the visible and UV regions. Typical chromophores are N=N, C=N, C=C and N=O. The precipitate obtained with aldehydes or ketones and 2,4-dinitrophenylhydrazine is an example.

This type of absorption is caused by the promotion of an electron in a π-bond.

Infrared spectra

A molecule can absorb energy in a number of ways:
- by movement — translational energy (heat)
- by the molecule rotating faster — rotational energy
- by vibration or bending of bonds in the molecule — vibrational energy

The energy for rotation is in the microwave region and the energy for vibration is in the infrared. Infrared spectroscopy relates to the absorption of energy, that increases the vibration in a molecule. The frequency of the infrared radiation absorbed depends on the nature of the bond that is vibrating.

> ℮ For a molecule to absorb in the infrared, the vibration must involve a change in the dipole moment of the molecule. Molecules with non-polar bonds, such as oxygen and nitrogen, do not absorb infrared radiation. This is why they are not greenhouse gases. Carbon dioxide is a non-polar molecule because the polarities of the two C=O bonds cancel. However, when the molecule vibrates in a bending or an asymmetric mode, the dipoles no longer cancel and it absorbs infrared energy. Therefore, carbon dioxide is a greenhouse gas. Water is polar and so absorbs infrared light. It too is a greenhouse gas.

An infrared spectrometer measures the amounts of radiation absorbed. It does this by splitting the incident beam of radiation into two. One beam passes through a cell containing a reference sample (usually solvent) and then goes to the detector; the other goes through the dissolved sample to the detector. The difference between the two amounts of radiation arriving at the detector is the amount absorbed by the chemical. The angle of the diffraction grating is slowly altered so that different frequencies sweep through the apparatus.

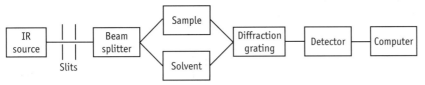

Figure 14.3
Representation of an infrared spectrometer

Different bonds in a covalent molecule absorb radiation of different frequencies, which are normally measured as wavenumbers. An infrared spectrum usually has a range from 4000 cm^{-1} to 600 cm^{-1}.

The C=O bond absorbs at around 1700 cm^{-1}, but the actual value depends on the other atoms attached to the C=O group. This is shown in Table 14.3.

Type of compound	Wavenumber/cm^{-1}
Aliphatic aldehyde	1720–1740
Aliphatic ketone	1700–1730
Aromatic aldehyde	1690–1715
Aromatic ketone	1680–1700
Carboxylic acid	1700–1725
Ester	1735–1750
Acid chloride	1815–1825
Amide	1640–1680

Table 14.3 Absorption frequencies of different C=O groups

Other types of bond absorb at different frequencies, but the actual value again depends on the neighbouring atoms and groups.

Bond	Functional group	Wavenumber/cm^{-1}
O–H	Alcohols (hydrogen bonded)*	3200–3600
	Alcohols (not hydrogen bonded)	3600–3700
	Carboxylic acids	2500–3300
N–H	Amines (hydrogen bonded)*	3300–3500
C–H	Alkanes	2850–3000
	Alkenes and arenes	3000–3100
C–C	Alkanes	1360–1490
C=O	See Table 14.3	
C=C	Aromatic	1450–1650
	Alkenes	1650–1700

*These peaks are very broad due to intermolecular hydrogen bonding.

Table 14.4 Absorption frequencies of some common groups

The region below about 1300 cm^{-1} is known as the fingerprint region. It shows a complex series of peaks that depends on the exact compound being analysed. Just as human fingerprints can be matched by computer to give a unique identification, so computer analysis of the fingerprint region can be used to identify a pure unknown organic substance.

Some infrared spectra are shown below.

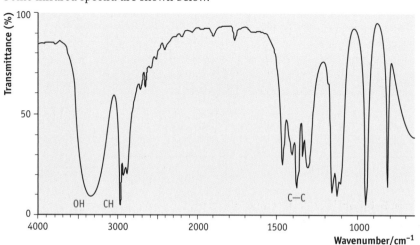

Figure 14.4 Infrared spectrum of propan-2-ol

In the infrared spectrum of propan-2-ol shown in Figure 14.4:
- the broad peak at around 3330 cm^{-1} is due to hydrogen-bonded O–H
- the peak at 2970 cm^{-1} is due to the C–H bond
- the peak at 1380 cm^{-1} is due to the C–C bond

Worked example

Examine the infrared spectrum of methylbenzene and assign the peaks at 3000 cm^{-1}, 2900 cm^{-1} and 1500 cm^{-1}.

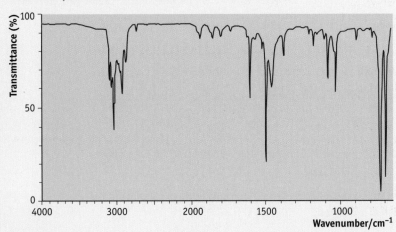

Answer

The peak at 3000 cm^{-1} is due to the stretching of the aromatic C–H bond.
The peak at 2900 cm^{-1} is due to the stretching of the C–H bond in the CH$_3$ group.
The peak at 1500 cm^{-1} is due to the aromatic C=C bond.

e Do not say that a group, for example the OH group, causes a peak. It is the covalent bond in the group that absorbs the infrared energy.

Worked example

Examine the infrared spectrum of ethanoic acid.

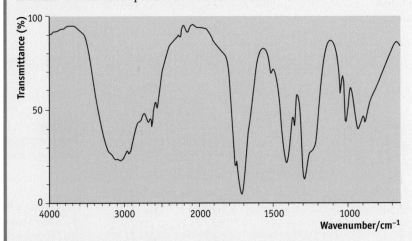

a Assign the peaks at 3000 cm^{-1}, 1700 cm^{-1} and 1400 cm^{-1}.
b Why is the peak at 3000 cm^{-1} very broad?

e The absorption by C–H bonds is often masked by the broad peak due to the O–H bond at similar frequencies.

Mass spectra

When a molecule, M, is bombarded by high-energy electrons, it becomes ionised:

$$M(g) + e^- \rightarrow M^+(g) + 2e^-$$

The molecular ion produced might subsequently break up into a smaller positive ion, X^+, and a radical, $Y\bullet$:

$$M^+(g) \rightarrow X^+(g) + Y\bullet$$

In a mass spectrometer, these positive ions are then accelerated by an electric field and deflected by a magnetic field.

The lighter ions are deflected more than the heavier ions and so a spectrum of ions of different masses is produced.

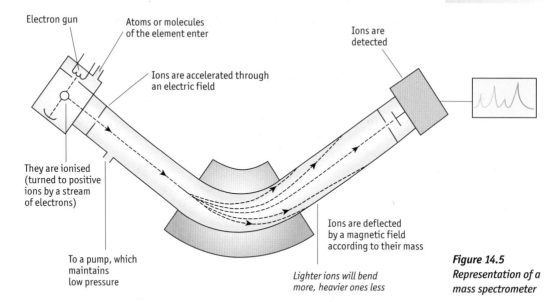

Figure 14.5 Representation of a mass spectrometer

The peak with the largest mass/charge ratio, m/e, is caused by the molecular ion. The peaks at lower m/e values arise from fragments of that ion.

The molecular formula can be deduced by comparing the m/e value of the highest peak with the empirical formula of the substance.

e In some texts, the mass to charge ratio is written as m/z, rather than as m/e.

14

Worked example

a An organic compound has the empirical formula, C_2H_4O. The largest m/e value in its mass spectrum is 88. Calculate the molecular formula of the compound.

b When phosphorus pentachloride is added to this compound, 1 mol of HCl per mole of the organic compound is liberated. Suggest possible formulae for the compound.

Answer

a The mass of $C_2H_4O = (2 \times 12) + 4 + 16 = 44$. This is half 88, so the molecular formula is $C_4H_8O_2$.

b As the HCl is produced in a 1:1 ratio, there can only be one –OH group in the molecule. Some possible substances are:

- $CH_3CH_2CH_2COOH$
- $(CH_3)_2CHCOOH$
- $CH_3CCH_2CH_2OH$
$\|$
O

Fragmentation of the molecular ion

The fragments give clues to the groups that are present in the molecule. A CH_3 group has a mass of 15 units and so an ion of mass $(M - 15)$ indicates that the substance has a CH_3 group:

$$(RCH_3)^+ \rightarrow R^+ + CH_3\bullet$$

The masses of some common fragments that are often lost are given in Table 14.5.

The mass spectrum of the substance in the worked example above (highest m/e value 88) also had peaks at m/e values 43 and 59. These fragments enable identification of the isomer.

m/e units	Group
15	CH_3
29	C_2H_5
31	CH_2OH
45	$COOH$
77	C_6H_5

Table 14.5 Common fragments lost

The three suggested formulae are:

- $CH_3CH_2CH_2COOH$
- $(CH_3)_2CHCOOH$
- $CH_3CCH_2CH_2OH$
$\|$
O

The m/e value of 43 is 45 units less than 88 and is caused by the loss of COOH. This discounts the third structure.

The m/e value of 59 is 29 units less than 88 and is caused by the loss of C_2H_5. This discounts the second structure.

Thus, only the first structure is possible.

Worked example

Study the mass spectrum of propanoic acid, CH_3CH_2COOH.

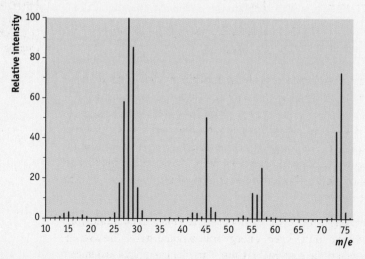

Identify the species responsible for the peaks at m/e values of 74, 73, 45 and 29 and state how they are formed.

Answer

The molar mass of propanoic acid is 74 g mol^{-1} and so the peak at 74 was caused by the molecular ion, $(CH_3CH_2COOH)^+$, produced by the removal of an electron from the gaseous molecule:

$$CH_3CH_2COOH(g) + e^- \rightarrow (CH_3CH_2COOH)^+(g) + 2e^-$$

The peak at 73 is caused by the molecular ion losing one of its hydrogen atoms.

$$(CH_3CH_2COOH)^+ \rightarrow (CH_3CH_2COO)^+ + H\bullet$$

The peak at 45 is 29 less than the molecular peak. It results from the loss of a C_2H_5 group and so is caused by the $(COOH)^+$ ion:

$$(CH_3CH_2COOH)^+ \rightarrow (COOH)^+ + C_2H_5\bullet$$

The peak at 29 is due to the $(C_2H_5)^+$ ion:

$$(CH_3CH_2COOH)^+ \rightarrow (C_2H_5)^+ + COOH\bullet$$

e Do not forget to put the positive charge on the formulae of the ions that produce the peaks in a mass spectrum.

Nuclear magnetic resonance

All nuclei in atoms are spinning. If a nucleus has an odd number of protons or an odd number of neutrons, its spin will produce a slight magnetic field.

The nucleus of a hydrogen atom, ^1H, produces a measurable magnetic field and the effect of an applied magnetic field on the nucleus of the proton can be studied.

If an external magnetic field is applied, the magnetic moment caused by the spinning nucleus will either be aligned with the applied field or be opposed to it. The former state is of lower energy. This is shown in Figure 14.6.

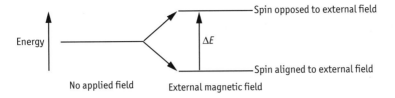

Electromagnetic radiation is absorbed as the spin of the nucleus flips from the lower aligned orientation to the higher energy opposed orientation. The frequency of the radiation that causes this is given by $v = \Delta E/h$. If a magnetic field of 15 kilogauss is applied, the splitting is such that radio waves of about 60 MHz are absorbed. The actual frequency depends on the environment of the nucleus and the strength of the applied magnetic field. Nuclei with spins that are aligned with the applied field will absorb the energy of the radiation and flip over to the spin-opposed state.

After a short time, normally of the order of a second, the nucleus spontaneously changes its spin and reverts to the lower energy spin-aligned state. The average time for this process is called the **relaxation time**. This change is what is detected in MRI (magnetic resonance imaging) scanning in hospitals.

Obtaining an NMR spectrum

The sample of the material, dissolved in a suitable solvent, is placed between the poles of a powerful electromagnet. Between the poles of the magnet there is also a radio-frequency coil that is then activated with oscillating radio waves. The absorption of these waves by the sample is detected and the results fed to a computer that shows the results as a trace.

The experiment can be carried out by:
- steadily altering the strength of the magnetic field and keeping the frequency of the radio waves constant
- keeping the magnetic field constant and sending pulses of radio waves of gradually increasing frequency through the sample

The extent of the splitting depends on the strength of the magnetic field. Therefore, the ΔE value of the hydrogen nuclei being investigated must be compared with that of a standard. The standard always used is tetramethyl-silane, $(CH_3)_4Si$ (TMS).

The sample is dissolved in a solvent that does not contain any protons. Carbon tetrachloride, CCl_4, is the usual choice. A small amount of TMS is added to provide the zero line for comparison and the sample is placed in the spectrometer.

Under these conditions, hydrogen nuclei in different chemical environments have different ΔE values. The extent to which they differ from the ΔE of the TMS protons is called the **chemical shift**, δ.

Low-resolution NMR

Low-resolution NMR investigates the value of the chemical shift and the area under the absorption peak (the peak height). The chemical shift indicates the environment of the hydrogen atom in the molecule and the peak height indicates the number of hydrogen atoms in that environment.

Chemical shift

The chemical shift, relative to the protons in TMS, depends mainly on the chemical environment of the hydrogen atom in the molecule. Some typical δ values are given in Table 14.6.

Group	δ (ppm)	Group	δ (ppm)
C–CH$_3$	0.8–1.2	CH$_2$OH	3.3–4.0
C–CH$_2$–C	1.1–1.5	C—C—OH (with H above and C below the central C)	3.2–4.1
C—C—H (with C above and C below)	1.5	H—C—C=O (in aldehydes, ketones, acids, esters and amides)	2.0–3.0
C–H on benzene ring	6.8–8.2	CHO	9.0–10.0
C=C–H in alkenes	4.5–6.5	COOH	10.0–12.0
C≡C–CH	1.8–2.0	C–OH	1.0–6.0*

* The value of the shift for hydroxyl hydrogen atoms depends on the solvent and the extent of hydrogen bonding and, therefore, it might be difficult to identify such compounds using NMR spectra alone.

Table 14.6 Chemical shifts of common groups containing hydrogen

The value of the chemical shift for a hydrogen atom attached to a benzene ring depends on the nature of the other substituents and their positions on the ring. Some chemical shift values are shown in Table 14.7.

Substituent	δ (ppm)		
	2-hydrogen	3-hydrogen	4-hydrogen
CH$_3$	7.1	7.2	7.1
COOH	8.1	7.4	7.5
OH	6.8	7.1	6.9
NH$_2$	6.5	7.0	6.6
Br	7.0	7.4	7.3
NO$_2$	8.2	7.4	7.6
COCH$_3$	7.9	7.4	7.6

Table 14.7 Chemical shifts for benzene-ring hydrogen atoms in the 2-, 3- and 4-positions, relative to a substituent in the 1-position

ⓔ Because this is so complex, you will not be asked to predict the exact number of peaks due to the hydrogen atoms attached to a substituted benzene ring. In many compounds the chemical shifts are similar and, therefore, a single slightly broadened peak is observed.

Peak height

The peak height is often indicated by a number above the peak. It can also be estimated by looking at the spectrum. Some spectra have an integration trace superimposed on the NMR spectrum. The NMR spectrum of ethoxyethane, $CH_3CH_2-O-CH_2CH_3$, with the integration trace added is shown in Figure 14.7.

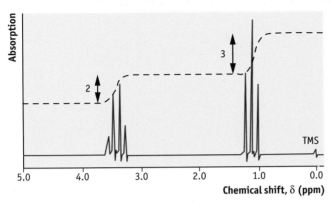

Figure 14.7
NMR spectrum of ethoxyethane with integrated trace

There are two different chemical environments for the hydrogen atoms — the CH_2 hydrogens and the CH_3 hydrogens. There are four CH_2 hydrogen atoms and six CH_3 hydrogen atoms, so the peaks heights are in the ratio 2:3.

The peak at $\delta = 1.0$ is caused by the hydrogen atoms in the CH_3 group; the peak at $\delta = 3.4$ is caused by the CH_2 hydrogen atoms.

ⓔ Do not state that the chemical shift is caused by a group. It is caused by the protons in the nuclei of the hydrogen atoms in that group.

The NMR spectrum of propanal is shown below:

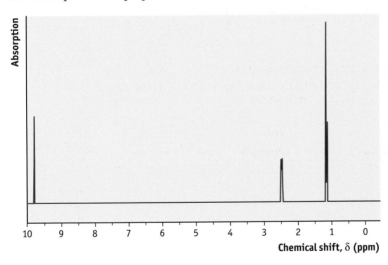

There are three peaks:
- The peak at $\delta = 9.8$ is caused by the hydrogen atom on the CHO group.
- The peak at $\delta = 2.4$ is caused by the two hydrogen atoms in the CH_2 group that is next to the CHO group.
- The peak at $\delta = 1.1$ is caused by the hydrogen atoms in the CH_3 group.

The areas under the peaks have not been calculated.

Worked example

Examine the NMR spectrum of propan-2-ol, $CH_3CH(OH)CH_3$, and identify the peaks.

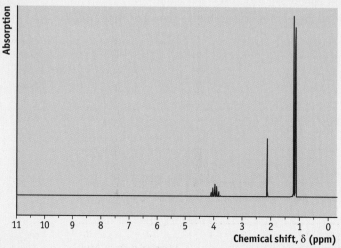

Note the splitting of the peaks in the spectrum of propan-2-ol.

Answer

The tall peak at $\delta = 1.1$ is due to the six hydrogen atoms in the CH_3 groups.
The peak at $\delta = 4.0$ is due to the CH hydrogen on the $CH(OH)$ group.
The peak at $\delta = 2.2$ is, therefore, caused by the hydrogen atom in the OH group.

High-resolution NMR spectra

If the spectrum is investigated with a high-performance spectrometer, the peaks are seen to be split. Splitting occurs because the magnetic environment of a proton in one group is affected by the magnetic field of a proton in a neighbouring group. If the field of a hydrogen atom is aligned with the applied field it is reinforced and increases the field on the neighbouring hydrogen atom.

Consider the effect of a proton in a CH group on the hydrogen atoms in the neighbouring CH_2 group:

- The CH hydrogen atom can have its spin aligned ↑ or opposed ↓.
- This results in two different fields affecting the CH_2 hydrogen atoms, so their peaks are split into two.
- The CH_2 hydrogen atoms affect the field on the CH hydrogen atom. Here, the situation is more complex because there are two neighbouring hydrogen atoms and there are three ways in which their spins can be aligned — ↑↑, ↑↓ or ↓↓. This results in the CH peak splitting into three. The effect of ↑↓ is the same as that of ↓↑, so one of the split peaks is twice as high as the others.

This process is called spin coupling or **spin–spin splitting**.

The rule is straightforward. If the proton of a hydrogen atom has n neighbouring hydrogen atoms, its peak will be split into $(n + 1)$ sub-peaks.

The only exception to this rule is that the hydrogen atom on an OH group does not normally cause splitting, particularly if it is hydrogen-bonded. This is shown by the high-resolution NMR spectrum of propan-1-ol, $CH_3CH_2CH_2OH$:

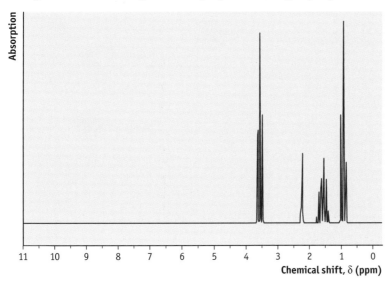

- The peak at 0.9 is due to the hydrogen atoms in the CH_3 group. It is split into three by the neighbouring two CH_2 hydrogen atoms.
- The peak at 1.5 is due to the hydrogen atoms in the middle CH_2 group. It is split into six by the five neighbouring hydrogen atoms.
- The peak at 3.5 is split into three. The peak is the caused by the two hydrogen atoms in the CH_2OH group. It is split into three by the two neighbouring hydrogen atoms.
- The peak at 2.4 is caused by the OH hydrogen. It neither causes splitting nor is split.

MRI

Magnetic resonance imaging is used as a diagnostic tool for medical problems in soft tissue and in collagen in bones. The technique is slightly different and requires extremely powerful electromagnets. This is achieved by cooling the metal core of the magnet to a temperature of 4 K with liquid helium. The metal then becomes a superconductor and high electric currents can be made to flow through it without any heat being produced. This results in an extremely powerful magnetic field of 10 kilogauss. Pulses of radio waves at around 40 MHz are then radiated through the patient and the relaxation time (p. 283) is measured. The hydrogen nuclei in soft tissue have a different relaxation time to those in harder tissue. Computers can generate pictures of slices through the part of the body being investigated and, therefore, problems can be detected. The patient suffers no ill effects because the procedure is non-invasive.

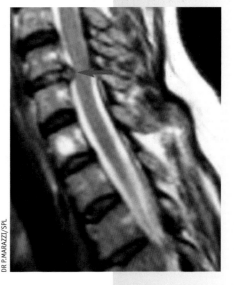

Coloured MRI scan of a patient with a slipped disc (arrowed)

DR P.MARAZZI/SPL

Questions

1 Calculate the energy of 1 mol of photons of green light of frequency 5.7×10^{14} Hz.

(Avogadro constant $= 6.02 \times 10^{23}$ mol^{-1}; Planck's constant, $h = 6.63 \times 10^{-34}$ J s)

2 Ba^{2+} ions are poisonous. Barium carbonate and barium sulphate are both insoluble in water. Explain why it would be dangerous to use barium carbonate, rather than barium sulphate, when taking X-rays of the human digestive tract.

3 Explain the difference in the origin of colour of a $[Cu(H_2O)_6]^{2+}$ ion in solution and a Ca^{2+} ion in a Bunsen flame.

4 Explain why water vapour is a powerful greenhouse gas.

5 Examine the infrared spectra, A and B, below. One spectrum is that of propanal; the other is that of propanoic acid.

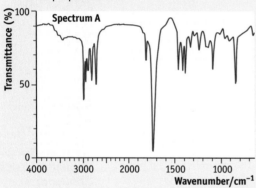

Spectrum A

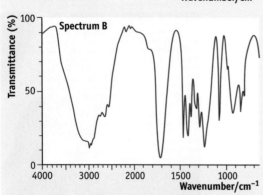

Spectrum B

Identify the peaks in A at 1715 cm^{-1} and 1421 cm^{-1} and the peaks in B at 2986 cm^{-1}, 1716 cm^{-1} and 1416 cm^{-1}. Hence, decide which spectrum is that of propanoic acid.

6 Consider a mass spectrometer. State:
  a how the positive ions are produced
  b how the ions are accelerated
  c how the ions are deflected

7 The mass spectrum below is that of propanone.

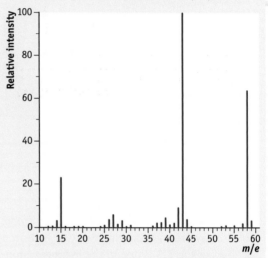

Identify the peaks at m/e values of 58, 43 and 15 and write equations to show the formation of the species responsible for these peaks.

8 Bromine has two isotopes, ^{79}Br and ^{81}Br, in approximately equal proportions. Sketch the mass spectrum of bromine in the range m/e 155 to 165.

9 Explain what is wrong with the following statements:
  a The infrared peak at about 1700 cm^{-1} is caused by the vibration of the carbonyl group.
  b The spinning of the CH$_3$ group in methanol causes a peak in the NMR spectrum at about $\delta = 3.5$
  c In a mass spectrometer, the molecular ion, $(CH_3CH_2OH)^+$, splits up as shown in the equation:

$$(CH_3CH_2OH)^+ \rightarrow (CH_3CH_2)^+ + OH^+$$

10 How many peaks would butanone, $CH_3CH_2COCH_3$, have in its low-resolution NMR spectrum? What will be the ratio of their heights?

11 How could low-resolution NMR spectra be used to distinguish between the isomers propan-1-ol and propan-2-ol?

12 The NMR spectrum of ethanol is shown below.

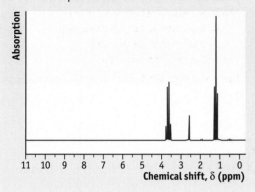

Absorption

Chemical shift, δ (ppm)

Identify the hydrogen atoms in the structure of ethanol that cause each set of peaks.

13 Explain why, in a high-resolution NMR spectrum, the hydrogen atoms in a CH_3 group cause the peak of a neighbouring hydrogen atom to split into four.

14 Search the internet and write short notes on MRI.

Organic analysis and synthesis

Chapter 15

Organic analysis

In organic analysis, care must be taken to follow the logic of the tests. For example, a positive test with Brady's reagent (2,4-dinitrophenylhydrazine) indicates that the unknown is a carbonyl compound but does not distinguish between an aldehyde and a ketone. If the unknown does not react with acidified potassium dichromate(VI) but gives a positive result with Brady's reagent then it must be a ketone. Aldehydes are oxidised by acidified potassium dichromate(VI), so a positive result in both these tests shows that the unknown is an aldehyde.

Tests for functional groups

C=C group

The test for the C=C group is to add bromine water. Compounds that contain a C=C group quickly decolourise the brown bromine water and do not give a precipitate.

Alkenes rapidly turn neutral potassium manganate(VII) from a purple solution to a brown precipitate at room temperature. However, aldehydes also do this.

Halogenoalkanes

Halogenoalkanes contain a halogen atom which, on warming with aqueous sodium hydroxide, is removed by hydrolysis. *Excess* dilute nitric acid is added to this solution to neutralise the sodium hydroxide. On addition of a solution of silver nitrate a precipitate is obtained. The equations for the reactions of a chloroalkane are:

$$RCl + OH^- \rightarrow ROH + Cl^-$$
$$Cl^-(aq) + Ag^+(aq) \rightarrow AgCl(s)$$

- A white precipitate soluble in dilute ammonia solution proves the presence of chlorine in the organic compound:
$$AgCl(s) + 2NH_3(aq) \rightarrow [Ag(NH_3)_2]^+(aq) + Cl^-(aq)$$
- A cream precipitate, insoluble in dilute ammonia but soluble in concentrated ammonia shows the presence of bromine in the organic compound:
$$AgBr(s) + 2NH_3(aq) \rightarrow [Ag(NH_3)_2]^+(aq) + Br^-(aq)$$
- A pale yellow precipitate, insoluble in both dilute and concentrated ammonia, proves the presence of iodine in the original organic compound:
$$AgI(s) + 2NH_3(aq) \rightarrow \text{no reaction}$$

The distinction between primary, secondary and tertiary halogenoalkane cannot be made by a simple chemical test. Analysis by mass spectrometry or NMR spectroscopy can be conclusive (pp. 280 and 282).

e Phenols also decolourise bromine water, but they give a white precipitate of a polybrominated phenol.

Alcohols

- Apart from phenols, compounds with an –OH group give steamy fumes of hydrogen chloride on the addition of solid phosphorus pentachloride:

  $ROH + PCl_5 \rightarrow HCl + RCl + POCl_3$

  $RCOOH + PCl_5 \rightarrow HCl + RCOCl + POCl_3$

Therefore, all alcohols and all carboxylic acids give a positive result. However, alcohols (unlike carboxylic acids) do not give bubbles of carbon dioxide on the addition of either sodium hydrogencarbonate or sodium carbonate.

- On warming with ethanoic acid in the presence of a few drops of concentrated sulphuric acid, all alcohols form esters:

  $ROH + CH_3COOH \quad CH_3COOR + H_2O$

If the product is poured into a beaker of dilute sodium hydrogencarbonate solution, the characteristic odour of an ester (like nail varnish, glue or fruity) will be detected.

- Primary and secondary alcohols turn orange acidified potassium dichromate(VI) solution to a green solution of Cr(III).Tertiary alcohols are not oxidised by acidified dichromate(VI) ions, so the solution remains orange.
  - This test can be modified to distinguish between primary and secondary alcohols, by distilling off the oxidised organic product as it is formed. If this is mixed with Tollens' reagent, only the oxidised product of the primary alcohol (an aldehyde) reduces the silver ion complex to give a silver mirror.
  - The oxidised product of the secondary alcohol (a ketone) has no reaction with Tollens' reagent, but (like all carbonyl compounds) gives a yellow-orange precipitate with Brady's reagent (2,4-dinitrophenylhydrazine).
- Alcohols, as well as carboxylic acids, have a broad band in the IR spectrum at approximately 3000 cm^{-1}. Carboxylic acids, but not alcohols, also have a peak at approximately 1700 cm^{-1} (p. 278).

Aldehydes and ketones

Both aldehydes and ketones give a yellow or orange precipitate when a few drops of 2,4-dinitrophenylhydrazine (Brady's reagent) are added. The equation for the reaction with ethanal is:

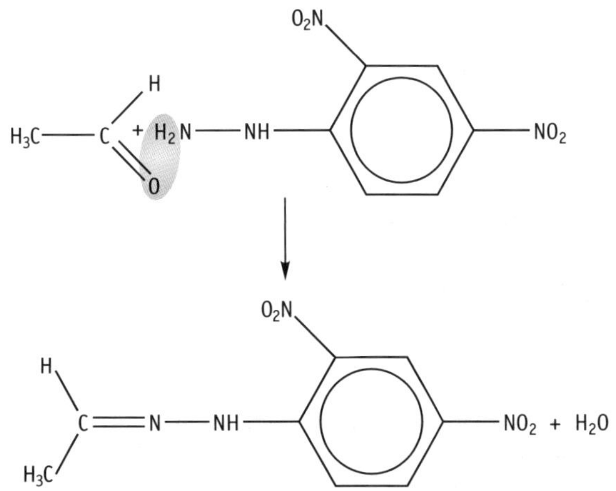

e Do not state that the appearance of steamy fumes of HCl with PCl_5 is a test for alcohols, because carboxylic acids (and water) also give the same result.

The sodium hydrogen-carbonate is used to neutralise any excess carboxylic acid, the smell of which might interfere with the detection of the smell of the ester.

e When a colour change indicates a positive result to a test, always give the colour of the solution *before* the test as well as after.

There are several simple chemical tests to differentiate between aldehydes and ketones:

- The carbonyl compound is warmed with Fehling's solution. Aldehydes give a red precipitate of copper(I) oxide. Ketones do not react. Therefore, the copper(II) complex in Fehling's solution is not reduced and the solution remains blue.

> **e** In these tests an aldehyde is oxidised to the salt of a carboxylic acid:
>
> $RCHO + [O] + OH^- \rightarrow RCOO^- + H_2O$

Distinguishing between an aldehyde and a ketone: left, Fehling's solution; centre, Fehling's solution that has been reduced by an aldehyde; right, ketones do not react with Fehling's solution

- The unstable Tollens' reagent is made by adding a few drops of sodium hydroxide to silver nitrate solution and dissolving the precipitate formed in dilute ammonia solution. If the carbonyl compound is gently warmed with Tollens' reagent, aldehydes give a silver mirror but ketones do not.

Silver mirror test for the presence of an aldehyde. Ketones do not react and the solution remains colourless

- On warming with potassium dichromate(VI), dissolved in dilute sulphuric acid, aldehydes turn the orange solution green. Ketones do not react, so the solution stays orange.

> **e** Primary and secondary alcohols also give a positive result with acidified dichromate(VI) ions. Therefore, their absence must first be shown by a lack of steamy fumes with phosphorus pentachloride.

The infrared spectra of aldehydes and ketones have peaks at about 1700 cm^{-1}, as do the IR spectra of all other compounds with a C=O group. This includes carboxylic acids, esters, amides and acid chlorides.

Aldehydes can be distinguished from ketones by examination of NMR spectra. The NMR spectrum of an aldehyde has a peak at $\delta = 9.0$–10.0, caused by the hydrogen atom in the aldehyde group, CHO.

The iodoform reaction

The formula of iodoform is CHI_3. It is a pale yellow solid that is insoluble in water. It has an antiseptic smell. Iodoform is produced when an organic compound containing the $CH_3C{=}O$ or $CH_3CH(OH)$ group is gently warmed with iodine mixed with sodium hydroxide solution.

- The only aldehyde that performs the iodoform reaction is ethanal.
- All methyl ketones give a yellow precipitate. The equation for the reaction of butanone is:

$$CH_3COC_2H_5 + 3I_2 + 4NaOH \rightarrow CHI_3 + C_2H_5COONa + 3NaI + 3H_2O$$

The products are a precipitate of iodoform and a solution of sodium propanoate and sodium iodide.

- Alcohols undergo this reaction if they can be oxidised to give rise to a $CH_3C=O$ group. Ethanol is the only primary alcohol that gives a precipitate of iodoform. The alkaline solution of iodine oxidises it to ethanal, which then reacts to give the precipitate:

$$CH_3CH_2OH + [O] \rightarrow CH_3CHO + H_2O$$
$$CH_3CHO + 3I_2 + 4NaOH \rightarrow CHI_3 + HCOONa + 3NaI + 3H_2O$$

The sequence is:

*ethan*ol → ethanal → iodoform + sodium *methan*oate

Methyl secondary alcohols are oxidised to methyl ketones and, therefore, give a positive iodoform test. For example, propan-2-ol gives a yellow precipitate with an alkaline solution of iodine:

$$CH_3CH(OH)CH_3 + [O] \rightarrow CH_3COCH_3 + H_2O$$
$$CH_3COCH_3 + 3I_2 + 4NaOH \rightarrow CHI_3 + CH_3COONa + 3NaI + 3H_2O$$

The sequence is:

propan-2-ol → propanone → iodoform + sodium *ethan*oate

Propan-1-ol does not undergo the iodoform reaction.

$$CH_3CH_2CH_2OH + [O] \rightarrow CH_3CH_2CHO + H_2O$$
$$CH_3CH_2CHO + I_2 + NaOH \rightarrow \text{no reaction}$$

Carboxylic acids

- Carboxylic acids as well as alcohols give steamy fumes of hydrogen chloride when phosphorus pentachloride is added:

$$RCOOH + PCl_5 \rightarrow RCOCl + HCl + POCl_3$$

An acid can be distinguished from an alcohol by the addition of a solution of either sodium hydrogencarbonate or sodium carbonate. With a carboxylic acid, bubbles of gas are seen:

$$RCOOH + NaHCO_3 \rightarrow RCOONa + H_2O + CO_2$$
$$2RCOOH + Na_2CO_3 \rightarrow 2RCOONa + H_2O + CO_2$$

The gas turns limewater cloudy.

$$CO_2 + Ca(OH)_2 \rightarrow CaCO_3 + H_2O$$

- If a carboxylic acid is warmed with ethanol in the presence of a few drops of concentrated sulphuric acid, an ester is produced. If the reaction mixture is poured into a dilute solution of sodium hydrogencarbonate, the characteristic smell of the ester can be detected.
- The infrared spectra of carboxylic acids have a broad band at approximately 3000 cm^{-1} and a sharp band at approximately 1700 cm^{-1}.

e The iodoform reaction is one of the few reactions in which a carbon chain is shortened by one carbon atom.

Aromatic compounds

Aromatic compounds burn with a smoky flame.

Phenol and phenylamine rapidly turn bromine water from brown to colourless, with the formation of a white precipitate, for example:

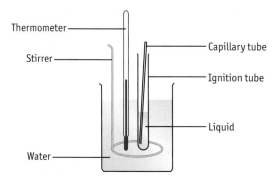

Identification of the specific compound

Once the functional group in the molecule has been identified by chemical or spectral tests, the question remains as to what is the exact formula of the specific compound. There are a number of ways of determining this.

Infrared fingerprint

The region of an infrared spectrum below about 1300 cm^{-1} is known as the fingerprint region because it is specific to a single compound. Thus, if the fingerprint region is checked against a database, the identity of the unknown can be found. This method requires the unknown sample to be pure, otherwise stray peaks caused by impurities will alter the spectral pattern.

Boiling point determination

The boiling point of an organic liquid can be determined and the value compared with those in a database.

The apparatus for boiling point determination is shown in Figure 15.1.

Thermometer —
Stirrer —
Capillary tube
Ignition tube
Liquid
Water —

Figure 15.1 Apparatus for the determination of boiling point

The method is as follows:
- Place a small amount of the test liquid in the ignition tube and, using a rubber band, attach it to the thermometer.
- Place the capillary tube in the liquid, with its open end below the surface.
- Clamp the thermometer in the beaker of water.

- Slowly heat the water, stirring all the time. When the stream of bubbles coming out of the capillary tube is rapid and continuous, note the temperature and stop heating.
- Allow the beaker of water to cool, stirring continuously. Note the temperature when bubbles stop coming out of the capillary tube and the liquid begins to suck back into the capillary tube.

The average of these two temperatures is the boiling temperature of the liquid.

As the beaker of water is heated, the air in the capillary tube expands and bubbles of air slowly come out of the tube. These act as nuclei on which the bubbles of boiling liquid can form. This prevents superheating, which is when the temperature of the liquid rises above its boiling temperature.

The temperature measured on cooling is when the liquid stops boiling.

Both temperatures are slightly inaccurate because there is a time lag before the thermometer can register the boiling temperature. Averaging the two cancels out this error.

There are two problems with this method:
- The boiling points of similar substances are often quite close together and can differ by less than the experimental error.
- Impurities, and variation in atmospheric pressure, alter the boiling point.

Ester	Boiling temperature/°C	Alcohol	Boiling temperature/°C
Ethyl ethanoate	77.1	Ethanol	78.5
Methyl propanoate	78.7	Propan-2-ol	82.4
1-propyl methanoate	81.3	2-methylpropan-2-ol	82.5

Table 15.1 Boiling temperatures of some esters and alcohols

ⓔ The terms 'boiling point' and 'boiling temperature' are interchangeable.

Melting point determination

The measurement of boiling point is not very reliable. Therefore, it is common practice for a liquid to be converted to a solid derivative. For example, a carbonyl compound can be converted to a 2,4-dinitrophenylhydrazine derivative. The derivative is then purified by recrystallisation and its melting point determined.

One method of determining melting point is:
- Insert some of the pure solid into a capillary tube and then attach the tube open end upwards to a thermometer with a rubber band.
- Place the thermometer into a bath of liquid. The liquid must boil at a higher temperature than the melting point of the solid being tested.
- Slowly heat the liquid bath, with constant stirring, and observe the solid in the capillary tube. Note the temperature when the solid melts.

Another method is:
- Place the solid in a boiling tube.
- Heat the boiling tube in a beaker of hot liquid (water if the solid melts below 100°C).

- When the solid melts, put a thermometer and stirrer in the molten solid and remove the boiling tube from the liquid bath.
- Allow the molten substance to cool, stirring the whole time, and read the temperature when the first crystals of solid appear.

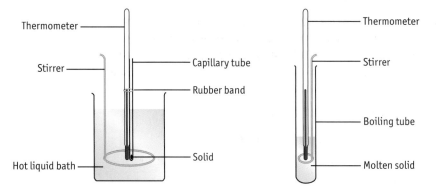

Figure 15.2 Apparatus for the two methods of melting point determination

Methods of purification

For spectral analysis and for the measurement of melting and boiling temperatures, substances need to be very pure

Simple distillation

Simple distillation can be used to:
- remove a volatile liquid from non-volatile substances
- separate two volatile liquids that form a homogeneous solution

The latter works only if there is a small amount of one of the two liquids present as an impurity. The neck of the flask and the still head act as a mini-fractionating column. Larger amounts of an impurity require fractional distillation for separation.

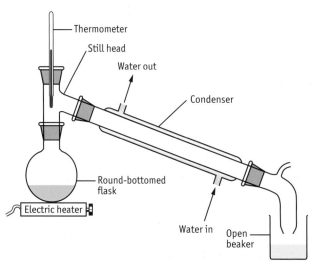

Figure 15.3 Apparatus for simple distillation

Fractional distillation

Fractional distillation can be used to:

- purify a liquid
- separate a mixture of two liquids

The impure liquid or mixture of liquids is placed in a round-bottomed flask and a fractionating column is fitted. The thermometer is positioned so that its bulb is opposite the side arm and a condenser is fitted to the side arm. The apparatus must be open either at the top of the adapter or where the distillate drips into the flask.

The liquid with the lower boiling temperature distils over first.

The theory behind this technique is based on **Raoult's law**.

> The partial vapour pressure of a liquid in a homogeneous mixture of liquids is equal to its mole fraction multiplied by its vapour pressure when pure.

$$p_A = \text{mole fraction} \times VP(\text{pure A})$$

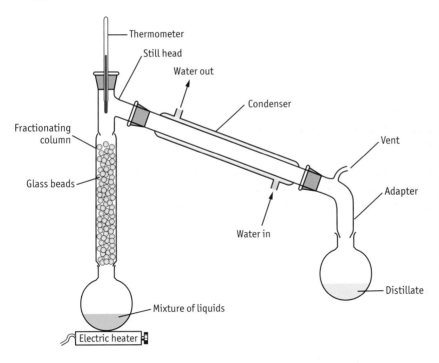

Figure 15.4 Apparatus for fractional distillation

Consider a mixture of benzene (boiling temperature 80°C) and methylbenzene (boiling temperature 111°C). Since benzene has the lower boiling temperature, it is more volatile. Therefore, it has a higher vapour pressure than methylbenzene.

This means that the vapour boiling off a mixture of benzene and methylbenzene will always be richer in benzene than the liquid from which it is boiling. This can be shown by a boiling temperature–composition diagram (Figure 15.5).

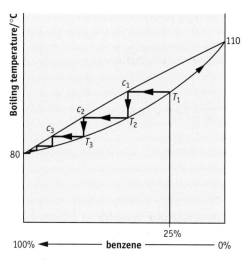

Figure 15.5 Boiling temperature–composition graph for a mixture of benzene and methylbenzene

The vapour follows the red zigzag line; the liquid in the flask follows the lower curve from T_1 upwards, towards the boiling point of the less volatile methylbenzene.

When a 25% mixture of benzene in methylbenzene is heated in the flask, it boils at a temperature T_1. The vapour coming off the liquid is richer than 25% in benzene. Its composition is given by c_1. As this vapour rises up the fractionating column, it cools and condenses, and then reboils at the new boiling temperature T_2. The vapour is now richer still in the more volatile benzene and its composition is given by c_2. This condenses and then reboils at a temperature T_3, giving a vapour of composition c_3. This process continues up the column. The higher up the column, the lower the temperature of the vapour. If the column is long enough, the vapour at the top is finally pure benzene, which passes at 80°C into the condenser. The liquid in the flask becomes steadily richer in the less volatile methylbenzene and its boiling temperature gradually rises as the percentage of benzene falls. When all the benzene has been removed from the liquid, pure methylbenzene remains and will boil off at 111°C.

Recrystallisation

Recrystallisation is the method used to purify solids. A solvent has to be found in which the substance is soluble when the solvent is hot, but insoluble (or very much less soluble) when it is cold.

The method is:
- Dissolve the impure solid in the *minimum* of hot solvent.
- Remove any undissolved impurities by filtering the hot solution through a fluted filter paper, using a *warmed* stemless funnel, into a conical flask.
- Allow the solution to cool.
- Filter the mixture of the pure solid and the solvent under *reduced pressure*, using a Buchner funnel. Collect the solid on the filter paper and discard the liquid, which will contain the impurities in solution.
- Wash the solid on the filter paper with a little ice-cold solvent and leave the solid to dry.

- Carefully remove the pure solid from the filter paper.

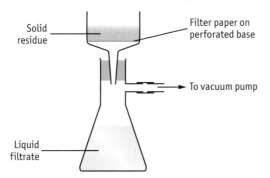

Solid residue

Filter paper on perforated base

To vacuum pump

Liquid filtrate

Figure 15.6 *Apparatus for reduced pressure filtration*

Benzoic acid is very soluble in hot water, but almost insoluble in cold water. Therefore, it can be purified by recrystallisation from hot water.

The compound formed by the reaction between an aldehyde or a ketone and 2,4-dinitrophenylhydrazine can be recrystallised from hot ethanol.

Organic synthesis

Organic synthesis is the construction of organic molecules using chemical processes. A particular synthesis may involve one or more intermediate compounds.

For a complex multi-step synthesis, it may be best to start by considering how the final product can be made and then work backwards to suitable original reactants.

An alternative technique is to determine whether the carbon-chain length has to be altered. If so, then the synthesis will involve one of the reactions below.

Increase in carbon-chain length

There are several ways in which the length of the carbon chain can be increased.

Nucleophilic substitution with KCN

Potassium cyanide reacts with primary, secondary and tertiary halogenoalkanes, RX. The reaction can be represented by:

$$RX + KCN \rightarrow RCN + KX$$

The conditions are heat under reflux in a solution of ethanol and water.

This reaction increases the carbon-chain length by one carbon atom. The product is a nitrile, which can be reduced to a primary amine or hydrolysed to a carboxylic acid:

$$RCN \xrightarrow[\text{2. Hydrolyse with } H_2SO_4(aq)]{\text{1. LiAlH}_4 \text{ in dry ether}} RCH_2NH_2$$

$$RCN \xrightarrow[\text{2. Add dilute acid}]{\text{1. Heat under reflux with NaOH(aq)}} RCOOH$$

ⓔ Alcohols do not react with potassium cyanide. An alcohol must first be converted to a halogenoalkane and then reacted with KCN.

Nucleophilic addition of HCN

Hydrogen cyanide reacts with aldehydes and ketones to form a compound with a –CN group and an –OH group on the same carbon atom:

$$\text{>C=O + HCN} \rightarrow \text{>C(OH)CN}$$

The conditions are that the reagents are mixed in the presence of a buffer at pH 8.

This reaction increases the carbon-chain length by one carbon atom. The product can be hydrolysed to a 2-hydroxycarboxylic acid:

$$\text{>C(OH)CN} \xrightarrow[\text{2. Add dilute acid}]{\text{1. Heat under reflux with NaOH(aq)}} \text{>C(OH)COOH}$$

For example, ethanal, CH_3CHO, can be converted to 2-hydroxypropanoic acid, $CH_3CH(OH)COOH$, by this method.

Use of a Grignard reagent

Grignard reagents have the general formula RMgX, where X is a halogen. They are prepared by mixing a halogenoalkane with magnesium in a solvent of dry ether (ethoxyethane).

Grignard reagents contain a δ^- carbon atom that will attack the δ^+ carbon atom in carbon dioxide, an aldehyde or a ketone. The initial product has to be hydrolysed with dilute acid.

Each of the reactions below uses dry reactants in dry ether, followed by acid hydrolysis:

- The reaction between carbon dioxide and a Grignard reagent, RMgBr, gives a carboxylic acid, RCOOH. The carbon-chain length is increased by one carbon atom.
- The reaction between methanal, HCHO, and a Grignard reagent, RMgBr, gives a primary alcohol, RCH_2OH. The carbon-chain length is increased by one carbon atom.
- With the exception of methanal, an aldehyde reacts with a Grignard reagent to form a secondary alcohol. The new increased carbon-chain length equals the number of carbon atoms in the Grignard reagent plus the number in the aldehyde. For example, ethylmagnesium bromide reacts with ethanal to give butan-2-ol:

$$C_2H_5MgBr + CH_3CHO \rightarrow C_2H_5CH(OH)CH_3$$

- A ketone reacts with a Grignard reagent to form a tertiary alcohol. For example, ethylmagnesium bromide and propanone react to form 2-methyl-butan-2-ol:

$$C_2H_5MgBr + CH_3COCH_3 \rightarrow C_2H_5C(OH)(CH_3)_2$$

Decrease in carbon-chain length

Iodoform reaction

Iodine and sodium hydroxide react with alcohols with a $CH_3CH(OH)$ group and carbonyl compounds with a $CH_3C=O$ group to form iodoform, CHI_3, and the salt of a carboxylic acid with one less carbon atom than the alcohol.

> e At A-level, you are required to know three methods for decreasing the length of the carbon chain.

Propan-2-ol and propanone each give sodium ethanoate. The general reactions are:

$$RCH(OH) \xrightarrow{I_2 + NaOH(aq)} CH_3RCOONa$$

$$RCOCH_3 \xrightarrow{I_2 + NaOH(aq)} RCOONa$$

The carboxylic acid can be formed from the salt by adding aqueous sulphuric or hydrochloric acid:

$$RCOONa + HCl \rightarrow RCOOH + NaCl$$

Aromatic ketones, such as $C_6H_5COCH_3$, also undergo the iodoform reaction.

Hofmann degradation reaction

Amides react with liquid bromine and concentrated aqueous sodium hydroxide to form a primary amine with one less carbon atom. For example, the Hofmann degradation of ethanamide produces methylamine. The general reaction is:

$$RCONH_2 \xrightarrow{Br_2(l) + NaOH(aq)} RNH_2$$

Aromatic side-chain oxidation

Aromatic compounds with a side chain joined via a carbon atom can be oxidised by heating under reflux with an alkaline solution of potassium manganate(VII). The organic product is an aromatic compound with a COO^- group on the benzene ring in place of the side chain.

Ethylbenzene, $C_6H_5C_2H_5$, methylbenzene, $C_6H_5CH_3$, and phenylethanone, $C_6H_5COCH_3$, all give the benzoate ion, $C_6H_5COO^-$. This ion can be protonated by a dilute solution of a strong acid to form benzoic acid:

$$C_6H_5COO^- + H^+ \rightarrow C_6H_5COOH$$

Other common transformations

Alkene to halogenoalkane

$$CH_2{=}CH_2 + HX \rightarrow CH_3CH_2X$$

Reagent: hydrogen halide, for example hydrogen bromide
Conditions: mix gases at room temperature

Halogenoalkane to alcohol

$$RX + NaOH \rightarrow ROH + NaX$$

Reagent: aqueous sodium hydroxide
Conditions: heat under reflux in aqueous solution

Alcohol to halogenoalkane

$$ROH + PCl_5 \rightarrow RCl + HCl + POCl_3$$

Reagent: phosphorus pentachloride, PCl_5, for chlorination; KBr and 50% sulphuric acid for bromination; moist red phosphorus and iodine for iodination
Conditions: mix reagents at room temperature

Primary alcohol to aldehyde

$$RCH_2OH + [O] \rightarrow RCHO + H_2O$$

Reagent: acidified potassium dichromate(VI)
Conditions: add oxidising agent to hot alcohol and allow the aldehyde to distil off

e Knowing these transformations will not only be useful in answering questions in synthesis. It is good revision of the earlier organic topics that may be tested in synoptic questions.

Primary alcohol to carboxylic acid

$$RCH_2OH + 2[O] \rightarrow RCOOH + H_2O$$

Reagent: acidified potassium dichromate(VI)
Conditions: heat under reflux

Secondary alcohol to ketone

$$RCH(OH)R' + [O] \rightarrow RCOR' + H_2O$$

Reagent: acidified potassium dichromate(VI)
Conditions: heat under reflux

Carboxylic acid to acid chloride

$$RCOOH + PCl_5 \rightarrow RCOCl + HCl + POCl_3$$

Reagent: phosphorus pentachloride
Conditions: mix dry reagents

Acid chloride to amide

$$RCOCl + 2NH_3 \rightarrow RCONH_2 + NH_4Cl$$

Reagent: aqueous ammonia
Conditions: mix at room temperature

Worked example

Deduce the necessary reagents and conditions and the intermediates for the conversion of benzene into the following compound:

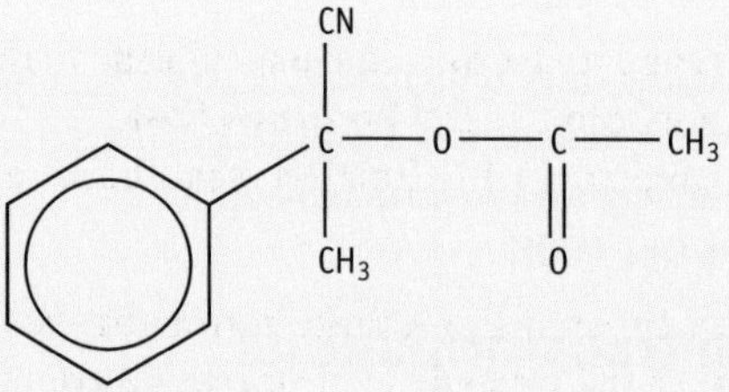

Answer
Working backwards:
The final product is an ester that can be made by the reaction between an alcohol and ethanoic acid or ethanoyl chloride.
The –CN and –OH groups on the same carbon atom come from the reaction of a ketone with HCN.
Working forwards:
A side chain has to be introduced into the benzene ring. This implies a Friedel–Crafts reaction. Since a ketone is required, the reaction is between benzene and ethanoyl chloride.
Step 1: reaction between benzene and ethanoyl chloride in the presence of anhydrous $AlCl_3$

$$C_6H_6 + CH_3COCl \rightarrow C_6H_5COCH_3 + HCl$$

Step 2: requires pH 8

$$C_6H_5COCH_3 + HCN \rightarrow C_6H_5C(OH)(CN)CH_3$$

Step 3:

$$C_6H_5C(OH)(CN)CH_3 + CH_3COCl \rightarrow$$

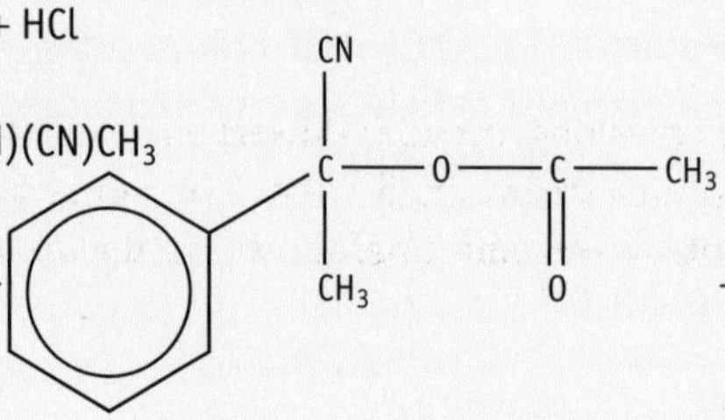

$+ HCl$

Methods of separation

Most organic reactions either do not go to completion or have side reactions. This means that the required product must be separated from the reaction mixture and purified.

Aqueous extraction

When an ester is prepared from a mixture of a carboxylic acid and an alcohol in the presence of concentrated sulphuric acid, an ester is formed in a reversible reaction. The ester is immiscible in water whereas the acids and alcohol are miscible. The ester can, therefore, be separated from the reaction mixture by the following technique:

- Add water to dilute the sulphuric acid and to dissolve the remaining carboxylic acid and alcohol.
- Pour the mixture into a separating funnel and run off the bottom aqueous layer.
- Add sodium hydrogencarbonate solution to the organic layer that remains and shake. This removes any acid dissolved in the ester.
- Run off the lower aqueous layer and then run the ester layer into a conical flask.
- Add some lumps of solid anhydrous calcium chloride to dry the ester.
- Decant the clear liquid into a round-bottomed flask.
- Distil the ester, collecting the fraction that boils at the appropriate temperature.

A similar method can be used to separate nitrobenzene from the nitrating mixture and to separate a halogenoalkane from the reaction mixture after it has been made from an alcohol.

> Care must be taken when shaking the organic layer with the sodium hydrogen-carbonate solution. Carbon dioxide will be produced and the pressure in the separating funnel must be carefully released.

Steam distillation

Steam distillation is used to extract a volatile liquid, which is immiscible with water, from a complex mixture. It is particularly useful for obtaining a substance that would decompose at its boiling point. It is used to extract perfumes from fruits and flowers. For example, lavender oil contains the compound linalool:

Linalool can be obtained by crushing lavender flowers and stalks with water and then subjecting the mixture to steam distillation. The liquid boils below the boiling temperature of both water and linalool, so no decomposition of the product takes place.

The procedure is as follows:
- Crush lavender flowers and stems in water and place the mixture in a flask.

- Steam distil and collect the distillate until pure water, with no oily droplets, distils over.
- Pour the mixture into a separating funnel and run off the aqueous layer.
- Add lumps of anhydrous potassium carbonate to the organic layer and leave until the product becomes clear.

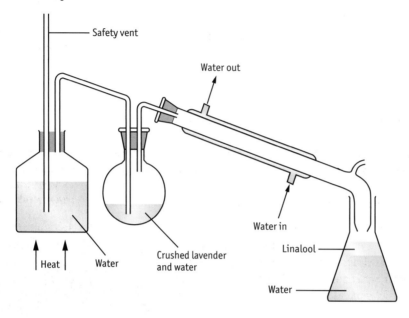

Safety vent

Water out

Heat   Water   Crushed lavender and water

Water in

Linalool

Water

Figure 15.7 Apparatus for steam distillation

Steam distillation is used to extract phenylamine from the reaction mixture after the reduction of nitrobenzene with tin and concentrated hydrochloric acid (p. 250).

Yields

Organic reactions rarely go to completion and there are usually competing side reactions. The yield is often as low as 60%. Purification processes also lower the yield. For instance, some solid will remain in solution during recrystallisation and a fractionating column will retain some vapour, so not all will be turned to liquid in the condenser.

If a synthesis requires three steps, each of which has a yield of 70%, the yield will be $0.7 \times 0.7 \times 0.7 = 0.34 = 34\%$. If the purification of the product is 80% efficient, the final yield will be $0.80 \times 34 = 27\%$.

Worked example
Benzene (molar mass 78 g mol^{-1}) can be converted into benzoic acid (molar mass 122 g mol^{-1}), which then has to be recrystallised. If 9.3 g of pure benzoic acid was made from 10.0 g of benzene, calculate the percentage yield.

e A common error is to work out the yield as mass of product × 100 divided by the mass of reactant. Making this mistake in this example would give the incorrect answer of 93%.

Answer

amount of benzene taken $= \dfrac{\text{mass}}{\text{molar mass}} = \dfrac{10.0\ \text{g}}{78\ \text{g mol}^{-1}} = 0.128\ \text{mol}$

theoretical yield of benzoic acid $= 0.128\ \text{mol} = 0.128\ \text{mol} \times 122\ \text{g mol}^{-1}$
$= 15.6\ \text{g}$

actual yield of pure benzoic acid $= 9.3\ \text{g}$

percentage yield $= \dfrac{9.3 \times 100}{15.6} = 59.6 = 60\%$ (to 2 significant figures)

Safety issues

It is assumed in A-level questions that the following safety precautions are always taken:

- Safety glasses and laboratory coats are worn at all times in all practical classes.
- Hands are washed before leaving the laboratory, particularly if toxic substances have been used.
- Food and drink are never consumed in the laboratory.

e Since these safety precautions are assumed, they are never awarded marks.

Special care must be taken with certain chemicals:

- Almost all organic chemicals are flammable. Flasks and test tubes containing them should not be heated directly with a Bunsen flame. A water bath or an electric heater should be used.
- If a chemical is harmful and can be absorbed through the skin, gloves must be worn.
- If a chemical has a harmful, irritating or poisonous vapour, the experiment must be carried out in a fume cupboard.
- If a chemical is corrosive, harmful, irritating or poisonous (toxic), gloves must be worn and extra care must be taken.
- Any substance suspected of being a carcinogen must not be used in a school laboratory.

e You are expected to be able to relate safety aspects to the specific hazards of the reaction or chemicals being handled.

Hazard symbols

GARRY WATSON/SPL

Questions

1 An organic compound X is thought to contain chlorine and iodine bonded to carbon atoms. Describe the tests that you would carry out to prove this.

2 Linalool is the major component of lavender oil. Its formula is

$(CH_3)_2C{=}CHCH_2CH_2C(CH_3)(OH)CH{=}CH_2$.

Describe the tests that would prove the presence of the functional groups in this molecule.

3 Spearmint oil contains the compound carvone. Use the results of the following tests that were carried out on carvone to deduce the functional groups present in the molecule. Justify your deductions from each test.

 a It turned brown bromine water colourless.

 b On warming with acidified potassium dichromate(VI), the solution remained orange.

 c It gave a yellow precipitate with Brady's reagent.

4 Tests on compound Y, $C_3H_4O_3$, gave the following results:

a When phosphorus pentachloride was added, steamy fumes that turned damp litmus red were observed.

b When a solution of sodium carbonate was added, a gas was evolved that turned limewater cloudy.

c A yellow precipitate was obtained when a solution of 2,4-dinitrophenylhydrazine was added.

d Orange acidified potassium dichromate(VI) solution turned green when warmed with Y.

e Y gave a negative result in the iodoform test.

Deduce the structural formula of compound Y.

5 This question concerns citral (found in lemon grass oil) and geraniol (found in rose oil).

Citral

Geraniol

a Describe a test to show that citral is an aldehyde.

b Describe a test to show that geraniol is an alcohol.

c Describe a test to show that both compounds contain a C=C group.

d In what way would the infrared spectra of citral and geraniol differ?

e Outline how citral could be converted to geraniol.

6 Compound Z has the following composition by mass: carbon, 55.8%; hydrogen, 7.0%; oxygen, 37.2%.

a Calculate the empirical formula of compound Z.

b Use the information below to deduce the structural formula of compound Z:

■ The largest m/e value in the mass spectrum of compound Z was 86.

■ Bromine water remained brown on the addition of compound Z.

■ No steamy fumes formed when phosphorus pentachloride was added to compound Z.

■ Addition of 2,4-dinitrophenylhydrazine to compound Z gave a yellow precipitate.

■ When Tollens' reagent was added to compound Z and the mixture warmed, a silver mirror formed.

■ When warmed with a solution of iodine in sodium hydroxide, compound Z gave a yellow precipitate.

7 An ester E has the molecular formula $C_7H_{14}O_2$. When heated under reflux with aqueous sodium hydroxide, followed by the addition of excess acid, it was converted into two compounds F and G:

■ Compound F has the following composition by mass: carbon, 54.5%; oxygen, 36.4%; hydrogen, 9.1%.

■ Compound F gives off carbon dioxide when added to a solution of sodium hydrogencarbonate.

■ Compound F has three peaks in its NMR spectrum.

■ Compound G does not give a precipitate with iodine and sodium hydroxide.

Deduce the structural formula of the ester E and write the equation for its reaction with sodium hydroxide.

8 When phenylamine reacts with ethanoyl chloride, a solid is formed that is soluble in hot water but insoluble in cold water. Describe how you could purify this solid.

9 Cyclohexanol (boiling point 161 °C) can be converted into cyclohexanone (boiling point 156 °C).

a State the reagents and conditions for this reaction.

b State how you would obtain a pure sample of cyclohexanone from a mixture containing it and 2% cyclohexanol.

c State how you would obtain a pure sample of cyclohexanone from a mixture containing it and 25% cyclohexanol.

10 Before cyclohexanone and cyclohexanol (produced as in question 9) can be separated, the organic substances, which are insoluble in water, have to be extracted from the reaction mixture.

a Describe how this would be achieved.

b How are traces of water removed from the organic substances?

c How would you know when the water removal was complete?

11 Draw a boiling-point–composition diagram for a mixture of cyclohexanol (boiling point 161 °C) and cyclohexanone (boiling point 156 °C). Use the diagram to explain how fractional distillation of a mixture containing 50% of each could be used as a method of separating the liquids.

12 Give the reagents, conditions and intermediates in the conversion of ethanol to propanoic acid.

13 Give the reagents, conditions and intermediates in the conversion of benzene to benzoic acid.

14 Give the reagents, conditions and intermediates in the conversion of ethanol to ethanoyl chloride.

15 Outline how propanoic acid could be prepared from methanol and bromoethane and no other carbon compound.

16 Outline how 1-phenylethanol, $C_6H_5CH(OH)CH_3$, could be prepared from benzene and one other organic reagent.

17 Outline how 1-propylamine can be prepared from butan-1-ol.

18 a Outline how you would convert $C_6H_5CH=CHCH_3$ into the following compound, M:

$$H_5C_6 - \underset{\underset{O}{\parallel}}{C} - \underset{\underset{O}{\parallel}}{C} - CH_3$$

b Identify the product formed by reacting compound M with iodine and sodium hydroxide.

19 12.6 g of benzene was nitrated and the nitrobenzene produced was reduced with tin and concentrated hydrochloric acid. After addition of sodium hydroxide, the phenylamine was steam-distilled out of the reaction mixture, washed, dried and redistilled. The mass of pure phenylamine produced was 6.75 g. Calculate the percentage yield.

20 It was required to prepare the compound $(CH_3)_2C(OH)CONH_2$ from propanone. A student suggested the following outline synthesis:

$$(CH_3)_2C=O \xrightarrow{\text{HCN}} (CH_3)_2C(OH)CN$$
$$\downarrow \text{H}_2\text{SO}_4\text{(aq)}$$
$$(CH_3)_2C(OH)COOH$$
$$\downarrow \text{PCl}_5$$
$$(CH_3)_2C(OH)COCl$$
$$\downarrow \text{NH}_3$$
$$(CH_3)_2C(OH)CONH_2$$

Explain why this sequence would *not* give the required product.

Applied organic chemistry

Chapter 16

Pharmaceuticals

Pharmaceuticals are synthetic chemicals that have a physiological effect on animals, including humans:

- They may be taken as pills or solutions, injected into the bloodstream or into muscular tissue or they may be absorbed through the skin.
- Those ingested into the digestive tract must be soluble, either under the acidic conditions of the stomach or under the alkaline conditions of the small intestine. Functional groups that can hydrogen-bond with water, and so become soluble, include the alcohol group –OH, the acidic group –COOH, the basic amino group –NH_2 or the salts derived from the latter two groups.
- To be absorbed through the skin, the drug must be lipid-soluble.

> **e** Lipids are mostly non-polar molecules of a biological origin that are relatively water-insoluble. Some, for example phospholipids, have a polar 'head' and two long hydrocarbon 'tails'. Phospholipids are esters. A phospholipid molecule is formed from glycerol, phosphoric acid and two carboxylic acids, each containing ten or more carbon atoms.

Examples of the difference in solubility can be seen in the behaviour of the two pain-relieving chemicals: aspirin and methyl salicylate.

Aspirin is slightly soluble in water. However, if the –COOH group is converted to the ionic –COO^- group by the addition of alkali, the aspirin becomes very soluble in water.

Aspirin
(ethanoylsalicylic acid)

Soluble aspirin
(sodium ethanoylsalicylate)

Oil of wintergreen
(methyl salicylate)

Methyl salicylate is the major constituent of Deep Heat and other creams and sprays that are used to combat muscle pain.

This compound is lipid-soluble, rather than water-soluble. Therefore, it is easily absorbed through the skin, where it acts as a painkiller on muscle tissue. The ester group and the benzene ring increase its solubility in lipids. Also, the phenolic –OH group in methyl salicylate is less water-soluble than the carboxyl –COO⁻ ion in ethanoylsalicylate, because it forms weaker hydrogen bonds with water molecules.

A molecule of ibuprofen has a long hydrophobic chain, which makes it lipid-soluble. However, it also has a –COOH group, which makes it slightly water-soluble and very soluble in the alkaline conditions of the small intestine.

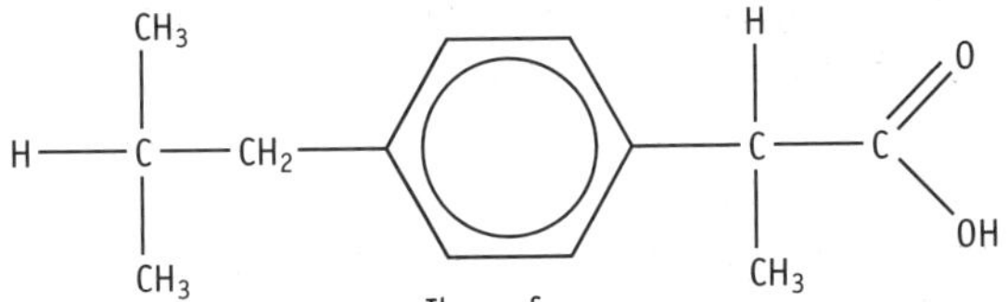

Painkillers

Ibuprofen

Ibuprofen can be swallowed as tablets or dissolved in a fatty cream and applied to the skin, where it is absorbed for relief of muscular pain.

Chloramphenicol (chloromycetin) is a powerful antibiotic:

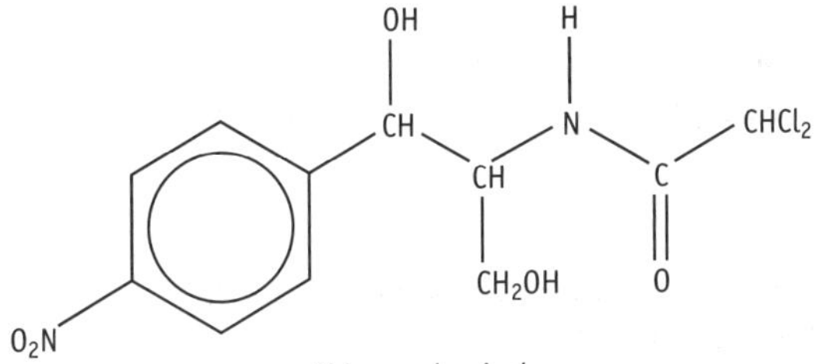

Chloramphenicol

The chloramphenicol molecule contains two alcohol groups and one amide group. Since these groups can form hydrogen bonds with water, chloramphenicol is very water-soluble. This has the advantages that it can be administered orally and passes quickly into the bloodstream. It is also neutral, so stomach acid does not affect its solubility. It has the ability to penetrate tissue, including that infected with pus, and pass through natural barriers, for example within the eye. It works by preventing protein synthesis in some bacteria, but does not affect the 'good' bacteria in the digestive system.

Esters, fats and oils

Esters

Esters are made by the reaction of an alcohol with a carboxylic acid or acid chloride. They have the general formula:

where R is a hydrogen atom or alkyl group and R′ is an alkyl group.

The ester methyl butanoate, which smells of apples, can be made by warming methanol with butanoic acid in the presence of a few drops of concentrated sulphuric acid:

$$CH_3OH + CH_3CH_2CH_2COOH \quad CH_3CH_2CH_2COOCH_3 + H_2O$$

Uses of esters

Esters are good solvents for organic substances that do not form hydrogen bonds. For example, ethyl ethanoate is used as a solvent for some glues and for nail varnish.

Esters are used for flavouring, particularly in boiled sweets. Pear drops are flavoured with the ester of 3-methylbutan-1-ol and ethanoic acid, which has the formula $CH_3COOCH_2CH_2CH(CH_3)_2$.

Esters as natural products

The smell of most fruits is mainly due to the presence of esters. Apples contain over fifty different esters, one of which is methyl butanoate. Oranges contain 2-octyl ethanoate, $CH_3COOCH(CH_3)(CH_2)_5CH_3$, and bananas contain 1-pentyl ethanoate, $CH_3COO(CH_2)_4CH_3$, and 1-pentyl butanoate, $CH_3CH_2CH_2COO(CH_2)_4CH_3$.

The flavour of a food is due to a combination of smell and taste. Smells are caused by the chemical responsible bonding to a protein in nerve endings in the nose, which stimulate a signal to the brain. Mammals have taste receptors in the mouth. In humans, receptors in the front of the tongue respond to sweetness and those on the edges to saltiness. Sourness is detected on the edges of the back of the tongue and bitterness in the middle of the back of the tongue.

◄ Some insects can detect taste through their feet.

Food is stored both in animals and in plants. The substances stored must be insoluble in water. In animals, food is stored as fats and in plants as vegetable oils. Both fats and oils are esters of propane-1,2,3-triol.

Fats and oils

Fats and oils are lipids. They are esters of high molecular mass acids (fatty acids) that have an even number of carbon atoms in the molecule and the alcohol, propane-1,2,3-triol (glycerol), $CH_2OHCHOHCH_2OH$.

The acids in fats are saturated and have the general formula, $C_nH_{2n+1}COOH$, where n is an odd number. Stearic acid, $C_{17}H_{35}COOH$ is a common constituent of animal fat.

Most vegetable oils are derived from polyunsaturated acids. These contain two or more C=C groups. They are more easily metabolised by humans than are animal fats and produce less cholesterol.

In vegetable oils, all the groups around a C=C double bond are in the *cis*-position. This means that the chains do not pack together very well, which in turn reduces the dispersion forces between the molecules. Therefore, oils are liquids at room temperature. Margarine is made from partially saturated vegetable oils that have been produced by the catalytic addition of hydrogen. This causes the molecules to pack more efficiently. Therefore, the oil is hardened and can be spread like butter.

Glyceryl tristearate is a typical saturated animal fat:

$$H_2C-O-\underset{\displaystyle O}{\overset{\displaystyle O}{\|}}C-C_{17}H_{35}$$

$$HC-O-\underset{\displaystyle O}{\overset{\displaystyle O}{\|}}C-C_{17}H_{35}$$

$$H_2C-O-\overset{\displaystyle O}{\underset{\displaystyle \|}{C}}-C_{17}H_{35}$$

Biodiesel

Vegetable oils cannot be used in an internal combustion engine because they would block the fuel injection system. Vegetable oils can, however, be hydrolysed by heating with aqueous sodium hydroxide. Long-chain acids can then be formed by acidification. If these acids are converted, using methanol, to their methyl esters, the result is a volatile liquid than can be used as a substitute for diesel.

Yellow-flowered rape can be seen growing in fields all over the UK. The seeds can be crushed to obtain rapeseed oil. This can be converted to the methyl ester of the component acids and is then sold as biodiesel or RME (rape methyl ester). In Asia, palm oil is the source of long-chain acids, which are then esterified for use as biodiesel.

Fertilisers

If plants are to grow quickly with a high yield, certain inorganic nutrients are needed. The most important are nitrogen, potassium and phosphorus. Most soils are deficient in these elements. Despite the word 'organic', organic fertilisers are mainly a source of inorganic nutrients; plants are unable to take up organic matter from the soil. Any organic fertiliser, whether manufactured or natural, is first broken down by soil bacteria to inorganic chemicals such as nitrates, phosphates and potassium salts.

Artificial fertiliser

ROBERT BROOK/SPL

The main element needed for growth is nitrogen. Since plant growth and harvesting remove nitrogen compounds from the soil, some nitrogenous fertiliser has to be added regularly . There are several ways of doing this.

Manufactured fertilisers

The common manufactured nitrogenous fertilisers are urea, NH_2CONH_2 (made from carbon dioxide and ammonia) and ammonium nitrate, NH_4NO_3 (made from ammonia and nitric acid). Table 16.1 shows some of the advantages and disadvantages of some manufactured and natural fertilisers.

Spreading manure

Natural fertilisers

Manure is a source of nitrates and is spread on the land. However, nitrates are soluble and are leached out. They may enter the water table and get into our drinking water. Too high a nitrate level in domestic water can cause problems, particularly to babies, so spreading manure or manufactured fertilisers is restricted in some areas and at certain times of the year.

Clover and other plants that have nodules containing nitrogen-fixing bacteria on their roots put nitrogen compounds back into the soil for absorption by the next crop.

Type	Fertiliser	Advantages	Disadvantages
Manufactured	Urea	Very high nitrogen content (56%); slow acting; easy to apply; no unpleasant smell	Very soluble so easily leached out; neutral so does not alter soil pH; not suitable for all soil types
	Ammonium nitrate	Fairly high nitrogen content (40%); acts rapidly on grasslands; easy to apply; no unpleasant smell	Very soluble so easily leached out; pH less than 7; can cause over-rapid growth
Natural	Manure	Improves soil condition; free to dairy farmers	Very low nutrient content; bulky, so needs much time and fuel for application; nitrates can be leached out; smells and encourages flies

Table 16.1 Advantages and disadvantages of some nitrogenous fertilisers

Polymers

Polymers are very long-chain molecules that are made by joining together thousands of smaller molecules, called monomers.

There are two types of polymer: addition and condensation.

Addition polymers

Molecules containing one or more C=C groups can be made to join together to form long chains. The simplest example is poly(ethene), made by polymerisation of ethene:

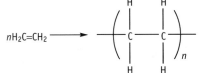

The repeat unit is shown in brackets on the right-hand side of the equation.

The repeat unit shows the monomer with its π-bond broken and 'continuation bonds' coming off each of the two carbon atoms that were π-bonded. The polymer consists of thousands of these repeat units joined together. This is indicated by the subscripted 'n' after the closing bracket.

Polymers do not melt at a fixed temperature — they soften gradually. The reasons for this are the varied chain length and the fact that the solid is not fully crystalline. It is more like glass, which is a supercooled liquid.

Monomers, for example ethene, can be polymerised by:
- free-radical addition. Ethene is heated with a trace of oxygen at a pressure of 1000 atm. The oxygen forms peroxide radicals that initiate a chain reaction (p. 259).
- ionic addition. Ethene is passed into a solution containing alkylaluminium compounds and titanium(IV) chloride. The chain grows from these substances and as the chains lie almost parallel to each other, the poly(ethene) produced has a higher density and a higher softening point, as well as a greater tensile strength.

The catalysts are called Ziegler–Natta catalysts.

Most addition polymers are produced by the polymerisation of monomers containing just one C=C group. Apart from Perspex and PTFE, these have the general formula for the monomer and for the repeat unit of the polymer as shown below:

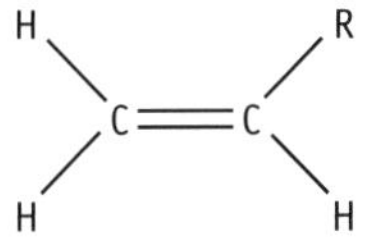

Monomer	Repeat unit of polymer

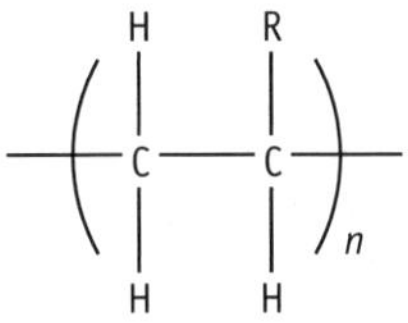

Some polymers, with different substituent R groups, and their main uses are shown in Table 16.2.

R group	Polymer	Repeat unit	Uses
H	Poly(ethene)	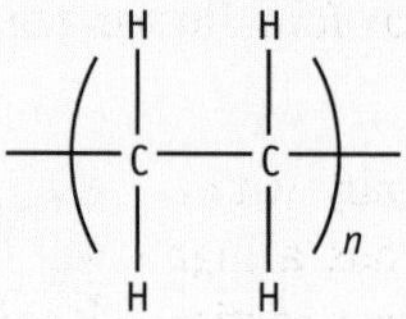	Low density — plastic bags; high density — food boxes, washing-up bowls, buckets, bottles etc.
CH_3	Poly(propene)	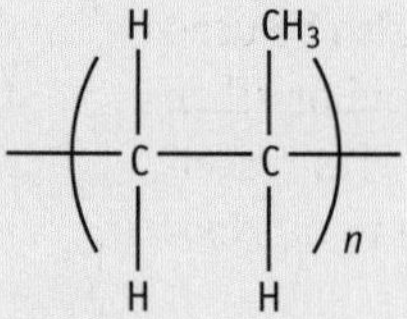	Ropes, plastic boxes
Cl	Poly(chloroethene) or PVC	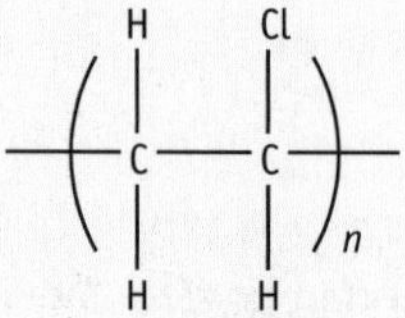	Water pipes, guttering, electrical insulation, window frames and window sills, waterproof clothing and Wellington boots
CN	Poly(propenenitrile) or Acrilan®	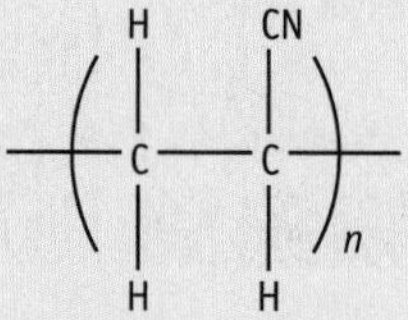	Fibres for clothing
C_6H_5	Poly(phenylethene) or polystyrene	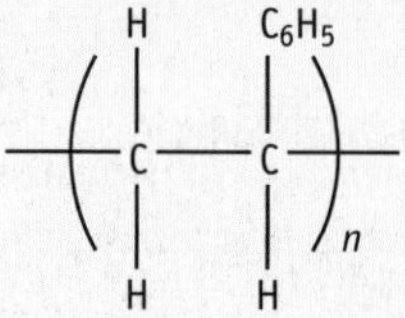	Thermal insulation, packaging for fragile articles
	Poly(methyl methacrylate) or Perspex®	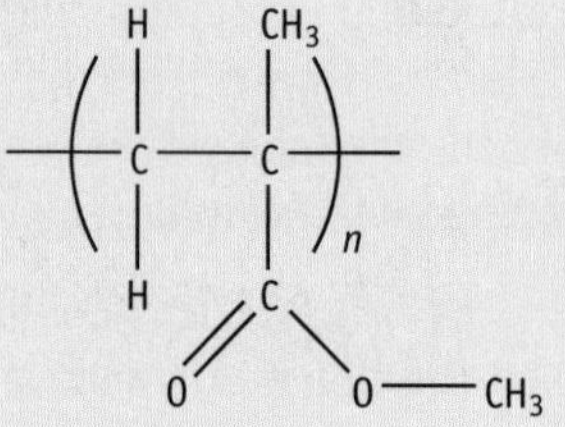	Rulers, a glass substitute (aeroplane cockpits)
	Poly(tetrafluoroethene) or PTFE	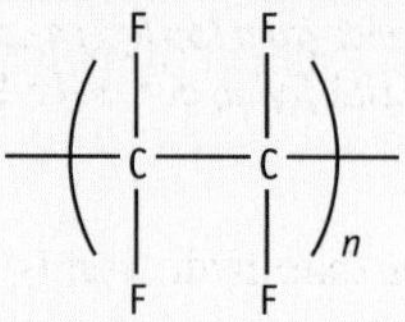	Non-stick coatings

Table 16.2 Polymers and their uses

ⓔ Note that all the repeat units have a carbon chain of two atoms. Only the R group varies.

The two addition polymers that do not have exactly the same general formula for the repeat unit are Perspex® and PTFE.

■ Perspex® is made by the addition polymerisation of methyl methacrylate.

The repeat unit contains two carbon atoms, but there are two substituted groups attached to one of the carbon atoms.

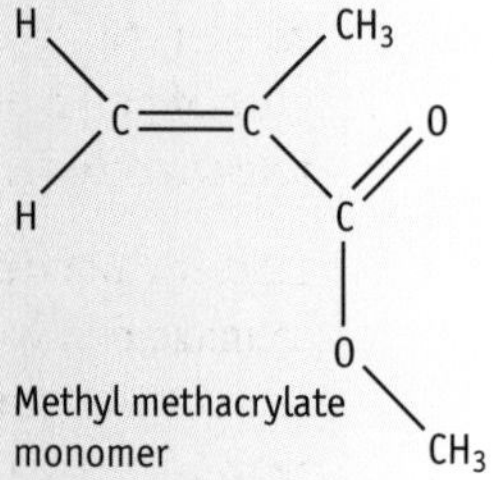

Methyl methacrylate monomer

- PTFE is the addition polymer from tetrafluoroethene, $CF_2=CF_2$. The repeat unit in poly(tetrafluoroethene) or PTFE has four fluorine atoms, and no hydrogen atoms, on two carbon atoms.

PTFE has the unusual property of being totally water-repellent. It is also almost frictionless and has a high melting point. These properties make it useful as a coating for non-stick frying pans and saucepans. It can also be used for low-friction bearings. It is not attacked by acid or alkali and is, therefore, used in burette taps. Since it is water-repellent, it is used to make a breathable lining in outdoor clothing such as Gore-Tex®.

Uses of polymers: Clockwise from top left: a car bumper, a Gore-Tex jacket, a non-stick frying pan and a PVC drain pipe

Isotactic polymers

When a polymer in which R is any group other than hydrogen is made using a Ziegler–Natta catalyst, the R groups all lie on the same side of the chain. This type of polymer is called an **isotactic** polymer. The chains are able to lie parallel to each other, so the intermolecular forces are much stronger.

Isotactic poly(propene) has a melting point above 100°C and is, therefore, used to make dishwasher-safe plastic containers. It is also used to make car bumpers, where strength is an important factor. Poly(propene) is found in fibres that are woven into carpets for outdoor use because it is non-polar and does not absorb water, unlike nylon, which contains C=O and N–H groups that can form hydrogen bonds with water.

Atactic polymers

Atactic polymers are made by free-radical addition. The R groups lie above and below the carbon chain in a random manner. The chains of an atactic polymer do not pack well and so it melts at a lower temperature than the isotactic form, which packs much more efficiently.

The isotactic and atactic forms of poly(propene) are shown in Figure 16.1.

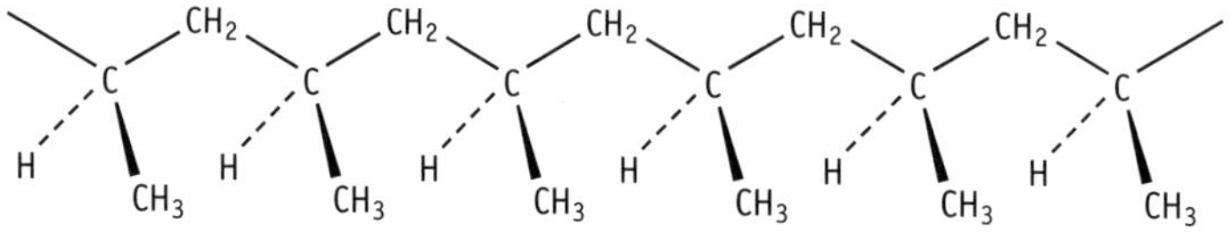

Isotactic poly(propene)

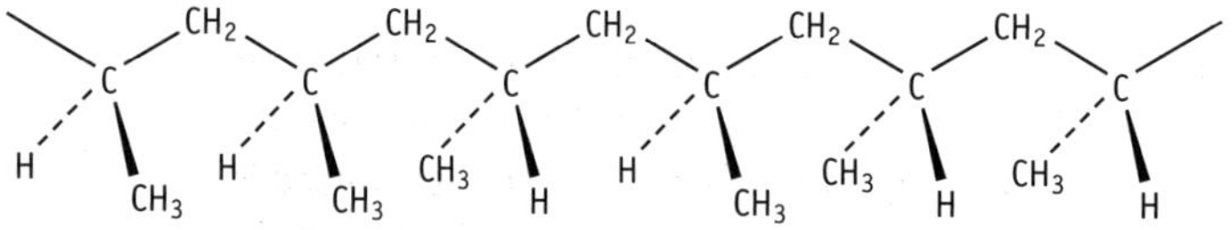

Actactic poly(propene)

Figure 16.1
Isotactic and atactic poly(propene)

Rubber

Natural rubber is a natural polymer of isoprene. The monomer has two double bonds. One of these breaks as the polymer forms, leaving the other double bond intact in the chain.

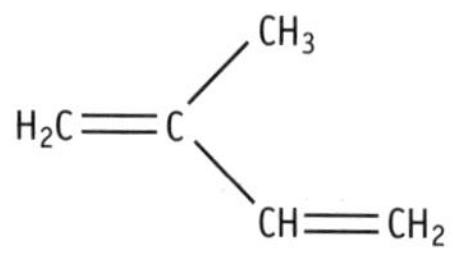

Isoprene

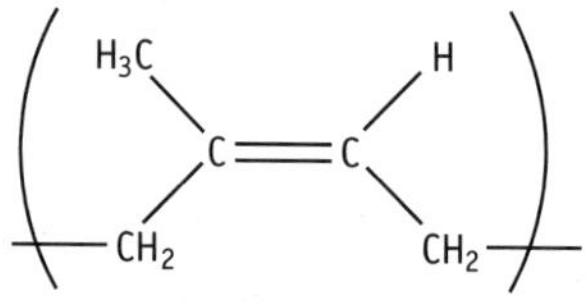

Poly(*cis*-isoprene)

Note that all the –H and –CH$_3$ groups are in the *cis*-position along the carbon chain.

Rubber latex is obtained from under the bark of rubber trees.

Synthetic rubbers are made by polymerising butadiene, CH$_2$=CH–CH=CH$_2$, and chloroprene, CH$_2$=CH–CCl=CH$_2$.

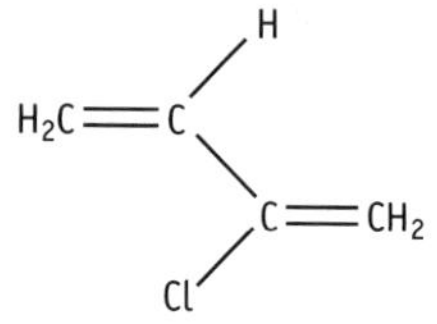

Chloroprene

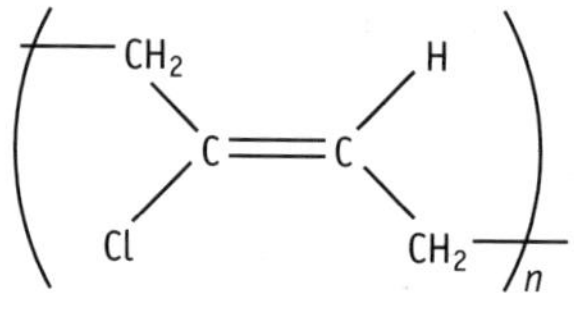

Poly(chloroprene) repeat unit

The rubber made from chloroprene is called neoprene.

This is an example of 1,4-addition. The double bonds break and one reforms in the middle of the molecule.

This is a 1,4-addition — possible only with dienes.

The name neoprene is derived from the Greek *neo*, which means new.

TOPFOTO

Natural and synthetic rubber have to be hardened before they can be used. The hardening process was invented by Charles Goodyear in 1839 and is called **vulcanisation**. Goodyear found that heating rubber latex with sulphur caused it to harden and become elastic. The sulphur atoms break some of the double bonds in the polymer and form cross-links between the chains.

Condensation polymers

When two different monomers form a condensation polymer, they join together with the elimination of a small molecule such as water, hydrogen chloride or methanol. Each monomer must have two functional groups, one at each end of the molecule.

Polyesters

Polyesters are made from a monomer that has two –COOH or two –COCl groups and another monomer with two alcohol, –OH, groups.

Terylene® is a polymer made from benzene-1,4-dicarbonyl dichloride:

and ethane-1,2-diol, CH_2OHCH_2OH. A molecule of hydrogen chloride is eliminated as each ester linkage is formed. The repeat unit of Terylene® is shown below.

The equation for this polymerisation is:

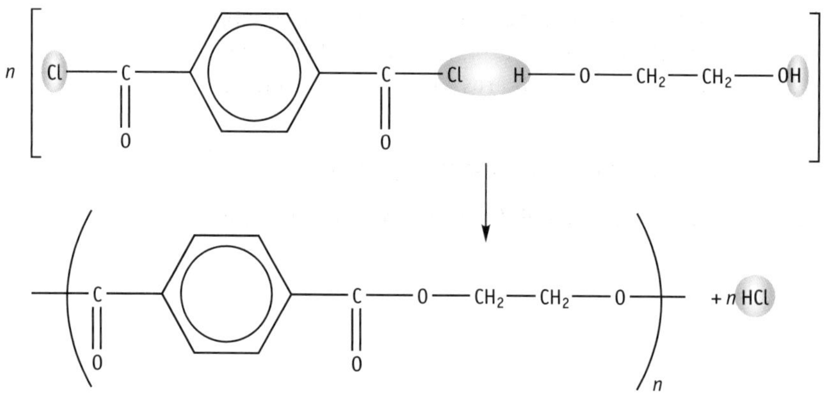

Polyesters such as Terylene® (also called Dacron®) are used as fibres. When mixed with cotton it makes a very hardwearing material called polycotton, which is used to make sheets, shirts and other articles of clothing.

Polyamides

Polyamides are condensation polymers of diacid chlorides and diamines.

Nylon-6,6 is a condensation polymer of hexane-1,6-dioyl dichloride:

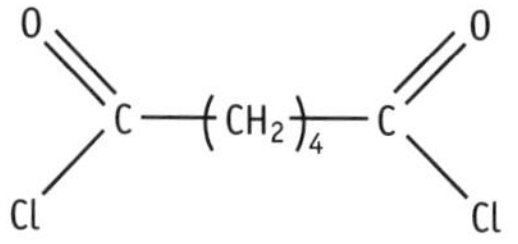

and 1,6-diaminohexane, $NH_2(CH_2)_6NH_2$:

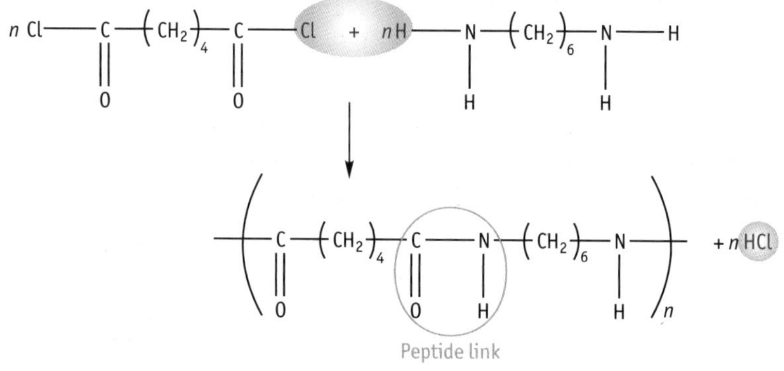

Peptide link

The repeat unit in nylon is shown below.

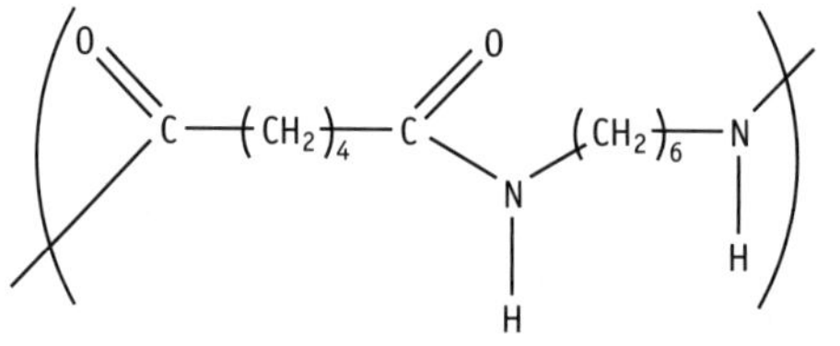

The nylon is spun and strengthened by stretching. It is then used to make nylon stockings, carpets and, when moulded, objects such as light switches.

ⓔ When you draw the repeat units of polyesters and polyamides, the ester and amide linkages must be drawn out in full, with the double bonds shown.

The strength of a polyamide is derived from the hydrogen bonds that form between the chains. Each hydrogen bond forms between the δ^+ hydrogen atom of an –NH group and the δ^- oxygen of a C=O group on another chain. Since water can also hydrogen-bond to these groups, nylon absorbs small amounts of water.

Other polyamides

The use of aromatic diamines gives rise to two important polyamides.

Nomex® is made from benzene-1,3-dicarbonyl dichloride and 1,4-diamino-benzene:

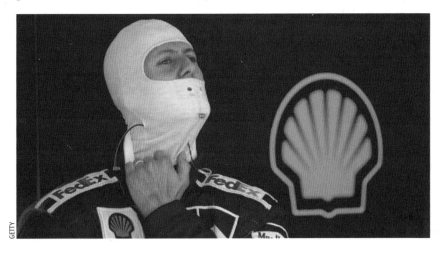

Repeat unit of Nomex

Nomex® melts above 400°C and is a poor conductor of heat. It is used to make fire-resistant clothing. Formula 1 racing drivers and Army Air Corps helicopter pilots wear Nomex® suits and firefighters' tunics are lined with Nomex®.

Formula 1 racing driver Michael Schumacher wearing Nomex®

Kevlar® is a polyamide made from benzene-1,4-dicarbonyl dichloride and 1,4-diaminobenzene. It is used to make bulletproof vests worn in dangerous situations by police officers, soldiers and TV reporters.

Kevlar can also be cold-drawn. The result is an extremely strong fibre. Cables made from Kevlar have the same tensile strength as steel but are five times lighter.

A police officer wearing a Kevlar® bullet-proof vest

◀ Cold-drawn means that the polymer has been pulled into threads; this aligns the chains and thus increases the inter-molecular forces between them.

◀ New synthetic polymers are being developed that are biodegradable.

Disposal of polymers

Bacteria that break down synthetic polymers have not yet evolved. Therefore, they are not biodegradable and are only broken down very slowly by light. This means that they stay in landfill sites, using up valuable space. If discarded in fields or by the roadside, they create ugly visual pollution.

Synthetic polymers can be destroyed by combustion. However, unless it is very carefully controlled, this method can result in toxic gases being released into the atmosphere. Burning PVC produces hydrogen chloride gas. Other polymers produce toxic substances, such as dioxins.

Plastics can be sorted, melted down and then re-used. However, this is not economically viable in countries where labour costs are high. Much of the waste plastic from the UK is sent to China, where some is re-used and the remainder incinerated.

Questions

1 Tylenol is a pain-relieving drug. It has the formula:

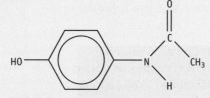

Tylenol

Explain why you would expect tylenol to be either water-soluble or lipid-soluble.

2 Explain why rapeseed oil has a lower melting temperature than butter.

3 Explain how a vegetable oil can be converted into a fuel for motor vehicles and domestic boilers.

4 Explain how soap removes oily dirt from clothing.

5 What are the advantages of using an organic fertiliser such as urea, compared with an inorganic fertiliser such as ammonium sulphate, $(NH_4)_2SO_4$.

6 But-2-ene can be polymerised. Draw the repeat unit of the polymer formed.

7 Draw the repeat unit of Kevlar.

8 Explain the difference between addition and condensation polymerisation.

9 2-hydroxypropanoic acid can be polymerised. Draw enough of the structure of the polymer to show *two* repeat units.

10 Polyamides and proteins both have peptide links between molecules in the polymer chain. Proteins are broken down by bacteria; polyamides are not. Explain why this is the case.

Practice Unit Test 5

Time allowed: 1 hour 30 minutes

(1) (a) Use the standard reduction potentials below to explain how Fe^{2+} ions can catalyse the oxidation of iodide ions, I^-, by persulphate ions, $S_2O_8^{2-}$.

$$S_2O_8^{2-}(aq) + 2e^- \quad 2SO_4^{2-}(aq) \qquad E^\circ = +2.01\,V$$
$$I_2(s) + 2e^- \quad 2I^-(aq) \qquad E^\circ = +0.54\,V$$
$$Fe^{3+}(aq) + e^- \quad Fe^{2+}(aq) \qquad E^\circ = +0.77\,V \quad \textit{(6 lines)}$$

(4 marks)

(b) Iron forms compounds that contain Fe^{3+} ions and compounds that contain Fe^{2+} ions. Zinc forms Zn^{2+} only.

Copy and complete the electron configurations below and explain why iron is classified as a transition metal whereas zinc is not.

Fe^{2+}: [Ar] ....

Zn^{2+}: [Ar] .... *(2 lines)* (3 marks)

(c) (i) Write an equation to show why an aqueous solution of hydrated iron(III) ions is acidic. *(1 line)*

(ii) Write an equation to show the ligand exchange reaction of hydrated iron(III) ions with cyanide ions. *(1 line)*

(iii) Explain why hydrated iron(III) ions are coloured. *(3 lines)*

(iv) Give an example of a reaction in which iron metal is a catalyst. *(1 line)* (7 marks)

(d) The concentration of iron(III) ions can be found by adding excess iodide ions and titrating the iodine produced against a standard solution of sodium thiosulphate.

The equations are:

$$2Fe^{3+} + 2I^- \rightarrow 2Fe^{2+} + I_2$$
$$I_2 + 2S_2O_3^{2-} \rightarrow 2I^- + S_4O_6^{2-}$$

A solution containing 1.00 g of impure iron(III) chloride, $FeCl_3$, was mixed with excess potassium iodide and the liberated iodine was titrated against a 0.200 mol dm^{-3} solution of sodium thiosulphate. The end point was reached after the addition of 27.3 cm^3 of sodium thiosulphate.

Calculate the percentage purity of the iron(III) chloride. *(space)* (5 marks)

Total: 19 marks

(2) (a) What is meant by:

(i) order of reaction? *(2 lines)*

(ii) rate of reaction? *(2 lines)* (2 marks)

(b) 1-bromopropane and sodium hydroxide react to form propan-1-ol and sodium bromide. The rate of this reaction was measured using different concentrations of hydroxide ions and 1-bromopropane. The results are shown in the table below.

Experiment	$[OH^-]$/mol dm^{-3}	[1-bromopropane]/mol dm^{-3}	Initial rate of reaction/mol dm^{-3} s^{-1}
1	0.25	0.25	1.4×10^{-4}
2	0.125	0.25	7.0×10^{-5}
3	0.50	0.125	1.4×10^{-4}

(i) Deduce the order of reaction with respect to hydroxide ions and to 1-bromopropane. Justify your deductions. *(4 lines)*

(ii) Write the rate equation for this reaction. *(1 line)*

(iii) Calculate the value of the rate constant. *(space)*

(iv) Write a mechanism for the reaction that is consistent with your answer to **(i)**. *(space)*   (10 marks)

(c) Explain, in terms of collision theory, how the rate of this exothermic reaction would alter with an increase in temperature. *(5 lines)*   (4 marks)

Total: 16 marks

(3) (a) Ethanamide, CH_3CONH_2, can be prepared in the laboratory from ethanol. Outline how this could be carried out, stating the reagents and conditions needed and identifying all intermediates formed. *(space)*   (6 marks)

(b) State and explain the differences in the NMR spectra of ethanol and ethanamide. *(3 lines)*   (3 marks)

(c) The infrared spectra of the two compounds are shown below as spectrum X and spectrum Y.

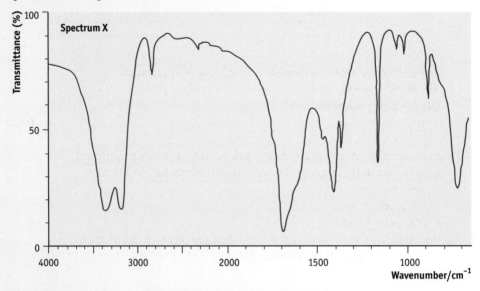

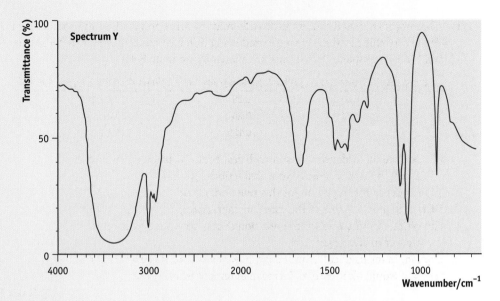

Identify which spectrum is for ethanamide, giving your reasons. (You may use the data in Tables 14.3 and 14.4 on page 278.) *(5 lines)* (3 marks)

(d) Tylenol is a secondary amide and a phenol:

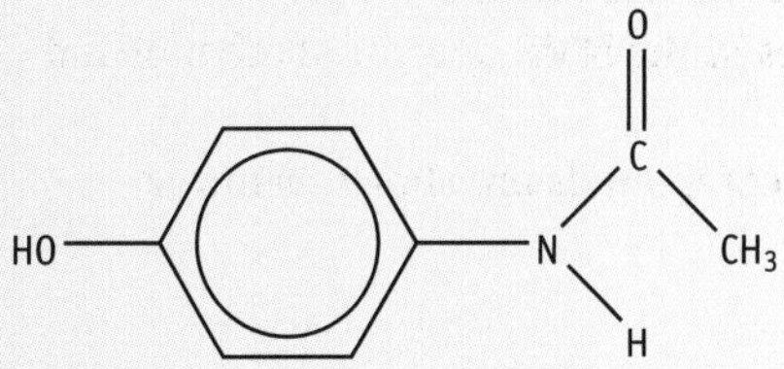

Tylenol

It is used in the USA as a painkiller. Predict its reactions with:
  (i) bromine water *(2 lines)*
  (ii) aqueous sodium hydroxide *(2 lines)* (2 marks)

Total: 14 marks

(4) (a) Ethene reacts rapidly with bromine, but benzene requires a catalyst of anhydrous iron(III) bromide. Write the mechanisms for the reaction of bromine with:
  (i) ethene *(space)*
  (ii) benzene *(space)* (7 marks)
(b) Use your answers to (a) to explain why benzene reacts by substitution whereas ethene reacts by addition. *(4 lines)* (3 marks)

(c) Write equations for the reactions of:
   (i) benzene with a mixture of concentrated nitric and sulphuric acids *(1 line)*
   (ii) benzene with ethanoyl chloride in the presence of a catalyst of anhydrous aluminium chloride *(1 line)*
   (iii) phenol with diazonium ions *(1 line)*   (4 marks)

                                            Total: 14 marks

(5) (a) Vanadium exists in the +5, +4, +3 and +2 oxidation states in its compounds. Explain why transition metals, such as vanadium, can form ions in different oxidation states whereas group 2 metals form ions in one oxidation state only. *(5 lines)*   (4 marks)

(b) When colourless sodium vanadate(v), $NaVO_3$, is added to water, a yellow solution is formed. This contains the $VO_2^+(aq)$ ion.
   (i) Write the equation for this reaction. *(1 line)*
   (ii) Explain why this is not a redox reaction. *(2 lines)*
   (iii) Explain what would happen to the colour of the solution if the pH were increased. *(2 lines)*   (4 marks)

(c) When a solution of sodium vanadate(v) is reduced by zinc and dilute hydrochloric acid, the following colour changes take place:
      yellow → green → blue → green → lavender
   Explain which ions are responsible for these colours. *(5 lines)*   (4 marks)

                                            Total: 12 marks

                                   Paper total: 75 marks

Unit **6B**
Synoptic

Synoptic

Chapter 17

The exam

Unit Test 6B is a synoptic paper that requires knowledge and understanding of all parts of the AS and A2 specifications. It examines the content of Units 1–5. The paper has two sections. Section A contains one compulsory question based on experimental results. Section B contains three questions, of which you have to answer two. The time allowed is 1 hour 30 minutes, worth 50 marks. This counts for 20% of the A2 or 10% of the whole A-level marks.

- Read the question. Questions usually change from one examination to the next. A question that looks the same, at a cursory glance, to one that you have seen before usually has significant differences when read carefully. Needless to say, candidates do not receive credit for writing answers to their own questions.

- Be aware of the number of marks available for a given part of a question. This is an excellent indication of the number of points that you need to make.

- If you start a question and then give up on it and answer the remaining two, do not cross out what you have written. The examiner will mark all that you have written and award marks for the best two answers.

- Look for words in **bold** in a question and make sure that you have answered the question fully in terms of those words or phrases. For example, if the question asks you to define a **dative covalent bond**, make sure that you explain the meaning of covalent bond as well as dative.

- Questions in Unit Test 6B will often involve substances or situations that are new to you. This is deliberate and is what makes these questions synoptic. Don't be put off by large organic molecules. They are nothing more than a collection of functional groups which, you may assume, react independently of each other.

Unit Test 6B has one assessment objective, A04. This is referred to as 'synthesis of knowledge, understanding and skills'. You should be able to:

- bring together knowledge, principles and concepts from different areas of chemistry, including experiment and investigation, and apply them in a particular context, expressing ideas clearly and logically and using appropriate specialist vocabulary

- use chemical skills in contexts that bring together different areas of the subject

Synoptic issues

This unit test will be synoptic assessment, which is the explicit drawing together of knowledge, understanding and skills learned in different parts of the A-level course. In Unit Test 6B, the questions draw on the content of the whole specification.

Practice Unit Test 6B

Time allowed: 1 hour 30 minutes

Section A

(1) A commercial fertiliser is labelled as consisting of potassium nitrate, KNO_3, and ammonium nitrate, NH_4NO_3. The procedure below can be used to estimate the amount of available nitrogen and potassium in the fertiliser.

4.67 g of the fertiliser was dissolved in water and the amount of NH_4^+ and NO_3^- ions was estimated.

(a) *Estimation of NH_4^+ content*

Excess dilute sodium hydroxide solution was added and the mixture heated. This caused all the ammonium ions to be converted into gaseous ammonia. The ammonia was bubbled through 50.0 cm^3 (an excess) of 1.60 mol dm^{-3} hydrochloric acid.

Reaction of ammonia

$$NH_3 + HCl \rightarrow NH_4Cl$$

The excess hydrochloric acid was titrated against a standard 0.400 mol dm^{-3} solution of sodium hydroxide. The titre was 42.5 cm^3 of sodium hydroxide.

$$HCl + NaOH \rightarrow NaCl + H_2O$$

Calculate the amount (moles) of ammonium ions in the 4.67 g sample of fertiliser. *(space)* (4 marks)

(b) *Estimation of NO_3^- content*

After all the ammonium ions have been converted to ammonia and driven off, the nitrate content can be estimated by adding aluminium foil to the alkaline solution of the fertiliser. This reduces all the NO_3^- ions into ammonia, which is then passed into another 50.0 cm^3 of 1.60 mol dm^{-3} solution of hydrochloric acid.

The excess hydrochloric acid was also titrated against the standard 0.400 mol dm^{-3} sodium hydroxide solution. The titre was 11.0 cm^3 of sodium hydroxide.

Calculate the amount (moles) of nitrate ions in the 4.67 g sample of the fertiliser. *(space)* (3 marks)

(c) Use your answers from **(a)** and **(b)** to calculate the percentage by mass of nitrogen and potassium in the fertiliser. *(space)* (5 marks)

Total: 12 marks

Section B

(2) (a) Boron and aluminium are in the same group of the periodic table.

(i) Explain why the first ionisation energy of boron is less than that of beryllium. *(3 lines)*

(ii) Boron forms a covalent chloride, BCl_3. Draw a dot-and-cross diagram showing the outer electrons in a molecule of boron trichloride. *(space)*

(iii) State and explain the shape of a boron trichloride molecule. *(3 lines)*

(iv) *Anhydrous* aluminium chloride sublimes to form molecules with formula Al_2Cl_6. Draw the structure of this molecule, labelling the different types of bond. *(space)*

(v) When *hydrated* aluminium ions are added to water, the solution becomes acidic. Write an equation to show this. *(1 line)*

(vi) Anhydrous aluminium chloride is used as the catalyst for the reaction of benzene with ethanoyl chloride. Write the equation for this reaction. *(1 line)*   (12 marks)

(b) (i) Write the equation that represents the standard enthalpy of combustion of benzene. *(1 line)*

(ii) When chloroethane burns, it forms carbon dioxide, water and hydrogen chloride:

$$CH_3CH_2Cl + 3O_2 \rightarrow 2CO_2 + 2H_2O + HCl$$

Copy and complete the Hess's law cycle below.

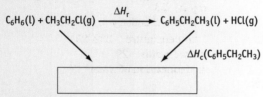

Substance	ΔH_c°/kJ mol^{-1}
$C_6H_6(l)$	−3267
$CH_3CH_2Cl(g)$	−1413
$C_6H_5CH_2CH_3(l)$	−4564

Use the cycle and the data in the table to calculate the standard enthalpy of the reaction:

$$C_6H_6 + C_2H_5Cl \rightarrow C_6H_5CH_2CH_3 + HCl \quad \text{(space)}$$ (5 marks)

(c) Aluminium hydroxide is amphoteric. Write equations to show how it reacts with (i) dilute hydrochloric acid and (ii) dilute sodium hydroxide. *(2 lines)*   (2 marks)

Total: 19 marks

(3) (a) Propanoic acid, CH_3CH_2COOH, has a higher boiling temperature than its isomer, methyl ethanoate, CH_3COOCH_3. Methyl propanoate, $CH_3CH_2COOCH_3$, has a higher boiling temperature than methyl ethanoate. Explain these differences. *(6 lines)* (5 marks)

(b) (i) Write the equation for the dissociation of propanoic acid in water and hence the expression for the acid dissociation constant, K_a. *(3 lines)*

(ii) Explain why a solution of propanoic acid alone does not act as a buffer solution when a small amount of acid is added. *(4 lines)*

(iii) Calculate the mass of sodium propanoate, CH_3CH_2COONa, that must be added to 100 cm^3 of 1.00 mol dm^{-3} propanoic acid solution to give a buffer solution of pH 5.20. (K_a for propanoic acid $= 1.3 \times 10^{-5}$ mol dm^{-3}) *(space)*   (9 marks)

(c) Identify the reagents needed for, and intermediates formed in, the conversion of propanoic acid to ethylamine, $CH_3CH_2NH_2$. *(4 lines)*   (5 marks)

Total: 19 marks

Paper total: 50 marks

Index

The periodic table

Group

Key:

| Molar mass/g mol⁻¹ |
| Symbol |
| Atomic number |

$$\text{Molar mass/g mol}^{-1}$$
$$\text{Symbol}$$
$$\text{Atomic number}$$

Period	1	2	3	4	5	6	7	0
1	1 H 1							4 He 2
2	7 Li 3	9 Be 4	11 B 5	12 C 6	14 N 7	16 O 8	19 F 9	20 Ne 10
3	23 Na 11	24 Mg 12	27 Al 13	28 Si 14	31 P 15	32 S 16	35.5 Cl 17	40 Ar 18
4	39 K 19	40 Ca 20	45 Sc 21	48 Ti 22	51 V 23	52 Cr 24	55 Mn 25	56 Fe 26	59 Co 27	59 Ni 28	63.5 Cu 29	65.4 Zn 30	70 Ga 31	73 Ge 32	75 As 33	79 Se 34	80 Br 35	84 Kr 36
5	85 Rb 37	88 Sr 38	89 Y 39	91 Zr 40	93 Nb 41	96 Mo 42	99 Tc 43	101 Ru 44	103 Rh 45	106 Pd 46	108 Ag 47	112 Cd 48	115 In 49	119 Sn 50	122 Sb 51	128 Te 52	127 I 53	131 Xe 54
6	133 Cs 55	137 Ba 56	139 La 57	178 Hf 72	181 Ta 73	184 W 74	186 Re 75	190 Os 76	192 Ir 77	195 Pt 78	197 Au 79	201 Hg 80	204 Tl 81	207 Pb 82	209 Bi 83	210 Po 84	210 At 85	222 Rn 86
7	223 Fr 87	226 Ra 88	227 Ac 89					

| 140 Ce 58 | 141 Pr 59 | 144 Nd 60 | (147) Pm 61 | 150 Sm 62 | 152 Eu 63 | 157 Gd 64 | 159 Tb 65 | 163 Dy 66 | 165 Ho 67 | 167 Er 68 | 169 Tm 69 | 173 Yb 70 | 175 Lu 71 |
| 232 Th 90 | (231) Pa 91 | 238 U 92 | (237) Np 93 | (242) Pu 94 | (243) Am 95 | (247) Cm 96 | (245) Bk 97 | (251) Cf 98 | (254) Es 99 | (253) Fm 100 | (256) Md 101 | (254) No 102 | (257) Lr 103 |